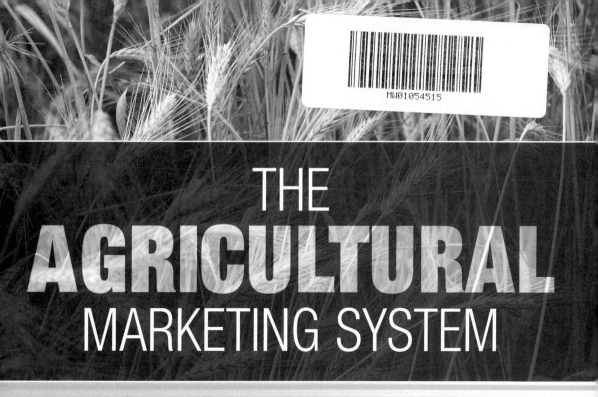

THE AGRICULTURAL MARKETING SYSTEM

SIXTH EDITION

V. James Rhodes

Jan L. Dauve

Joseph L. Parcell

UNIVERSITY OF MISSOURI–COLUMBIA

HOLCOMB HATHAWAY, PUBLISHERS

Scottsdale, Arizona

Library of Congress Cataloging-in-Publication Data

Rhodes, V. James.
  The agricultural marketing system / V. James Rhodes, Jan L. Dauve, Joseph L. Parcell. — 6th
ed.
         p. cm.
  Includes bibliographical references and index.
  ISBN-13: 978-1-890871-68-0
  1. Farm produce—United States—Marketing. 2. Agriculture—Economic aspects—United
States. I. Dauve, Jan. II. Parcell, Joseph L. III. Title.

  HD9005.R47 2007
  630.68'8—dc22

                                                                              2006016827

Copyright © 2007 by Holcomb Hathaway, Publishers, Inc.

Holcomb Hathaway, Publishers, Inc.
6207 North Cattletrack Road, Suite 5
Scottsdale, Arizona 85250
480-991-7881
www.hh-pub.com

10 9 8 7 6 5 4 3

ISBN 978-1-890871-68-0

All rights reserved. No part of this publication may be reproduced,
in any form or by any means, without permission in writing from the publisher.

Printed in the United States of America.

CONTENTS

5   The Domestic Market: A Developed Economy   93

6   The International Market   115

PART II   THE MARKETING SYSTEM   135

7   Pricing and Exchange Systems and Alternatives Within the Marketing–Procurement Channel   137

8   Providing the Optimum Varieties and Qualities   161

9   Place and Time Aspects of Marketing   183

10   Understanding and Applying Hedging Using Futures, Options, and Basis   201

11 Participation and Leadership in the Marketing–Procurement Channels   229

12 Marketing by Farmer Groups: Collective Action   247

13   Processor Procurement Systems   271

PREFACE

During the past ten years, the agricultural value chain has evolved in scope and target market. The focus of this text has always been, and remains, on training future managers, decision makers, and opinion leaders as to the economic drivers of the agricultural value chain. Globalization has changed the way agricultural marketing must be taught, as has the increase in the number of student scholars without firsthand experience in agriculture. The content of this book reflects an increased focus on the global agricultural environment. We believe this book will be valuable to those trying to understand the agriculture value chain.

This edition differs from earlier editions in important ways. In addition to updating exhibits to reflect the global agriculture value chain, we have rewritten the chapters relating to the understanding and use of futures markets. We have placed more focus on quality-based marketing and contracting, which are becoming dominant means of market transactions in the agriculture value chain. Other revisions include the following:

- Agricultural and food policy issues have been integrated throughout the book instead of being treated in separate chapters.
- We have reduced the discussion of industry and sector structure, as structure is a dynamic facet that now changes more quickly than a book is revised.
- We have further emphasized the book as a reference for learners and a supplement to knowledge in the teacher–learner interaction.

We would be remiss without addressing the question of why we devote an entire book to the agricultural marketing system. In a developed country such as the United States, we find that agriculture accounts for over 12 percent of gross domestic product and over 16 percent of total employment. Each of the various sectors of the agriculture marketing system contributes in important ways to the overall value of agriculture and to the domestic economic engine.

In emerging economy countries, economic reliance on agriculture can exceed 80 percent of gross domestic product and involve over 90 percent of a country's population. In addition, the level of spending on food varies considerably by country. Although in this text we have tried to consider global concerns when most relevant, a comprehensive look at the geopolitical and economic consequences of trade and industry globalization are beyond the scope and intent of this book.

As a greater number of non–agriculture persons play important roles in agribusinesses, the need for a text such as this one grows. This book offers readers an understanding of how decisions at one level in the value chain impact all other levels and explores if, how, and when the system changes and evolves as a result of cumulating individual decisions.

We hope you share our enthusiasm over the sixth edition of *The Agricultural Marketing System.*

ACKNOWLEDGMENTS

We would like to thank the following individuals, who reviewed the manuscript for this edition and made constructive suggestions for its improvement: Jeff Beaulieu, Southern Illinois University–Carbondale; Clark Springfield, Texas A&M University; and Rick Whitacre, Illinois State University. We appreciate their help.

VJR
JLD
JLP

Julia, thanks for your support and love. This edition of *The Agricultural Marketing System* is dedicated to the memory of J. Bruce Bullock, a colleague and friend, and an impetus for the sixth edition.

JLP

MARKETING, MARKET COMPETITION, AND CONSUMER MARKETS

The term *marketing* has many different meanings. Chapter 1 defines this concept and comments on some of the popular notions about it. The *micro*, or firm-oriented, definition of marketing is distinguished from a *macro*, or more global, definition of marketing.

Point of view is important in marketing. In this section, the point of view is generally that of firm managers (farm or agribusiness) as they survey the environment within which they operate. Managers of firms involved in marketing must deal with their competitive environment. How that competitive structure shapes and limits their options as managers is discussed in Chapters 2 and 3. Managers must also understand the ways in which prices are determined in the markets for their products, the topic of Chapter 4.

Although there is a vast market beyond the borders of the United States for many of its farm commodities, the domestic market is larger than the foreign one, and agribusinesses are generally much more interested in the domestic market. Chapter 5 discusses the important characteristics of the domestic market.

Many firms, however, are deeply involved in marketing abroad. In fact, early in the twenty-first century, global markets have a growing influence on U.S. agricultural industry, and global political and economic factors directly impact demand for U.S. products and influence prices. For example, the changing Chinese political environment and growing Asian economy have allowed many U.S. agribusinesses to increase commodity exports to Asia. On the other hand, the finding of BSE (bovine spongiform encephalopathy) in the U.S. cattle herd in late 2003 caused most countries around the world to discontinue importing U.S. beef. Chapter 6 discusses the unique aspects of international markets.

0.00

AGRICULTURAL MARKETING: AN INTRODUCTION

PREVIEW

- Agricultural marketing can be observed from various viewpoints: farmer, processor, retailer, consumer, policy maker, or detached citizen. These viewpoints make a difference in what we observe.

- The macro, or "big picture," view of global marketing is one of a complex, finely tuned machine that daily delivers an enormous amount of food and fiber to consumers.

- Marketing participants, such as farmers, processors, and retailers, see marketing as a set of specific profit-seeking business activities directed to satisfy their customers. This micro view of marketing emphasizes the problems and opportunities facing firm managers as they implement marketing decisions.

KEY TERMS

agribusiness

behavioral systems approach

consumer sovereignty

fallacy of composition

functional approach

institutional approach

macro marketing

marketing channel

micro marketing

micro procurement

gricultural marketing is a shopper pushing a grocery cart through the checkout counter as the cash register reads the Universal Product Code (UPC) on the items passing across the scanner. It's a fast-food worker preparing at 11 A.M. for the impending lunch rush at a Taco Bell. It's a commercial on your radio extolling the benefits of a new sport drink.

These are some of the sights and sounds of agricultural marketing that you may have experienced. Here are some that you may not have experienced firsthand: A tanker maneuvers into a dock at San Paulo, Brazil, to load thousands of metric tons of soybeans headed for Beijing. A packer–buyer at a Texas feedlot studies the latest market prices before entering the manager's office to bargain over the price of 200 Angus steers in pen 112. In Alberta, the Canada Wheat Board is conducting a public hearing on wheat prices for the upcoming year, and an economist for the dominant wheat cooperative in the Alberta area is presenting testimony. In Chicago, futures trading activity has moved at a furious pace in the corn and wheat pits since the market opened because of unexpected news the previous evening of much reduced prospects for grain crops in Argentina. A businessman in Capetown, South Africa, ponders alternatives after learning that the branch railroad serving his elevator will likely close in 90 days. The product manager of a large food processor in London wonders if she should recommend they begin market testing a replacement product based on the declining market share of one of her firm's oldest brands of breakfast cereals. In the Salinas Valley of California, a USDA inspector is grading truckloads of fresh produce before they start east. In the Mideast, farmers are delivering seed cotton to the local gin.

All those activities (and many others) add value in agricultural marketing. The market values involved run into billions of dollars (see Exhibit 1.1). The many businesses involved in agricultural marketing are known as **agribusinesses.** Every reader will fit somewhere into this system. Surely you are and will be a consumer, because food is the ultimate necessity. You might earn your living and develop as a professional in some part of this complex system. This text cannot train you for such specific positions as product manager, elevator manager, market news reporter, grain futures trader, fruit and vegetable grader, or merchandising manager. It can, however, teach you much about the marketing "game" that will help to prepare you for any career in agribusiness.

This book's purpose is twofold. First, by describing the principal structures and workings of the agricultural marketing system, we hope to provide an orientation that will help you—as a consumer, business person, and citizen—understand the developments and issues within it. Some of the processes and issues will be much the same a decade from now. Some processes and issues will surely be different, but many will be understandable if you think in terms of a market system.

EXHIBIT

1.1   Food marketing sales.

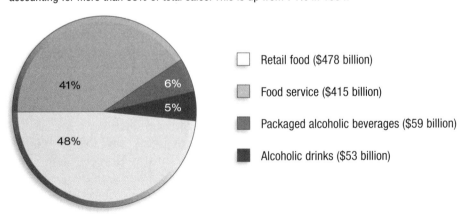

Food marketing sales in 2002 topped $1 trillion, with retail food store and food service sales accounting for more than 88% of total sales. This is up from 74% in 1994.

- Retail food ($478 billion)
- Food service ($415 billion)
- Packaged alcoholic beverages ($59 billion)
- Alcoholic drinks ($53 billion)

41%
6%
5%
48%

Source: USDA; Food CPI, Prices, and Expenditures. Compiled by the Economic Research Service.

Our second purpose is management oriented. We introduce you to ways of approaching many of the practical problems facing today's farmers and agribusiness. Examples include how to reduce commodity price uncertainty by contracting and how to reduce loss of market share by analysis of a product's life cycle. We also discuss the ways that supply and demand can guide a manager's decisions regarding supply response.

These two purposes overlap. A modern manager needs to understand something of the whole system to see his or her niche in it. Similarly, by understanding how to use a variety of approaches to the managerial problems of various market participants, a student will better understand the economic forces that affect the total food marketing system.

Powerful forces are at work, and these are the mainsprings that make a market system function, causing the continuous flows and adjustments of orders and products to keep the shelves of thousands of supermarkets stocked every day of the year. One of these forces is biology. A distinguishing characteristic of agricultural marketing is the biological nature of the products. Biological lags of months or years typically separate the actual delivery of a marketed item from the decision to produce it. For example, nearly six months are required to raise a hog, and it may take years before forestry or nut products can be marketed after the initiation of production. Much of the uniqueness in the food marketing system stems from this biological influence.

The system gradually changes as new products, new methods, and new systems of marketing or procurement are adopted and old ones fade away. The agricultural marketing system is a global one, and you should recognize that cultural differences often influence food purchasing decisions and that forces of change can come from across the globe. For example, from Exhibit 1.2 you can see that Japanese consumers have a strong preference for fish. So, a U. S. agribusiness may want to market food and food ingredient products to Japanese food firms that are complementary to fish consumption. Or, as vice-president of a grain merchandising business, you might have to decide where to invest in new facilities—New Orleans or Port of Santos, Brazil. Considering the change in percentage of production between the U. S. and Brazil as shown in Exhibit 1.3, you may decide to invest in a facility in Port of Santos. Similarly, the forces of public opinion and public policy constantly influence the marketing system.

THE MACRO VIEW OF MARKETING

The typical textbook approach to agricultural marketing has been a macro view—a description of the total system for marketing food and fiber. The "who" and "what" questions are given most emphasis, with some attention to "how" and "why." The boundaries of agricultural marketing are often said to be the farm gate and the final consumer. We formally define **macro marketing** as the performance of all business activities involved in the forward flow of goods and services from producers to consumers.

EXHIBIT

1.2 Consumer food expenditures by country.

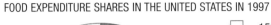

FOOD EXPENDITURE SHARES IN THE UNITED STATES IN 1997

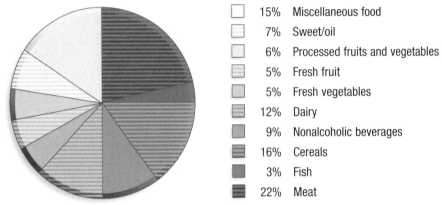

☐	15%	Miscellaneous food
☐	7%	Sweet/oil
☐	6%	Processed fruits and vegetables
☐	5%	Fresh fruit
☐	5%	Fresh vegetables
☐	12%	Dairy
☐	9%	Nonalcoholic beverages
☐	16%	Cereals
☐	3%	Fish
☐	22%	Meat

FOOD EXPENDITURE SHARES IN JAPAN IN 1997

Miscellaneous food	13%	☐
Sweet/oil	8%	☐
Processed fruits and vegetables	7%	☐
Fresh fruit	6%	☐
Fresh vegetables	10%	☐
Dairy	6%	☐
Nonalcoholic beverages	6%	☐
Cereals	14%	☐
Fish	18%	☐
Meat	12%	☐

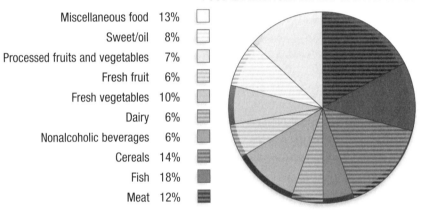

FOOD EXPENDITURE SHARES IN THE UNITED KINGDOM IN 2002

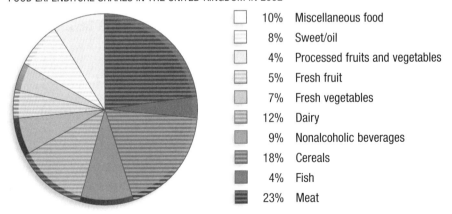

☐	10%	Miscellaneous food
☐	8%	Sweet/oil
☐	4%	Processed fruits and vegetables
☐	5%	Fresh fruit
☐	7%	Fresh vegetables
☐	12%	Dairy
☐	9%	Nonalcoholic beverages
☐	18%	Cereals
☐	4%	Fish
☐	23%	Meat

Source: Top: Consumer Economic Survey, 1997, U.S. Dept. of Labor Statistics. *Center:* National Survey of Family Income and Expenditure, 1997, Japanese Statistics Bureau. *Bottom:* Expenditure and Food Survey, 2002, United Kingdom Office for National Statistics.

EXHIBIT
1.3   Country production of soybeans as percentage of global production.

	Argentina	Brazil	China	United States
1999–2000	13%	22%	9%	45%
2001–2002	16%	24%	8%	43%
2003–2004	18%	28%	8%	36%
2004–2005	17%	30%	8%	35%

Source: USDA, 2006.

Exhibit 1.4 presents a macro view of the **marketing channel**—the set of firms that move a commodity from the farm to the consumer—for a typical agricultural commodity. The configuration reflects the fact that the commodity is concentrated into larger quantities handled by fewer firms as it moves to processors and then is broken down into smaller quantities as it moves to many retailers and even more consumers. Assemblers, processors, wholesalers, and retailers collaborate with farmers in the forward flow of the agricultural commodity from farm producers to consumers. Value is added at each stage. A packaged steak at the supermarket has a considerable value to a consumer. An equivalent amount of beef in a carcass at the packing house or on the hoof at the feedlot has far less consumer value, because the consumer cannot use the product in those forms and quantities. The forward flow of commodities and products is driven by a return flow

EXHIBIT
1.4   Stages in a marketing channel.

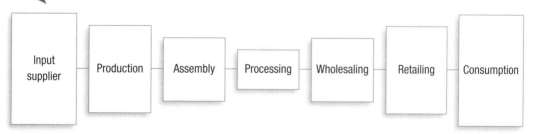

EXHIBIT

| **1.5** | The institutional approach. |

Players	Institutions	
Assemblers	Corporations	Futures/options
Order buyers	Cooperatives	Marketing orders
Commission agents	Organized markets	Generic checkoffs
Processors	Forward contracts	Retailer affiliations
Wholesalers	Contract production pools	Fast-food franchises
Brokers	Regulatory bodies	
Retailers		

of both dollars spent by domestic and foreign consumers and information about consumer preferences. Everyone in the system depends on the other people in the system performing their tasks.

In viewing agriculture marketing from the macro perspective, one can adopt an institutional, functional, or behavioral systems approach or some combination of the three.

Institutional Approach

One macro approach, the **institutional approach,** emphasizes the key institutions and institutional players—the "who" of marketing (see Exhibit 1.5). It is easy to list some of the people who do specialized marketing tasks. Those involved in handling commodities and those who work in pricing are often referred to as "middlemen," regardless of their gender. After all, in the flow between farmers and ultimate consumers, they are in the middle. Middlemen have classifications such as retailers, wholesalers, brokers, commission agents, and order buyers. Processors are also an important part of the marketing process, combining raw materials into the final products that you and I consume. Their decisions as to product design and merchandising may often be crucial in determining how well a particular item sells and, in turn, the level of demand for a particular farm commodity. Consider, for example, how the successful processing and merchandising of margarine increased the demand for vegetable oils (e.g., soybeans) and reduced the demand for butterfat and thus milk. Other important players include the government agencies that provide public services, such as market information and commodity grades, and those that regulate various aspects of marketing, from honest weights to product safety.

Institutions may be thought of as organized systems of behavior, such as organized markets, alliances, joint ventures, corporations, cooperatives, and marketing orders. An understanding of each of these is essential to an understanding of agricultural marketing. Some of the "whys" of marketing can best be understood in terms of these various institutional groups and their particular interests. For example, producers and commodity associations may oppose environmentalists and government concerning manmade river rise on the Missouri river, involving the issue of protecting an endangered species at the expense of limiting barge traffic or farm ground being flooded. One looks first at these institutions in appraising how a marketing innovation or new legislation might be received. The National Corn Growers Association, for example, has been instrumental in furthering renewable fuels legislation to enhance ethanol production.

Functional Approach

Another macro approach, the **functional approach,** emphasizes the functions performed in marketing. This is a "what" approach, focusing on specialized activities within the marketing process. The usual classification of functions is shown in Exhibit 1.6.

Obviously, the exchange functions—*buying* and *selling*—are important. Intelligent buying or selling is almost impossible without adequate market information, which requires the function of *market intelligence gathering.* Most sellers sell from inventories, so *storage* is essential to their business. Inventories require *financing.* The holding of valuable inventories (whether wheat or Wheaties, hogs or Hormel hot dogs, soybeans or Silk soy milk) involves risks of value changes; therefore, institutions have developed to facilitate *risk bearing.* Many buyers of agricultural commodities will buy unseen only if the commodity is graded. Hence, *standardization* becomes essential. Final consumers are interested in finished products and not raw

EXHIBIT

1.6   Classifications of functions in the marketing process.

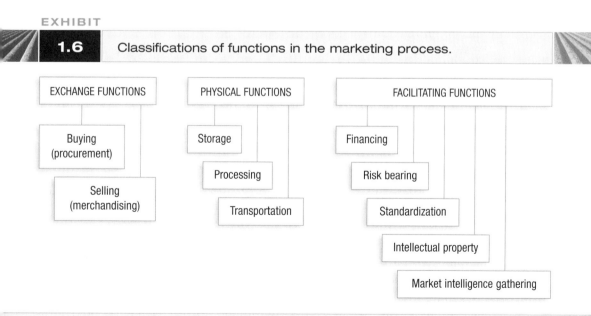

materials; thus, *processing* is necessary and is quite significant for some commodities. Few products are consumed where they are produced and so *transportation* to processors or end users is required.

The functional approach to studying marketing has several advantages. First, it helps us see what must be done. Those critics who talk of eliminating the middleman (to the presumed benefit of farmers or consumers) must face the fact that the job would remain to be done even if the middleman were "removed." It may be, of course, that some efficiencies could be gained by rearranging who performs which functions, and a study of functions may help market participants achieve such gains. The second advantage of the functional approach is that it simplifies a complex economy and reveals similarities that are not apparent when we focus on the "who" of marketing. We see that most of the players, such as farmers, retailers, processors, and assemblers, are each involved in buying and selling. Moreover, each group of players faces the problems of storage and transportation, of financing and risk bearing, of managing intellectual property, and so on.

Behavioral Systems Approach

A third macro approach is the behavioral systems approach. To some extent, the **behavioral systems approach** combines both of the previous approaches. This approach focuses on the interdependence and coordination of all the participants and all the functions of the entire system. It focuses on the flow of products as it is facilitated by a flow of market intelligence and on those firms and institutions where major decisions are made and where market leadership is exercised. Such an approach examines market power in the system and the leadership roles exercised by large or innovative firms. It shows how differing market structures require different types of production and marketing decisions.

In the 1990s the behavioral systems approach spawned contract production and marketing to enhance control of value, risk, and decision rights (functional and institutional elements). For example, a hog processor might offer a marketing contract to a would-be supplier in order to control quality (functional) to meet a special retailer need (institutional).

THE MICRO VIEW OF MARKETING

The micro approach to marketing is more typical of the modern business marketing text. **Micro marketing** is defined as the performance of business activities that direct the forward flow of goods and services to customers and accomplish the farmer's or the firm's objectives.[1]

The micro approach, although much narrower than the macro view, is still quite inclusive. Selling and buying are central to the micro concept of marketing, but they are only a part of it. In the micro view, marketing includes packaging, storage, transportation, pricing, financing, and even product design insofar as these activities direct the flow of goods and services to customers. Moreover, marketing includes the identification of consumer demands and their translation into a set of decisions as to what to produce, how much to produce, what channels to use, and how to promote products.

Central to the micro view of marketing is the purpose of accomplishing the firm's objectives. Firms seek to direct and control the flow of goods and services to their customers because they perceive control as essential to their objectives. Profit making is presumably a central objective of firms, although that objective need not preclude specific concerns such as increasing sales volume or selecting safe market strategies.

A merit of the micro definition of marketing is the emphasis on the active role required of the firm's management. In today's world, good products occur seldom enough. Few customers will ever know about the best of products if it is not marketed effectively. An effective micro marketing program involves more than a satisfactory price and a few ads. Effective marketing may involve numerous other conditions of satisfactory merchandising, including the assurance of availability at the right places in the proper packaging. Effective marketing is Subway developing a new product, the low-carb wrap, naming it the Atkins Friendly Fresh Wrap, and then spending millions promoting it. Effective marketing is ADM developing healthy new food products such as Novasoy brand soy isoflavones and then spending millions promoting the line.

Should we apply micro marketing ideas to farmers? Many farmers do not engage substantially in micro marketing activities. Nonetheless, these concepts do apply to farmers. The fact that farmers typically lack power over marketing activities is central to explaining not only much of what happens in agricultural marketing but also the frustration of many farmers with marketing. Granted, a few farmers (such as purebred livestock breeders or independent seed producers) do have an effective micro marketing program. Some other farmers are trying to engage in collective action to achieve an effective marketing system. The micro view of marketing is relevant to farmers as they seek to direct the flow of commodities from their farms in ways that will best serve their objectives.

The micro definition of marketing specifies a flow forward to the customer, who may be the final household consumer or an intermediate user. Thus, position in the market channel affects a firm's view of marketing. From the point of view of farmers, the assembly and processing of their commodities in their own cooperative is viewed as marketing. However, from the point of view of a corporate processor, assembly and processing is not likely to be called marketing. Because most business marketing texts begin with the manufacturer rather than the farmer, they typically do not define manufacturing or processing as marketing. Agricultural (farm) marketing is distinct from business marketing in that agricultural marketing often refers to timing, whereas business marketing refers to product strategies.

This book adopts, wherever possible, the micro viewpoint, which is managerial in orientation. It conceives of marketing problems as problems

facing the manager, whether he or she is a farmer, an assembler, a processor, or a retailer. All of these market participants employ various strategies
to solve marketing problems every working day. This is not a how-to book
for solving management problems, but it does strive for the manager's
micro orientation and will be valuable to readers who have (or anticipate
having) managerial responsibilities. For this reason, it may be helpful to
consider some of the manager's perceptions.

THE MICRO PROCUREMENT VIEWPOINT

All marketed commodities proceed down a one-way street.
Agricultural commodities move from farmer to processor to consumer, not the reverse. Like any object, their movement may be the
result of someone either pushing or pulling. In market channels, the guiding force may be a push (from the sellers) or a pull (from the buyers). As
suggested by both the institutional and the behavioral systems approaches,
it is important to know where the guiding forces originate.

Procurement at the micro level is defined similarly to micro marketing,
except that it is concerned with the flow to the firm rather than the flow
from the firm to its customers. Thus, we can rephrase the definition of
micro marketing to fit procurement. **Micro procurement** is the performance of business activities that direct the flow of agricultural commodities
to a firm to satisfy its objectives. Procurement obviously involves many of
the same activities as marketing, but it is viewed from a different vantage
point. Procurement is more than the single act of buying, just as micro
marketing is more than the single act of selling. To a modern agribusiness
firm, procurement generally involves an organized set of activities.
Procurement, to a corporate processor like Cargill, may involve buying,
assembling, storing, financing, and transporting grain and soybeans to its
processing plants; procurement, to a retailer, may involve determining
product specifications of a line of soups bearing its own retail brand, finding a processor, and then purchasing, financing, transporting, and
warehousing those soups.

Micro Procurement in a Macro Marketing Context

If one firm's marketing program is another firm's procurement program,
why bother with the distinction? It will require most of this text to show
why. The range of decision options open to a manager varies greatly with
his or her freedom and ability to develop a procurement and marketing
system. Farmers tend to be typical of those firms that have neither a
strong procurement nor a strong marketing program. Thus, many farmers exercise little control over the design, pricing, and handling of the
inputs they buy and of the commodities they sell. Some processors may
have a strong procurement program but may be limited in their marketing options because they face customers who have strong procurement

programs of their own. Other processors have both strong procurement and marketing programs.

To analyze managerial options as they exist at various levels of the marketplace, we must first distinguish between micro procurement and micro marketing options. The multiple marketing procurement nodes in the agricultural marketing channel are the focus of this textbook.

PULLING THE VIEWPOINTS TOGETHER

This text is eclectic. It reflects the institutional macro approach in that it focuses progressively on market participants—farmers, handlers, processors, wholesalers, retailers, food service units, and consumers—and in that it examines various institutions, such as futures options. It contains chapters and subsections that examine such functions as standardization, storage, transportation, and risk bearing. Following the behavioral systems approach, we place emphasis on how price and other devices coordinate a complex system. Processors are usually important leaders in the agricultural marketing system, and their key role in both procurement and marketing is highlighted. Much attention is given to how shifts in supply or demand change prices and thus change the signals to market participants. The "bonus" element in this text is the business emphasis—the managerial point of view. With that micro orientation, we examine how and why farmers make output choices while most other participants make price choices. From the micro orientation we examine strategies for handling commodity price risk and show how value chain participants link together as affiliates to cut costs.

Imagine that you are the vice-president for a national beef packer. Your firm has a 15-year-old beef slaughtering plant in a southern plains state. Its capacity is 500,000 head per year. Profits the last two years have been $5 per head. One of your competitors has started construction of a one-million-head capacity plant (slaughtering and processing) just 20 miles away. You estimate that the competing plant will have costs $10 per head below yours because of newer technology. What action do you recommend to your boss?

Imagine that you are the merchandising vice-president of a major food processor. Your firm's labs have just achieved a technological breakthrough: they have developed a cheap method of producing soy proteins with texture and flavor characteristics almost identical to those of a good steak. What sort of marketing program will you develop to exploit this marketing opportunity? How will you coordinate the value chain to get this commodity transformed into a product?

As stated earlier, this is not a manager's how-to book, but it does relate to managerial problems and solutions. After studying this text, you should have a better appreciation of these (and other) marketing and procurement problems and of managerial and economic perspectives.

MARKETING: AN APPRAISAL

Whether or not you expect to earn your living in the agricultural marketing system, you as a consumer and a citizen ought to develop an informed opinion about the system's performance. Following are a few questions and answers to help you begin thinking about the performance of our agricultural marketing system.

Is Our Agricultural Marketing System Unfair to Farmers?

Of the average consumer dollar spent on food in recent years, the marketing agencies got about 80¢ and left only 20¢ for the farmers who produced the food. Sometimes the ratio is higher than that—a cereal manufacturer may spend more on the box than the farmer receives for the grains and other ingredients that fill it.

Marketing cooperatives, bargaining associations for many specialty crops, industrywide advertising campaigns urging people to "eat more beef" or "drink more milk," and holding actions are all examples of farmers' attempts to influence and participate in marketing.

As you will learn from reading this book, basic economic principles help to explain why farmers receive such a small share of each consumer dollar spent on food, fiber, and fuel. Economic principles also will be used to explain why farmers have received an increasingly smaller portion of this dollar over time. Factors such as biological lag, low opportunity cost, and near perfect competition mean that farmers are in the position of "taking a price" rather than "making a price." Some agribusiness participants argue that market power by middlemen is the cause of farmers losing their fair share, but economics drives allocation of value between market chain participants.

Does the Marketing System Operate Efficiently?

It is easy to find achievements in our food marketing system that seem truly marvelous. Fantastic quantities of perishable products are moved quickly and efficiently across great distances to the shelves of supermarkets and food service firms. Spoilage is minimal, food safety is high, and variety and quality are rarely exceeded in any other country in the world.

By means of a market system too complex to be understood by most of its participants, the farm prices of a product such as wheat are determined daily, or even minute by minute, for almost every elevator in the world from Hartsburg, Germany, to Sydney, Australia. The differences in the prices of wheat from place to place or day to day usually can be explained logically in terms of the market. One of the merits of a market system is that it economizes on information. Market participants do not have to understand all that is going on throughout the system for the system to work effectively.

Are Consumers Served Properly?

Even if we can defend the operational efficiency of our marketing system, what about consumers? Are they served properly? In a market economy, much emphasis is properly given consumers. Their consumption is said to be the ultimate goal of the system, and their expenditures make the system operate. If sufficient numbers of consumers decide that they do not like to shop in supermarket X or to eat in restaurant Y, those firms will wither away. If sufficient numbers decide that they prefer broilers to beef for most meals, then broiler producers will prosper and beef producers will not. No agricultural product or agribusiness has a guaranteed attraction to buyers. Each must continue to earn its position in the marketplace. This concept is known as the economic doctrine of **consumer sovereignty,** whereby consumers, through their independent purchases, direct all production and market activities. Consumers, voting with their dollars, determine the winners and losers in the marketplace.

Can Sellers Influence Consumer Demand?

Every student should be aware of the other side of the coin—the fact that millions of dollars are spent every year to influence consumers. Consumers frequently are persuaded to buy through appeals to their emotions. (Next time you see a soft drink spot on TV, compare the emotional versus the informational content.) People can be persuaded to attribute desirable characteristics to one product and not to another even though they are identical from an objective point of view. This fact, of course, is one of the reasons that firms, including farmers, seek to exercise leadership in the marketing system. For example, when dairy farmers awake to find that soy milk processors are aggressively merchandising milk substitutes, they are seldom content to say, "Let the consumer be the judge." Instead, they say, "Let's band together to advertise milk" or "We should organize our own processing cooperative to merchandise our products." For the moment, we need not judge whether such reactions are in the public interest or even in the best interest of farmers in the long run. The point is that agribusinesses and farmers frequently influence consumers to buy the products or services that they have to sell.

Most large public food firms, such as Altria, Coca-Cola, Kellogg's, McDonald's, and Wal-Mart, have been highly successful in influencing consumers' demands for their specific products. Their influence on the diet and lifestyle of consumers is considerable. On the other hand, for many commodities, the influence of sellers on consumers' choices is moderate or nearly nonexistent. In these cases, a successful marketing program must be consumer oriented, in the sense that it must be concerned with achieving consumer satisfaction. That satisfaction can be supplied partly through effective packaging, advertising, and other attributes, if the product or service is within the ballpark of consumer demand. If it is not within that ballpark, some other product or service will likely push it off the supermarket shelves.

One of the goals of this text is to help you think within a framework in which you can perceive both the benefits of the domestic and global market system and the ways in which it fails consumers and producers.

SOME CONCLUDING COMMENTS

What you know already about marketing gives you a base on which to build. However, you will encounter many terms in the study of marketing that are new or that are used much more precisely than they are used in the media. You will encounter new information and ideas that can give you additional ways of analyzing marketing behavior. You may also encounter information and concepts that challenge some of your present beliefs.

Marketing and Economics

A prior study of economic principles is essential to understanding marketing, but economics and marketing are not the same subject. Economic principles concern those problems common to any society: What is produced in what quantities? How, and by whom, are goods and services produced? For whom shall goods be produced?[2] The marketing system is only a part of the entire economy, so the field of marketing is narrower than economics. But economic principles certainly apply in the agricultural marketing system. Firms at each stage of the marketing system, from farmers to retailers, add value to the foods and fibers. Among the many competing food commodities (wheat, corn, pork, and so on) and even more competing food products (Michelob Ultra, Green Giant frozen sweet corn, and Hormel Hams, for example), market forces determine the kinds, qualities, and quantities that reach consumers. Similarly, decisions are made as to whether wheat is stored on farms or in terminal elevators, whether meat packing plants are located near the big-city consumption centers or out in the country near the livestock, and whether we are offered hamburgers in four-ounce or two-ounce patties—all on the basis of market forces.

In another sense, marketing is broader than economic principles. Other disciplines, such as psychology and management science, are helpful in dealing with managerial problems. Marketing certainly tends to be less abstract and more institutional than economic principles. We get more into the nitty-gritty of everyday experience, and we learn more about how things actually work and spend less time thinking about economic forces at large. Again, our approach to marketing frequently emphasizes the firm manager's individual perspective rather than a social perspective.

Micro and Macro Again

It is appropriate to emphasize again that you are being asked to think at two different levels. On the micro level, you are asked to think like a manager of a farm or an agribusiness firm as you look at marketing and procurement problems and opportunities. On the macro level, you are asked to look at a bigger picture—at the way the total marketing system or some large part of it works. Each level of approach is helpful to understanding the other level, as long as you keep both in mind.

Thinking in macro terms takes practice. What seems so obviously true from an individual point of view may not be true from a systemic point of view. All of us have experienced that truth in one way or another. For example, think about spectators at a football game. It is obvious to an individual spectator that he or she can see a play better by standing up. But when everyone stands up, do they see any better than if they all had stayed seated? In your economic principles course, you most likely read about the **fallacy of composition:** what is true for a part (or for an individual) is not necessarily true for the whole (or for the entire group). It is easy to find examples of the fallacy of composition in marketing. You may say to yourself, "If I adopt this new merchandising technique, I should be able to double my market share from its present 5%." What if all of your competitors arrived at the same decision? Could each and every one double their market share? Does that mean that you should not bother adopting this new technique? What happens to your market share if competitors adopt it and you do not?

SUMMARY

1. Agricultural marketing, as defined from a macro (social) perspective, is the performance of all business activities involved in the forward flow of food and fiber from farm producers to consumers.

2. In the micro (individual firm) perspective, agricultural marketing is defined as the performance of business activities directing the forward flow of goods and services to customers and accomplishing the objectives of a particular firm (farmer or agribusiness).

3. The one-way flow to market is guided by leading firms in the marketing system. Such firms may organize and guide their procurement (purchasing) as well as their marketing. Micro procurement is defined as the performance of business activities that direct the flow of agricultural commodities to a firm to satisfy its objectives. Large processors often have strong procurement and marketing programs.

4. Most agricultural marketing texts have a macro viewpoint. They may focus mainly on the functions performed, such as buying, selling, storage, transporting, and financing, or they may focus more on the institutions or types of firms, such as processors, brokers, wholesalers, and retailers. Usually, emphasis is on the coordination and interdependence of all market participants and an examination of market pricing and techniques of coordination that knit everyone into a system. This text goes one step further by emphasizing the managerial

viewpoint of micro marketing and micro procurement—that of real firms facing real problems.

5. The study of agricultural marketing includes concepts, terms, and facts not included in the study of economic principles. There is, however, much application of economic principles, because marketing is an economic activity. Competition among market participants is an important force in coordinating the flow to market. Economic incentives drive most decision making.

STUDY QUESTIONS

1. Why would American soybean producers care about the weather in South America? Is this distinction macro, micro, or a mixture of micro and macro?

2. Distinguish between micro marketing and micro procurement. What do they have in common?

3. What function relates best to a broker trading grain futures on the Chicago Board of Trade?

4. Is the satisfaction of consumers essential to the accomplishment of a firm's objectives as stated in the definition of micro marketing?

5. Who is the "consumer"? Think of your own personal and family experiences as a consumer.

6. If you were a dairy farmer, would you like the dairy processors to advertise milk and milk products (e.g., cheese or ice cream)? Why or why not?

7. Can you identify a case where falling consumption was evident for a food product? Why was this?

8. Select a high-income and a low-income country and compare their agricultural marketing systems. Who are the producers, processors, consumers, and regulators?

CLASS EXERCISE

For this exercise, your instructor will place you into groups with a different agricultural commodity assigned to each group. Most of the end-of-chapter exercises in the book will build from this initial exercise.

For the agricultural commodity assigned, each group member should separately research the commodity using the Internet and other resources and then discuss the following questions:

1. Where is it produced?
2. When is it planted or born?
3. When is it harvested or slaughtered?
4. How many production cycles does it turn?
5. How much does it cost to produce?
6. How much is it worth?
7. Which agribusinesses buy it?
8. What are five end-user products that come from it?

Each group should then prepare to lead a class discussion on the assigned commodity.

 NOTES

1. Adapted from E. Jerome McCarthy, *Basic Marketing: A Managerial Approach,* 5th ed. (Homewood, IL: Richard D. Erwin, 1975), p. 19.
2. P. A. Samuelson, *Economics,* 10th ed. (New York: McGraw-Hill, 1976), pp. 17–18.

CHAPTER

2

THE COMPETITIVE ENVIRONMENT

PREVIEW

- Participants in marketing, whether businesspeople or farmers, need to understand the environment in which they operate. The competitive nature of their markets is a significant part of the marketing environment.

- The competitor in perfect competition (atomism) faces different problems and copes in different ways than a competitor in monopolistic competition or an oligopoly because of the opportunities and constraints of the environment.

- Competitive models are useful tools to help marketing management better understand their environment and the causes of market reactions.

- Economic concepts such as demand, supply, economies of size, long run, marginal revenue, marginal cost, and opportunity cost are helpful in understanding and predicting market variables.

KEY TERMS

diseconomies of size

imperfect competition

industry

law of demand

law of supply

market

market model

monopolistic competition

oligopoly

perfect competition

price leader

price maker

price taker

product differentiation

Marketing requires many kinds of decisions. Sellers decide what to produce; when, where, and how to sell; how to price; and how to deal with dissatisfied customers. Buyers decide what to buy and, if they are commercial buyers such as meat processors, make complex decisions about what, when, where, and how to buy; how to price; and how to deal with dissatisfied sellers. These decision makers are organized into individual businesses called *firms*. Whether a firm involves only a family (as is true of many farms) or thousands of people (as is true of Coca-Cola), it is a basic decision-making unit in marketing.

Marketing takes place within a **market,** which is defined as all the possible buyers and sellers of a product or commodity. For convenience, the final buyers who buy to consume are called *consumers*. The various firms that produce and participate in marketing may be sellers, buyers, or both. Thus, a particular market always involves both buyers and sellers; it may involve only firms, as when farmers sell wheat to elevators, or it may include both firms and consumers, as when you shop at a supermarket.

A *set of competing firms* producing similar products or a commodity in a market is called an **industry** (e.g., the meat processing industry or the restaurant industry). Alternatively, Burger King is a firm competing in the restaurant industry.

The competitive environment within a market has a powerful impact on the market alternatives available to a firm. A major objective of this chapter is to help you understand the implications of this statement.

MARKET MODELS

A model is a simplified representation—such as the model trains or model airplanes you may have played with as a child. Perfect competition, oligopolistic competition, and monopolistic competition are models of competition. Economists use these **market models** because they aid in understanding and talking about real markets. The next sections provide an overview of each model. In later chapters, you will encounter numerous descriptions of firms operating in various market environments. The discussions of these models will help you understand the marketing alternatives available to firms.

Perfect Competition

Your economic principles text likely gave much attention to a type of competitive market called *pure,* or *perfect, competition.* This text uses the term **perfect competition.** One important characteristic of such a competitive environment is that it is made of many competing firms (usually sellers, but they could be buyers), each of which is too small for its independent decisions to influence the market in a way perceptible to the firm. Another important characteristic is that all of the firms sell the same commodity, so buyers do not care which seller they buy from. Your principles text probably used the production of an agricultural commodity like canola or soybeans as an example of a homogeneous product required for perfect competition. It is tough to find commodity examples outside of farming. There are some relatively homogeneous products, such as gasoline, that consumers could consider as commodities. Still, we often have a favorite filling station because of its convenient location, the other products and services sold there, or the friendliness of its employees, so that the product is not truly interchangeable.

Although we recognize that perfect competition is an unusual marketing environment, it is one polar extreme instructive in itself and in helping us understand other types of markets. How does a firm act within a perfect market? Its marketing alternatives are limited. Promotion by a single firm does not pay because buyers treat one firm's commodity the same as its rival's commodity. Price is determined by supply and demand forces outside the control of the firm, so it must accept price as a given. A firm in a perfectly competitive environment is a **price taker**—a market participant that buys or sells such a small part of the market's total that its most important decisions involve responding to price levels with appropriate decisions about output. So competition among firms under perfect competition is primarily cost based.

A perfectly competitive firm (Exhibit 2.1) has a short-run, U-shaped average cost (AC) curve. This keeps the firm "small" because it cannot produce output QB as cheaply as can two competitive firms, each of which is producing the smaller amount, QA. Any firm in the *short run* will have a U-shaped average cost curve because there is not time for it to adjust its fixed factors (plant), and so it encounters diminishing returns. By definition of the *long run,* there are no fixed factors, so there are no diminishing returns. Rising average costs in the long run are called **diseconomies of size.** If perfectly competitive firms did not have U-shaped cost curves, they would not be forced to remain relatively small. If a competitive firm grows large enough to affect prices, then perfect competition no longer exists, and the firm's marketing alternatives change.

A farmer's set of marketing decisions varies with the farm's size, commodity product mix, individual or group sales, and whether it is selling directly or indirectly to consumers. Traditionally farms produced commodities, and there was no point in promotion unless it took place across the entire industry. The industrialization of farming has altered the relationship so that more farmers are producing commodities with specific characteristics; thus, they are more amenable to being differentiated or fitting into particular niche markets.

A perfectly competitive firm faces a horizontal demand curve because, as a price taker, it faces "a going price" for whatever amount it sells. The going price is determined by levels of market demand and supply. As a profit-making firm it adjusts its output to equate its marginal costs (MC) to the going price. You recall from your principles course why profit is maximized

EXHIBIT

2.1   Perfectly competitive firm, short run.

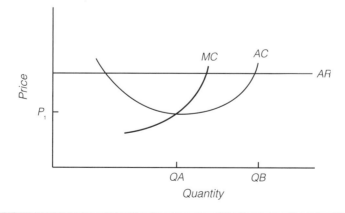

at the output where $MC = P$ marginal revenue *(MR)* when generalized to all market structures. At a smaller output, the extra revenue *(P)* from a unit of sales is greater than the extra costs *(MC)*, so the firm increases profits by expanding output. At a larger output than that where $MC = P$, the extra revenue is less from a unit of sales than the extra costs, so the firm increases profits by reducing output.

When price *(AR)* is above P_1, the firm earns nice profits; at price P_1, it earns only the "normal profits" necessary for that business to operate that are of average costs *(AC)*; at prices below P_1, it incurs losses, and it will eventually shut down temporarily or permanently if losses are too great. Thus, on the production side, a perfectly competitive firm can do little but adjust output up or down as prices change. The firm has more choices on the marketing side. That is, the firm has choices about when to sell that are frequently made independently of its production decisions. The choices cannot be shown on Exhibit 2.1, but they are discussed in later chapters. One adaptation of our analysis to market realities is to say that any firm adjusts its production to an expected price, which may or may not be the price actually received.

Besides many competitors and a homogeneous product (commodity), a third important characteristic of a perfectly competitive market is easy entry or more competitors when prices are good (highly profitable) and exit of some competitors when prices are bad (unprofitable). We will look at these longer-run characteristics of competitive adjustment later in the chapter. Entry and exit are extremely important aspects of markets. Entry increases total sales and erodes the prices and profits obtained by existing sellers. On the other hand, exit from a perfectly competitive market reduces total sales (output) and relieves pressure on each of the remaining sellers by allowing a higher price and greater share of total sales.

It is hard for a firm in perfect competition to make really big profits. Price is the same for every seller, so having lower costs is one way to excel. Thus, perfect competition pressures firms to reduce costs. That is usually good for consumers.

Imperfect Competition

We live in a world of differentiated products and services. As buyers, we prefer to buy a particular hamburger sold by a specific firm or a specific pizza delivered to our home or residence hall. A seller of a differentiated product operates in a very different competitive environment from that of a seller of a commodity. The firm under **imperfect competition** usually finds it profitable to advertise and otherwise promote its own product or service. The seller finds that, within limits, it can set its prices. In fact, it is expected to set and post such prices if it sells to consumers. Even a food processor selling to retailers sets its prices for its differentiated products, although it may negotiate prices with retailers on commodities (such as some fresh meats). Those firms that set price or negotiate it with those on the other side of the market are called price setters, price searchers, or **price makers.**

Monopolistic Competition

When a market contains many firms, each competing to sell a product or service that is somewhat different, this market is called **monopolistic competition.** A better term might be *differentiated competition,* because *monopolistic* can be misleading. Monopoly (one seller) is far different from monopolistic competition (many sellers), so do not confuse them, and do not try to save time by referring to the latter as *monopoly.* There is so much competition among the many sellers that the price results often appear similar to those of perfect competition. As the many firms compete to sell their similar products, they tend to reduce prices about as far as their costs will allow. The big difference that buyers can see between monopolistic and perfect competition is the combination of a variety of products and prices and promotional messages. Even in a fairly small city, a pizza lover may choose among many sizes and tastes, and among free home delivery, a pickup window, or eating in a variety of restaurant atmospheres. When **product differentiation** exists, buyers perceive significant differences among the products or services offered by various sellers. Each seller is the only seller (monopoly) of his particular pizza combination—thus the name *monopolistic competition.*

Compared to a farmer, the pizza restaurant has many more management decisions to make. A pizza restaurant owner must decide how to market, which involves decisions about the size, location, and atmosphere of her restaurant; whether to offer delivery; what days and hours to be open; ingredients, pricing, general advertising, and special promotions; drinks and associated foods to serve; and so on. Menu decisions, especially pricing, are constrained by what her competitors are doing. One of the striking differences from perfect competition is that the monopolistic competitor does not make the output decisions. Sales volume (output) is a partial result of marketing decisions about product, price, and promotion. She sells all that her market allows her to sell at any given price. As shown in Exhibit 2.2, a firm manager in monopolistic competition faces a declining demand curve, so that sales quantity is limited by the price that is set—the higher the price, the lower the sales. What one must not forget is that the *height* of the sales curve, *AR,* which affects the prices and profits, is influenced greatly by the decisions made about the product, its promotion, and the total of all nonprice competition. A firm may make above-average profits over a long period for either or both of two rea-

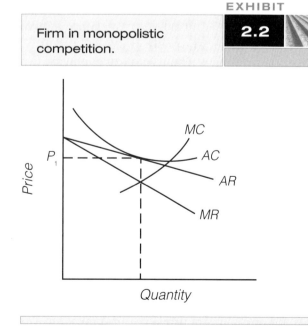

EXHIBIT

2.2

Firm in monopolistic competition.

sons: (1) lower costs than rivals (as in perfect competition) or (2) a better accepted product than rivals that yields a higher price.

Entry and exit are easy in monopolistic competition and cause much the same effects as in perfect competition. That is, any significant increase in demand, with its resulting growth in profits for each seller, will cause sufficient entry into the industry that average profits return to their previous level.

Oligopoly

Within numerous markets, a typical firm may be viewed as large in relation to its market. An extreme example might be a market containing only one, two, or three sellers. An isolated village in Wyoming and its surrounding area may be served by only two food stores. Both stores are small firms, but they are large in relation to the small market. Many retail markets are local because people prefer not to drive long distances to buy groceries. Outside urban areas, markets are numerically small and are served by only a few competitors. On the other hand, some regional or national markets are served by relatively few firms that are giant by most measures, such as Wal-Mart and Kroger.

Marketing competition among a few firms of fairly similar size is called **oligopoly.** Purchasing competition among a few firms is called *oligopsony.* The chief characteristic of an oligopoly is a high degree of interdependence; in making strategic decisions, each firm considers the possible reactions of each of its rivals. If you and I share a pie, the bigger the piece I eat, the less you get. So it is if you and I share a market. Such interdependence produces a basic uncertainty. A firm's sales depend not only on its strategies but also on how its rivals react to its strategies. A small cut in price might lead to a profitable jump in sales if competitors do not react—or to an unprofitable loss of sales if rivals more than match the price cut.

Typically, there is product differentiation among rival oligopolists. Conceptually, an oligopolistic firm faces a demand curve sloping much like that shown in Exhibit 2.2 for the firm in monopolistic competition. The important distinction is that any marketing decision, such as changing promotion or changing price, may incur a reaction by one's rivals that moves and reshapes that demand curve. Thus, a firm competing with only a few others faces a continual strategy problem. Often, all concerned adopt some sort of "live and let live" policy that means each seldom makes any really major (i.e., dangerous) shifts in prices or in other marketing strategies. For example, if two grocery stores serve a neighborhood, each may use the same suggested markup supplied by the distributor so that their prices and margins are much the same. An oligopolistic firm still considers whether promotion or price change might be profitable, but the manager does so within the context of whether it may incur a reaction from rivals. It is no longer as simple as saying: To maximize, one equates *MR* to *MC.*

Entry into oligopoly is typically not easy. If it were easy, there would be more firms. If a firm must have one-third of the market to have enough volume to be efficient, then an entrant has to be strong enough to force out an incumbent (existing) firm. That is much more challenging than gaining the 1% market share necessary to becoming the ninety-ninth firm in an industry that already has 98 firms. Moreover, there may be other special reasons, such as patents for many pharmaceuticals, locations, government regulation, or deeply held brand loyalties (such as Coke and Pepsi), that make it costly (or occasionally impossible) for potential entrants to gain the necessary market share. Difficulty of entry has long-run profit implications that will be explored later in the chapter.

In some oligopolistic industries, the rivals sell a commodity rather than differentiated products. Because buyers are then likely to be highly responsive to any price differences, the sellers must generally set the same price or else engage in a dangerous price warfare until one or more collapse. Warfare is the exception. The tricky marketing challenge is changing prices when changes in costs or demands make it important to do so. Some firm usually leads with a price change, acting as a **price leader,** and all the rivals in the industry quickly change their prices as well. In some industries, the same firm may initiate price changes for several years. In some markets, the same markup is accepted by everyone. For example, a retail price may be 25% above wholesale, and all prices will change together. Thus, the marketing alternatives for a commodity oligopoly differ from those of a differentiated oligopoly in the following ways: pricing is even more sensitive, dollars spent in promotion are few because the individual promoter has to share the benefits with rivals, and little or no attention is given to product research and development. Exhibit 2.3 compares the main models of market competition.

EXHIBIT

2.3   Market models compared.

MODELS

CHARACTERISTICS	PERFECT COMPETITION	MONOPOLISTIC COMPETITION	OLIGOPOLY (SELLER) OLIGOPSONY (BUYER)	MONOPOLY (SELLER) MONOPSONY (BUYER)
Nature of product	Homogeneous	Differentiated	Homogeneous/differentiated	Differentiated (patent)
Number of firms	Many	Many	Few	One (legally exists with government regulation)
Ease of entry for new firms	Easy	Fairly easy	Difficult	Very difficult to impossible
Market strategies	Timing of sales	Set price, brand names, promotion, product design, and packaging	Set price; if differentiated then establish brand name, promotion, product design, and packaging	Set price based on marginal cost equal to marginal revenue

SUPPLY AND DEMAND

ow do economists reconcile supply-and-demand analysis with market models? Supply-and-demand analysis can ignore firms and their considerations about price making and interdependence. For certain purposes, such as determining price levels or explaining the typical impact on market prices of a shift in consumer attitudes, supply-and-demand analysis is all we need. However, there are also important, logical ties between market models and supply-and-demand analysis.

Demand Changes for a Perfectly Competitive Firm

Supply-and-demand analysis best fits the perfect competition market model, where the price is determined by economic forces for a given commodity and the sellers accept (take) the price. Price makers in the other models, however, are not immune from the forces of supply and demand, so we can usually approximate results in those markets by analyzing supply and demand.

You will recall from economic principles that supply generally is not a single amount but rather a schedule of alternative quantities that will be offered for sale at different prices. The **law of supply** states that sellers will ordinarily offer more at higher prices than at lower prices, if other things hold constant. Thus, a supply curve will generally slope upward and to the right. The logic behind the law of supply is that to increase the output of any commodity (X), its producers must bid inputs (resources such as labor, land, machines, and services) away from the production of other items. It is likely that some of these new resources will be not only more costly but also less well adapted to producing commodity X. These are two reasons that average production costs may rise as output increases.

To refresh your memory of demand concepts, we will review them briefly. *Demand* is defined as the schedule of alternative quantities that a buyer or buyers will purchase at different prices. The **law of demand** states that the quantity of a good purchased will increase as its price is reduced. This downward sloping demand curve can be explained by the concept of diminishing marginal utility. Suppose that you pay $3.80 for a sandwich. You decide to buy one, so its utility to you is worth the cost. However, if the price of that sandwich were lower, say $2.97, you might decide to buy two sandwiches. Presumably, the price would have to be even lower (say $2.00) before you would buy three. The example suggests why your demand curve for sandwiches has a negative slope—why you will buy more units at a lower price than at a higher price. Consider now that some people who like sandwiches more than you do might each buy one at a price of $5.00, whereas others would not buy a sandwich at $2.97 but would at say $1.69. Thus, the slope of the demand curve reflects the increased number of buyers as prices go down, plus the likely increased purchases of each buyer as prices go down.

You will recall also that demand can shift. For example, in the late 1990s the poker game Texas Hold 'Em was virtually unknown. By 2004 demand increased for playing the game as television coverage caused consumer preference for and awareness of Texas Hold 'Em. This is a consumer preference change that caused the demand curve to move to the right. A demand curve may shift for various reasons—we discuss some of them in Chapter 4.

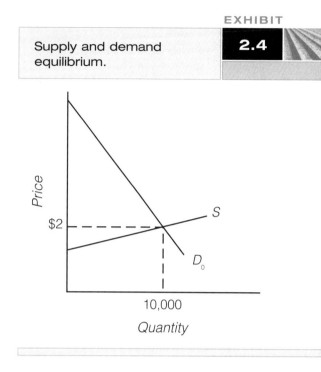

EXHIBIT **2.4**

Supply and demand equilibrium.

As illustrated in Exhibit 2.4, price equilibrates the two schedules of supply and demand at a single quantity and a single price (for a given time period). Price must be $2 when supply is S and demand is D_0. At any price lower than $2, the would-be buyers want a larger quantity (more than 10,000) than the would-be seller will sell (they offer less than 10,000). At any price higher than $2, the would-be sellers offer more than 10,000, whereas the would-be buyers are willing to buy fewer than 10,000 units. Thus the price of $2 is the only price that can last; it is the only price that satisfies the market forces.

Over time, the supply schedule may shift to the right or the left. For example, the supply curve for hogs will shift to the left after a short corn crop raises feed prices. Gains in the efficiency of producing hogs, such as more pigs farrowed per sow, will shift the supply schedule for hogs to the right. Whereas the supply shift in the first example was temporary (the supply curve will shift again with the next change in the cost of feed), the second example ordinarily represents a permanent shift. In the past decade, the real price of hogs (price adjusted to compensate for general inflation of all prices) has fallen a few dollars per hundredweight because of a relatively stable demand for hogs and steady gains in the efficiency of production that have gradually shifted the supply curve to the right.

Suppose that demand shifts to the right, as illustrated by D_1 in Exhibit 2.5. If this demand shift were sudden, the immediate impact might be for the price to jump to $4 (the price at which 10,000 units will clear the market) before any supply response. However, the existing sellers would soon expand at these profitable prices, and their increased sales, as shown by the short-run supply curve S_{SR} in the exhibit, would drive the price down to $3. Given a longer time, new sellers would enter the market, and eventually the price would fall back to $2.30, where the long-run supply, S_{LR}, cuts the D_1 demand curve. This new price of $2.30 would prevail until there is another shift in demand or supply. To summarize, the short-run market adjustment to the demand shift produced a price of $3, whereas the long-run adjustment produced a price of $2.30.

2.5 Short- and long-run supply-and-demand adjustments.

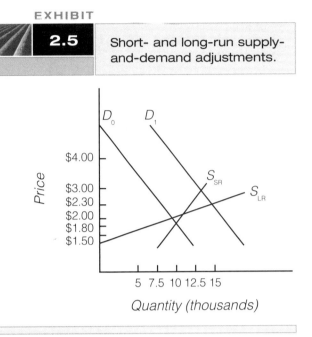

The practical lessons to a seller or marketing manager are (1) to increase output quickly in response to price rises and (2) to make longer-run responses in terms of what the price is likely to be after everyone has adjusted rather than where price is now. The fact that price did not fall when one seller quickly increased output does not mean price will not fall when additional sellers increase their output. Such joint expansion will reduce market price. Those two strategies are not foolproof, of course, but if the price rise is due to a demand increase, they generally will pay off.

Now let's tie these supply-and-demand illustrations to the costs and revenues of perfectly competitive firms. Suppose that each of 500 firms is producing 20 units per period at the original industry price of $2. When a demand shift causes a price jump above $4, a typical competitive firm expands output as rapidly as possible and soon has its output up to 25 units (Exhibit 2.6a). However, as it and other firms each expand output to 25 units, the price falls to $3, as explained before ($500 \times 25 = 12,500$). At a $3 price, the competitive firm is in short-run equilibrium, its $MC = \$3 = MR$, and its profits are abnormally high. This short-run equilibrium, however, is disrupted by the entry of more sellers, so that the price eventually falls to $2.30. (Remember that a key characteristic of perfect competition is easy entry and ready exit.) Costs of all sellers may be bid up in this process of industry expansion. Thus, $2.30 (instead of $2) becomes the new long-run equilibrium price because the sellers are willing to provide a total output that will clear the market at $2.30 (Exhibit 2.6b). The various positions over time for the firm are charted in the exhibit as points 1, 2, 3, and 4, where AC_1 represents the average costs after the increase in long-run costs. This would cause the short-run supply curve to shift to the right, now intersecting D_1 and S_{LR} at a price of $2.30.

In the real world, most changes in demand are much smaller than the change just discussed. Such a large shift in demand would probably be caused by a major change in the attitudes of many prospective buyers or the addition of many new buyers to the market. Such a major change may occur during the introduction of a new, highly promoted product, but it seldom occurs for a farm commodity. A change in demand of 1% for beef, pork, or broilers during a year would be a significant change in the real world. Our example used a much larger shift in demand to make it easy for you to see.

EXHIBIT

2.6   Short-run and long-run adjustments of a firm in perfect competition.

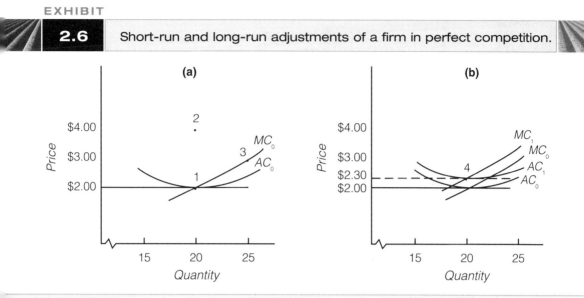

Demand Changes in Monopolistic Competition

Monopolistic competition reacts in its own way to a change in demand. A change in demand to a price maker is first signaled by a change in the number of orders or the amount of business transacted, not by a change in price (as in perfect competition). Changes in demand are not likely to be felt uniformly when there is product differentiation. In fact, sometimes demand may be shifting from some competitors' products to others in the industry. If so, McDonald's sales could be decreasing, for example, while Burger King's sales were rising (with prices constant at both firms). Price changes depend on decisions of the price maker. Although we can predict the direction these decisions will take, we cannot be very precise as to timing and magnitude. For example, small changes in demand may be ignored. As in perfect competition, a large increase in demand will almost certainly lead to higher prices and quantities. Moreover, the same short- and long-run considerations are relevant to the extent that entry is easy.

Imagine that per capita incomes are rising, fuel prices are falling, and the popularity of fast-food service is rising. Thus, the demand curves faced by most (perhaps all) fast-food restaurants shift to the right. Suppose that a particular restaurant (R) has had price set at P_1 for the past dozen accounting periods and has regularly achieved sales of Q_1. If we can assume that the revenue and cost curves $(AR_1$ and $AC)$ facing R are as shown in Exhibit 2.7, then Q_1 and P_1 are, respectively, the profit maximizing output and price. The dot above Q_1 at the level of P_1 and on the average cost curve indicates that R's average revenue is equal to its average cost, so it is making normal profits but no more. Remember that R chooses the price, whereas the flow of customers determines whether it reaches output Q_1. Now suppose that the above-mentioned improvement in general demand occurs. Assume that R is pleased to

EXHIBIT

2.7   Changes in demand experienced by a firm in monopolistic competition.

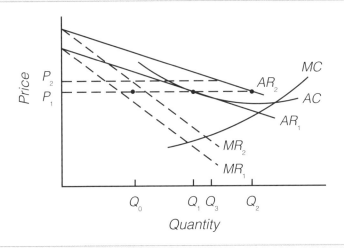

discover that sales have increased to Q_2. Given that R hasn't changed the price, a new average revenue AR_2 is indicated by the dot above Q_2 at a level with P_1. Have profits risen? Of course. Average profits per unit of sales have risen (the AR now exceeds AC), and sales are also up. What should R do? Perhaps nothing more than enjoy it! Perhaps it should think about building another fast-food restaurant in a good location somewhere! With sufficient information, the new demand curves facing the restaurant, shown by AR_2 and MR_2, can be determined. If so, then R can determine the new profit maximizing price. In the example shown, the new profit-maximizing price, P_2, is above the old price, P_1, and the new best output is more than the old output, Q_1.

Because R can adjust to either sales increase (i.e., Q_2 or a Q_3 between Q_1 and Q_2), will the industry be in equilibrium? The usual assumption is that anytime AR exceeds AC, there will be entry. What will be the impact of these entries on R? We may assume that each entrant will get a small share of the market and that R will lose a tiny bit of market to each entrant. Eventually, then, R finds that sales are declining. If general demand for fast food stabilizes and entry continues, then R may eventually find itself back in the $P_1 \, Q_1$ situation. Of course, if R did buy another fast-food restaurant when times were good, it now may have two restaurants, each operating at a point approximating $P_1 \, Q_1$.

This process of market adjustment typically takes several years. Perhaps you have seen it happen. For example, a small city has a sizable increase in population. For a while, the restaurants are crowded by the influx of new-comers, and restaurant profits rise. But soon, new restaurants are built, and eventually the typical restaurant in that city is no busier than it was before the increase in demand, and profits return to their old level.

What if a general decrease occurred in the demand for fast-food servic-es? Then R would discover that sales per accounting period have fallen to

Q_0. What should R do? It should tighten cost controls. It may experiment with moving price up or down, but the charts give little hope that R can break even. A price increase offers more hope than a decrease, although we would have to develop a new set of revenue curves to prove that. (Because demand has shifted to the left, new revenue curves are needed.) The more likely remedy is that some fast-food restaurants will have to drop out. As they leave, their ex-customers will shift to the remaining firms, and gradually the demands of the survivors will shift back toward the $P_1 \, Q_1$ equilibrium.

Notice the parallel between perfect competition and monopolistic competition. A shift to the right in demand increases profits, whereas a shift to the left causes losses. Profits and losses are a guide in both models to resource allocation as extra profits stimulate entry into the industry and losses stimulate exit from it. Note also the differences. When the firm is the price taker (perfect competition), a *price* variation signals a demand change and leads the manager to do something about output. When the firm is a price maker (monopolistic competition), a *sales* variation signals a demand change and leads the manager to consider doing something about price. Prices do change less frequently in monopolistic competition than in perfect competition because the price maker controls them, but output is less under control. Notice that neither firm can control both output and price. The price taker sets output (in anticipation of a certain price) and leaves price to be determined in the market. The price maker sets price (in anticipation of a certain output) and leaves the quantity of sales to be determined in the market. Needless to say, profits are not guaranteed by either market model—if there are too many competitors (or costs are rising rapidly or management is bad), any firm may encounter losses.

Demand Changes in Oligopolistic Markets

In oligopolistic markets, a demand increase is experienced by an individual seller as an increase in the volume sold, as was true in monopolistic competition. A seller faces the same questions as in monopolistic competition: whether to raise prices and/or expand facilities. Two extra considerations apply: (1) How will one's rivals react to any actions? (2) If profits are really great, will one or more new sellers try to enter the industry? If entry is greatly feared, the seller might hold down her own prices to make entry less attractive. The seller might build more capacity to meet the greater demand and also to discourage any potential entrants. On the other hand, in the case of some effective barriers to entry, the existing sellers may experience the same high profits in the long run that prevailed in the short run.

Suppose that a general decrease in demand is experienced that impacts all sellers by cutting their sales. Will sellers cut price? Perhaps, although each will probably move cautiously to avoid a price war. Usually a small, temporary fall in demand can be endured without any price changes. A small and more permanent fall in demand may reduce profits from good to minimal.

Another significant difference between the perfect competitor and his counterpart in monopolistic or oligopolistic competition is their possible

2.8   Impacts of a large decline in demand in alternative market models.

MARKET MODELS

SITUATIONS	PERFECT COMPETITION	MONOPOLISTIC COMPETITION	OLIGOPOLY
First indication of a demand decline	Price falls	Orders or sales decline for most firms	Orders or sales decline for most firms
Likely first reaction of a firm	Cut output	Cut output, change promotion	Cut output or change promotion
Later reactions of a firm	Nothing new	Likely alter price or experiment with nonprice variables	Likely alter price or experiment with nonprice variables
What happens in the long run	Numerous firms exit	A few firms exit	Possibly an exit
Impact of exits on each remaining firm	Raises prices	Strengthens demand and increases sales	Strengthens demand and increases sales
Comparison of equilibrium prices before and after the decline in demand	Later price a bit lower	Later price likely a bit lower or the same	Not predictable

reactions to changes in demand (Exhibit 2.8). The latter two have the additional competitive tools of changes in their product and promotion. A fall in demand may be met by an increase in advertising or a remodeling of the restaurant, for example. In an uncertain world, there is no guarantee that these actions will be profitable, but they are important marketing options that may be effective and likely will be tried.

We will return many times to the point that effective product differentiation leads to market behavior that is significantly different from that of undifferentiated commodities. Supply-and-demand analysis explains the market behavior of firms marketing commodities. Something more than supply-and-demand analysis is essential to explain the market behavior of firms marketing highly differentiated products.

OLIGOPSONY AND MONOPSONISTIC COMPETITION

Although most of this chapter focused on competitive models involving sellers, buyers also often compete. Ask the managers of competing grain elevators about the competition to buy grain, or ask meat processors about the competition to buy slaughter livestock. If there are only a few buyers competing in a market, this mirror image of oligopoly is called *oligopsony.* If there are numerous rather than few buyers, it is called *monopsonistic competition.* Note the slight alteration in spelling, which is a tip-off to whether the sellers or the buyers are the market being considered. It may seem strange that there could be product differentiation among buyers. Differentiation among buyers is less common than among sellers, but it does frequently exist. The location of the buyer, the personalities of its employees, the adequacy of its facilities, and the way it does business (reliability of payment and fairness and promptness in handling complaints) are a few examples of how a firm may differentiate its procurement operations. We will see later that although the competition among farmers often resembles perfect competition, the competition among the outlets that are buying their livestock or crops often resembles oligopsony or monopsonistic competition.

SUMMARY

1. Marketing managers operate in markets in which they buy and sell. Competition is not the same in all markets. A marketing manager's competitive tools vary among firms and especially between firms that are not in markets resembling perfect competition.

2. Some markets resemble the perfect competition model. We analyzed these markets with firm cost and revenue curves and industry demand. Price is determined by the intersection of the industry forces of supply and demand. Thus, price is outside the control of any firm in the perfect competition model: the firm is a price taker. Prices in perfect competition generally move in the same direction as any change in costs or in demand. However, time lags are important. A price jump in the short run may be largely erased in the long run because industry output is altered by the entry or exit of firms.

3. Some markets resemble the model of monopolistic competition. The large number of firms resembles the perfect competition model. The chief difference is that each firm sells its own differentiated product(s) rather than a standardized commodity. Each firm is a price maker. The marketing alternatives of firms are much broader than in perfect competition.

4. Some markets resemble the model of oligopolistic competition, or competition among the few. Product differentiation is typical, although not universal. Firms are price makers. There are many ways in which oligopolists may compete. Their performance may be much like that of monopolistic competitors at one extreme or like a single monopoly at the other. Each competitor has to worry about the reaction of its rivals and the possibility of entry of new competitors. The marketing alternatives of these firms are as broad as in monopolistic competition. Frequently, there is greater reliance on competition by means of new products and promotion because direct price competition is dangerous.

5. The ability to make price is not a license to steal. In monopolistic competition, price makers typically receive normal profits that are not so large as to attract entrants. We examined cases in which a decline in demand forced price makers out of business. A price follower in oligopoly feels that she cannot change her price except when a competitor (a price leader) changes his price. That kind of price maker operates under severe constraints. Nevertheless, marketing managers are aware that they are price makers and know the degree of freedom that they have. Certainly, price makers must accommodate broad swings in demand or in costs, but the mechanism is less automatic than the supply-and-demand forces that control price for price takers.

6. Whereas an increase in demand is perceived by a competitive seller as an increase in price, it is perceived by a seller in monopolistic competition or oligopoly as an increase in quantity sold. In all three markets, an increase in demand will increase short-run profits but not necessarily long-run profits.

7. Price is not the only variable of competition. Managers with differentiated products and budgets for promotion seek to control in a limited way the position of demand curves for their products and services. Some firms spend large amounts on developing and merchandising new products. Others may respond to a price cut of a competitor by increasing their TV ads. In numerous ways the marketing of differentiated foods by processors is quite different from the marketing of commodities by farmers.

8. Although our discussion focused on sellers, it is important to realize that buyers also operate in various environments that are similar to those of sellers. Buyers are constrained by the market in which they operate and by shifts in demand and costs.

STUDY QUESTIONS

1. Of what use is a market model? How do we relate it to reality?
2. Why does perfect competition simplify both marketing and procurement for a manager?
3. What is meant by the entry and exit of firms? Why are entry and exit easy or difficult in the various market models?
4. How do demand curves vary in the different market models? How does each affect managerial behavior and planning?
5. What is a supply-and-demand model?
6. Suppose that through some cultural revolution one-half of Americans became vegetarians and would no longer eat any kind of meat.

Assume that beef producers compete in perfect competition, and use supply and demand curves to explain the impact. What would happen in the short run to beef prices and the profits of beef producers? In the long run?

7. Which of the following are standardized commodities and which are differentiated products?

hard red winter wheat	oranges
Wheaties	Arrow shirts
corn	Folgers coffee
packaged cake mixes	cigarettes
potatoes	

8. What kind of market power is possessed by a firm that has a highly differentiated product?

9. Why is it more difficult to predict the impact on price of a demand shift in oligopoly than in perfect competition?

10. Sam Browne operates a little restaurant on Main Street. He prices "Browneburgers" at the same price as the popular four-ounce hamburgers of the fast-food restaurant out on the highway. Is Sam a price maker or a price taker? Do you see any advantages to Sam in adopting such a pricing strategy?

11. Why do most firms strive to become oligopolists? How might this affect a market over time? Is the impact different in different markets?

 CLASS EXERCISE

In your commodity group, use the agricultural commodity assigned in Chapter 1 and choose one agribusiness from your answer to Question 7 of the Chapter 1 exercise. Investigate the agribusiness and identify the following aspects:

1. Size
2. Sales
3. Scope of product line
4. Worth (if public)
5. Number of employees
6. Locations globally
7. Market structure
8. Industry sector

Prepare to present your findings to the class.

3

FUNCTIONS, STRUCTURE, AND ALTERNATIVES IN THE AGRICULTURAL MARKETING SYSTEM

PREVIEW

- Agribusinesses conduct most marketing activities. They provide most of the transportation, storage, and processing that add place, time, and form utilities as farm commodities are transformed into consumer products and transferred to the final buyer.
- Several economic factors affect where a plant or firm locates.
- Many agribusinesses are commodity handlers. The task of maintaining adequate margins for their services is a daily challenge to their managers.
- Some agribusinesses have achieved effective product differentiation and have obtained a degree of latitude in pricing.
- Agribusiness firms range in size from one-person shops to corporate giants.
- Farm and agribusiness relationships continue to evolve because of changes in demand and technology.
- The marketing alternatives of farmers are influenced by many factors, such as their size, location, and climate.
- Farm output does respond to price incentives. That response is often slow and complicated, and it can be understood only in terms of the biological lags in the production of most agricultural commodities.

KEY TERMS

biological lags
business logistics
commodity
commodity handling
concentration ratio
conglomerate
convenience yield
economies of size
expected prices
inelastic
margin maker
market intelligence
perishability
product marketing
realized prices
risk bearing
standardization

gribusiness marketing firms are frequently termed *intermediaries*. The term is apt, from the farmer's and consumer's point of view, as they see agribusiness firms located between them. But the term has some misleading connotations because intermediaries are often conceived of as having a passive, subordinate role. The opposite is closer to the truth. Most of the action in marketing takes place in the agribusiness firms. Agribusiness firms are a diverse group, and some do have a passive, service role, but most do not. It is more accurate to think of agribusiness as the control center of the food-and-fiber system. It is also appropriate to look at farms as agribusinesses, as they make more efforts to differentiate their products and to "connect" with other agribusinesses.

Like the food processor, the farmer is concerned with what to sell and how much, the selling price or prices, how to promote the availability and virtues of his products, and what intermediaries to use if direct sales to final consumers are not feasible. The typical farmer is more limited than the food processor in his choice of commodity–product mix, and, unlike the food processor, is a price taker rather than a price maker, able to promote only through group efforts, and less able to select intermediaries or to negotiate with them. To understand the context affecting farmers' decisions about their marketing, we need to understand a few key points about U. S. farmers and the nature of farming:

1. Much of U. S. agricultural production fits relatively well with the competitive firm model. That is, there are many relatively small producers of mainly homogeneous commodities who can rather easily begin or cease production.

2. A particular farmer's choices of which commodities to produce are related to such factors as soil, climate, distance to market, economies of size, risk, government programs, environmental factors, collective efforts, and expected relative prices.

WHAT TO PRODUCE AND MARKET

We turn to the fundamental marketing decision for a farmer. What mix of commodities or products should he sell, and how much should he sell? The simple answer is that he chooses the most profitable, given the degree of risk that he is willing to take. Risk, of course, is affected by yield and price variability. These decisions in global regions like North America and Europe are constrained by soil characteristics and climate.

Diversity describes American agriculture. More than 200 commodities are produced. A few commodities, such as cattle, are produced in virtually every state. On the other hand, some commodities are concentrated in regions such as the Corn Belt or the Wheat Belt. Some specialty crops are grown only in a single region, such as hops in the Pacific Northwest.

Distance to market is important. For example, most cattle are fed in the High Plains, stretching from the Texas Panhandle through Oklahoma, Colorado, Kansas, and Nebraska. Although feeder cattle and feed are available almost everywhere, any farmer who is more than 500 miles from the belt of feedlots and cattle processing plants is going to worry about distance to markets when he considers cattle feeding as a market alternative. For $65 per hundredweight cattle, a shrink of 2% *more* when shipped 250 miles compared to 25 miles has an extra shrink cost of $1.30 per hundredweight, plus the additional trucking costs. Most livestock are slaughtered within 100 miles of their production. Generally, most market outlets are concentrated in the heavy production areas of a commodity. Individual or small producers not in those heavy production areas may have to hunt for market outlets.

Through much of American history, the size of the production unit did not seem to matter much. There were dairy herds of 10 cows and others of 5,000. A farmer might have fed 20 steers while a specialized feedlot fed 5,000. Increasingly, however, **economies of size** do matter. Whenever a specific range of large-sized operators can produce at significantly lower average costs per unit than can other sizes, we refer to that size range as possessing economies of size. Therefore, anyone thinking about producing a commodity is wise to consider whether she can attain an economic size of unit. A farmer who tries to produce less than several hundred acres of a major field crop or raise less than several thousand hogs or to keep less than 400,000 laying hens is going to be at a disadvantage in competing with the larger producers. These economies of size in producing a particular commodity have been pushing farmers toward much more specialization. Whereas her grandparents may have produced four or five kinds of livestock and poultry and a half dozen crops, today's farmer is more likely to specialize in two or three crops with no animals or to specialize in only one kind of livestock.

Biology and Marketing

The biological timing of farm output is an important characteristic affecting marketing. The biological lag in production differentiates agriculture from all other industries. The dairyman and the egg producer have a daily output that goes to market daily or every other day. These are nonstorable commodities. In contrast, there are many annual crops that are harvested only in the fall. These are storable commodities. To avoid dependence on once-a-year sales, those farmers can resort to a number of devices that separate the once-yearly marketing from the actual selling. For example, harvested corn can be stored in grain bins until it is ready to go to market. Many of the producers of annual crops must consider the degree of **perishability** (the process of a food losing its desirable characteristics, and thus its value, over time), an important characteristic. Some commodities, such as strawberries and milk, must be marketed very quickly under controlled temperatures to avoid spoilage. At the other extreme, commodities such as cotton store well for many months with only minimal environmental protection. Obviously, the expenses and the pace of physical marketing tend to be greater for the more perishable items. Moreover, the types of pricing and other coordination mechanisms are affected by the degree of a commodity's perishability.

There is considerable variety within any commodity. Some of the variety is deliberate—a Delicious apple tastes different from a Jonathan. Other variations derive from differences in production and marketing—disease or storms may pit the apple's skin, and incorrect storage may speed its spoilage. The biological nature of farm commodities presents special challenges and opportunities to farmers in controlling the qualities they market.

HOW MUCH TO PRODUCE: SUPPLY
RESPONSE AND BIOLOGICAL LAGS

How much to produce? The textbook answer is easy: A competitive firm chooses the short-term output where marginal cost is equal to price. The biggest problem is that the market price will not be known until months or even years after the production decision is made. The individual farmer perceives price to be unaffected by her output decisions. As a price taker, she reacts with output changes that are rational in terms of **expected prices** (prices estimated months or years before actual harvest or production of the commodity). Typically, she engages in production without knowing what price level will be realized. Short-term price variability is greater for some commodities than for others. The lettuce producer has usually been more confident of prices a year ahead of time than have been producers of many other commodities.

The **biological lags** in agricultural production cause farmers to make production decisions on the basis of expected rather than **realized prices,** which are often quite different. Planting decisions for major crops such as corn and soybeans are made in the spring as much as seven months ahead of fall harvest; the lag for winter wheat is closer to ten months. Beef cattle can seldom be produced from conception to slaughter weight in less than 30 months. A nut or fruit tree may not bear during the first three or four years and may not reach peak production for another six to ten years. Farmers may estimate their expected prices in various ways. Presumably, farmers look at current prices and modify them by their evaluation of how supply and demand may change them before harvest. Even experts in price prediction occasionally make sizable errors in predicting prices as much as six months ahead of time.

The realized price will be affected by the time of sale, the size of the crop, and possible shifts in demand during the production period. The size of a crop can frequently vary as much as ±20% because of weather and other factors beyond the effective control of farmers. Moreover, at the time of the planting decision, the farmer does not know the total intentions of his fellow producers, so he does not even know the intended size of the total crop, let alone the realized size. (How could he know the intended total size when he and other farmers are still deciding?)

Any consideration of agricultural supply response must distinguish between individual commodities and all of agriculture. For example, each year at the planting season, farmers can shift some land fairly readily among corn and soybeans and wheat. The short-run supply curve for an individual commodity is ordinarily **inelastic** (a 10% change in price brings about less than a 10% change in output). The commodity mix actually produced in any given marketing season or year is frequently far from optimal. In terms of the relationships between production cost and market price in any given year, farmers may produce too many hogs and too few beef cattle, too much soybeans and too little corn, or vice versa. Therefore, prices received by farmers are frequently very poorly related to costs incurred in production (in the sense discussed in Chapter 2).

There are differences among commodities, of course. One cannot readily switch between commodities, such as hogs and chickens or rice and cranberries, when facilities or land is highly specialized. As many producers become increasingly specialized (as cattle ranchers or feeders or hog producers or turkey raisers), they ordinarily have no effective choices among alternative commodities. Their most effective strategy is to keep producing at their most efficient level regardless of whether next period's expected prices are low or high. Their most basic long-run marketing choice is to look regularly at long-term price prospects and decide whether they should expand substantially their operation or close it down.

Farmers also need to decide what to produce. Two important distinctions need to be considered in regard to farmers' choice of what to produce: commodities vs. differentiated products and crops vs. livestock.

Commodities vs. Differentiated Products

Most farmers produce commodities. A **commodity** is an economic good that can be legally produced and sold by almost anyone. Agricultural items (e.g., corn, wheat, cotton, grapes, and melons) and minerals (e.g., iron ore) are the principal examples. In contrast, as discussed in Chapter 2, a *differentiated product* is an economic good that belongs to a single seller and that often may be patented, copyrighted, or trademarked to the exclusive use of that seller. If I feed Hereford steers and sell them for slaughter, I am selling a particular class (Hereford steers) of a commodity (cattle). If I produce and sell a particular line of Hereford bulls, I am selling a differentiated product. If my bulls have been proven to be superior sires and I promote that fact, I will be able to negotiate premium prices for my differentiated product. The packer who slaughters my steers is likely to convert them into another set of commodities such as beef steaks, roasts, and ground beef. However, if the ground beef is formulated for the world's largest fast-food chain, it may be resold in a bun as a differentiated product because of other ingredients and brand. In this text, we try to use the two terms (*commodities* and *products*) as just defined; however, it is common, and often confusing, to use them interchangeably.

Recall from Chapter 2 that the significance of selling a commodity versus a differentiated product lies in the greater number of marketing alternatives open to the seller of products. Because he controls the supply of the item, he can price it and reap the benefits of promotion. However, producers of commodities typically cannot set prices; nor can they benefit from individual promotion because there are many other sellers of that same commodity. One benefit of being a price taker is that a farmer can ordinarily sell any quantity of a commodity without depressing the price. *The seller of a differentiated product does not face an unlimited demand at the price he sets.* In other words, he usually would like to sell more units than the buyer will purchase.

Another characteristic of many commodity markets is easy entry. Because the commodity is not exclusive property, it is usually easy for others to begin producing it whenever prices are profitable. Thus, farmers soon learn that good prices usually do not last very long because increased production drives price back down. In economic terms, the short-run supply curve shifts to the right through entry. Experience leads farmers to be careful in anticipating how long good prices for a commodity will last.

Most farm commodities are processed before they reach consumers. In fact, many products (e.g., McDonald's hamburgers) reaching consumers are derived from several farm commodities. This raw material characteristic of many farm commodities is one of the reasons that most marketing functions are performed by agribusiness rather than farmers.

Crops vs. Livestock

Another useful distinction is between the production of crops and the feeding of animals. Because most cropping involves thousands of acres of land, it is not as easily supervised as is work in more confined areas such as a factory. Consequently, except for high-value commodities such as certain fruits and vegetables, most cropping tends to be in family-sized operations. Much animal production, on the other hand, is quite adaptable to factory-type operation. Cattle feedlots; hog farrowing and feeding; broiler, turkey, and egg production; and even dairying require little space, permit much substitution of capital for labor, permit effective labor specialization, and generally resemble factory operations.

Historically, animal production generally began on crop farms in the humid areas; the big exception was grazing of cattle and sheep on western ranches. Animal production was an efficient way to "market" grain, hay, especially the pasture production. The splitting of crop and animal production that has been underway for 40 years or more is virtually complete in poultry, advanced in cattle feeding, and well underway in hog production. These days, poultry rarely eat feed produced on the same farm or even on adjoining farms.

AGRIBUSINESS CONTROL

Agribusinesses possess the preponderance of power in many market channels. Sometimes their power is in pricing. First-handler firms such as grain elevators, hog buying stations, and vegetable processors are quite interested in the size distribution of the farms they deal with. These procurement firms frequently make concessions to attract the business of the larger farm producers. For example, the transaction cost of dealing with four large farmers is less than that of doing business with 20 smaller farmers. This will be discussed in greater detail in the section on collective action.

More often the power is in organizing many of the activities in the channel, in determining the form in which final products reach consumers, and in affecting directly or indirectly the volume of sales. The great volume of margarine or vegetable spreads and yogurt or frozen custard products sold today and the reduced volume of butter and traditional ice cream products reflects the technical developments and merchandising of agribusiness, not of farmers. The great growth in sales of chicken strips, ground beef, french fried potatoes, and pizza undoubtedly reflects not only consumer demand but also marketing by agribusiness, particularly by the fast-food chains. Many other examples could be given of the extent to which agribusiness exercises formidable influence over the whole food-and-fiber system.

Agribusinesses engage in two different types of marketing. The first is **commodity handling.** Farmers sell commodities, and so any agribusiness buying "at the farm gate" buys commodities. Those firms that specialize in milk, eggs, fresh fruit, and fresh meat tend to be highly price competitive because the commodities offer few or no profitable opportunities for advertising and promotion. Large portions of these items proceed through the marketing channel to consumers in essentially a commodity form. Each commodity encounters some degree of processing, but in this type of marketing it usually arrives at retail in an unbranded, undifferentiated form. Second, **product marketing** agribusinesses transform raw commodities into bread, frozen entrees, baby foods, instant mashed potatoes, and so forth and then merchandise them as branded products such as Pillsbury, Banquet, Gerber, and Healthy Choice. This provides profitable opportunities for promotion and reduces the emphasis on price competition.

There is, of course, no neat boundary between those two classifications. Major firms often engage in both; a big food company, such as Pillsbury, may buy grain, mill flour, and manufacture and merchandise cake mixes. Moreover, the past half-century has seen a strong trend toward more product marketing and less commodity handling.

The category in which a firm operates has deep significance in many respects, including the terms of competition. Agribusiness firms handling undifferentiated commodities generally experience considerable price competition, for example, when ADM and Cargill buy commodities. Such firms find it difficult to obtain the market security associated with loyal customers. They have great difficulty finding much latitude as price makers and, like farmers, are often price takers. On the other hand, the marketers of highly differentiated food products experience reduced price competition, have the market security of loyal customers, and have more latitude as price makers. Obviously, a major reason for the trend of the past half-century toward more marketing of products and less handling of commodities is that many agribusiness firms find the former to be a much more attractive business. The impact or expansion of product differentiation and branding continues to increase its impact on the entire channel.

Most differentiation is developed near the consumer end of the market channel by processors, retailers, and food service firms. At the farm end of the market channel, agribusinesses are almost entirely engaged in handling commodities.

We turn now to a number of functions that describe some of the things that agribusiness firms, including farmers, do.

MARKETING FUNCTIONS

The most visible and generally the most costly aspects of agricultural marketing are the *physical functions:* transportation, storage, and processing. These may be collectively referred to as **business logistics.** These functions will be discussed first, followed by the functions of buying and selling, standardization and market intelligence, and financing and risk bearing.

Transportation

Unless you have a secret desire to jockey an 18-wheeler down the highway, transportation may appear to be an unglamorous aspect of marketing. Glamorous or not, a moment's thought will convince you that a major task of marketing is simply hauling food from field and feedlot to retailer, usually with several intermediate stops along the way.

There are many reasons that agricultural transportation costs will always be significant. Because unit costs of transportation are relatively low, regional specialization in production has been highly developed. Producers and consumers, on the average, are located far apart. Much of our fresh and frozen fruit and vegetables are hauled across the continent from California to the populous centers of the East Coast. Transporting such long distances in refrigerated trucks or railroad cars is expensive but worth doing. Livestock are assembled from farms, ranches, and feedlots scattered from Florida to Washington, then hauled to slaughter. The resulting meat products are frequently transported hundreds of miles to distribution centers. Then they are delivered over congested city streets to thousands of retailers.

Most transportation of agricultural commodities and products is provided by agribusinesses, not farmers. Much is provided by transportation firms—truck lines, railroads, barges, and ocean freight. The remainder consists of do-it-yourself services provided by assemblers, processors, wholesalers, and retailers.

Market prices guide agribusinesses in their transportation decisions. If wheat is selling for $3 a bushel at location A in South Dakota and for $3.45 at location B in Minneapolis and if wheat can be transported for 40¢ a bushel from A to B, then the incentive is clear. For grains, cotton, and some other commodities, agribusiness trading companies seeking opportunities to buy, sell, and transport at a profit constantly scan a worldwide network of prices. The profit per unit can be tiny and still be adequate when the volume involves thousands of units per transaction.

Storage

"A thing has to be somewhere." Some farmer or agribusiness must furnish storage of every product until it is consumed. Grain for a year in a metal bin or in a huge concrete elevator, beef carcasses for a day in a packer's cooler, canned vegetables for six months in a packer's warehouse—all these are part of the vital marketing function of storage.

Storage is the primary activity of some specialized agribusinesses but is a necessary secondary activity of most other agribusinesses. The storage specialists are the big grain elevators, the warehouses for cotton and tobacco, and the cold storage warehouses for perishable products such as frozen foods. These storage specialists typically help to spread out the consumption over a year of an agricultural good that is harvested once a year. But some storage is necessary for even those products produced daily, such as milk and eggs. Each firm in the market channel finds it essential to maintain sufficient inventory to meet the demands of its customers.

Thus retailers, wholesalers, and processors all maintain some storage as a normal part of doing business. A processor will often store or offer incentives for its suppliers to store a product even though there is a negative expected return to storage. For example, if Cargill's corn milling operation has an end-user contract for delivering a certain quantity of high-fructose corn syrup each of the next six months, then Cargill must have a corn supply for the next six months to ensure meeting contract obligations. The cost of breaking the end-user contract is greater than paying market incentives to ensure ample corn supply. The value of storage in situations like this one is termed the **convenience yield.** That is, even during times when macro-level incentives don't signal storage to be profitable, at the micro-level a firm may be required to offer storage incentives.

Processing

Processing, the manufacturing phase of marketing, is a technologically sophisticated phase. If you are a food science student, you appreciate the science that goes into processing food economically, swiftly, and safely. For the rest of us, a simpler description will suffice. Processing of most goods typically involves inspecting and sorting. For animals and poultry, it involves slaughtering and cutting up. Processing may also involve curing and sausage making or grinding and baking. Packaging is also important. For perishables, cooling is frequently a necessity. Then there are complicated activities such as baking, canning, preparation of frozen dinners, and so on. These activities often transform commodities into potentially differentiated products capable of being merchandised. Processing varies in cost, complexity, and relative importance. For example, compare broilers to cake mixes.

An important concept in commodity processing is *separability of commodities*. This concept refers to the fact that every commodity processed yields several coproducts. A processed steer yields steaks, roasts, hamburger, hide, offal, and bone meal. A processed bushel of wheat yields wheat middlings, flour, and gluten, and a bushel of corn in ethanol production yields ethanol, distillers, dried (or wet) grains, and CO_2. Processing and the subsequent marketing of the various coproducts must be a fully integrated process to support firm profitability. For example, the fact that a pork processor has a good profit stream for hams does not mean that all other coproducts (e.g., bacon, loins, chops, hide) will yield similar profit streams.

From a macro point of view, processors convert commodities to forms more suitable for consumption. In a simple case, they take fluid milk from huge tank trucks, pasteurize it, standardize the butterfat to a rate such as 2% or 0.5%, and put the milk in convenient consumer-sized containers. In more complicated cases they produce products such as Tombstone pizzas, Pillsbury cake mixes, or Hanes shirts, all blended from numerous raw materials.

From a micro point of view, many agribusinesses have found that processing is an essential and profitable business activity in directing the forward flow of products to consumers. In any developed nation, consumers are willing to pay for a broad range of processed items. Most consumers want convenience and variety. They want foods that can be stored for long periods and yet can be prepared quickly. They want foods that are tasty as well as safe and nutritious. Several agribusiness empires have been built by processors who have catered successfully to this vast consumer market.

Buying (Procurement) and Selling (Merchandising)

Common to most agribusiness firms are the exchange functions of buying and selling. The wheat in the slice of toast someone ate this morning may have been purchased by a local elevator, who sold it to a terminal elevator in Kansas City or Minneapolis, who then sold it to a flour miller, who sold the flour to a baker, who sold bread to the local retailer. Because relative prices directly affect incomes of buyers and sellers, the exchanges are of considerable interest to those involved. Buying and selling of commodities are essential functions performed routinely and cheaply. As we will see later, the merchandising of branded products is a more complex and expensive form of selling.

The flow of agricultural products to consumers requires an enormous number of sales transactions. For example, how many total changes in title per year are involved in transferring, say, 103 million hogs from 70,000 producers to 664 meat packers, who then sell billions of pounds of cuts and sausages to thousands of retailers, who resell them to 123 million households? Imagine the labor and expense involved if every single transaction required 30 minutes of haggling! The simple, efficient transfer of ownership from farmer to consumer is one of the great, unseen accomplishments of marketing.

Even if there were no physical functions of storing, transporting, and processing, we cannot imagine consumers buying their pork directly from farmers. The exchange inefficiencies of 123 million households shopping and buying from 70,000 farmers is staggering. Marketing intermediaries make exchange much more efficient by reducing the number of transactions among many sellers and many buyers.

It may be apparent already that procurement is as important an effort for agribusiness as is marketing. Agribusiness has taken such a lead in organizing its procurement that it is as accurate to speak of an agricultural procurement system as an agricultural marketing system.

Agribusinesses have generally taken a more aggressive lead in procurement than have farmers in marketing because of their greater economic size. Although there are exceptions, the firm with $10 million or $100 million in assets is better able to assume certain coordination risks and to expend resources on organizing a procurement system than is the typical farmer. Similarly, the larger organization has the legal and financial expertise to develop new methods of doing things, whereas the typical farmer lacks such expertise. The larger organization also usually has lower unit costs because of economies of size.

Standardization and Market Intelligence

Standardization and market intelligence are related functions. Both are concerned with providing market participants with the information essential to deal with one another in competitive markets. As might be expected, both have different meanings in commodity markets than with branded products and services.

Standardization concerns the development and use of constant measures of quantity and quality of various goods. In an undeveloped society, a buyer and seller may dicker over the price of some cows or hogs in so much money per head. In our economy, slaughter steers may be priced at so many dollars per hundredweight, and their carcasses are priced at so many dollars per hundredweight if they are Choice, yield grade 3s or at a different price if another grade. The point is that communication and trading within the marketing channel—and indeed within large agribusiness firms—depend on standardized measurements of quantity and quality.

Agricultural commodities are usually diverse in quality despite persistent efforts to reduce the diversity. The larger share of heterogeneity arises from the biology of reproduction. However, a small share of heterogeneity derives from economic demands for varying qualities. In either case, it is as important to measure the quality of apples in a standardized way as it is to measure the size of the container of apples in a standardized way.

Standardization of commodities is an integral part of **market intelligence,** which is data about current volumes of sales, current and future prices, and events that may influence upcoming prices and sales. Imagine yourself as a market reporter charged with informing cattle producers about today's prices in a particular market for slaughter—if you could report neither weights nor grades. Your report might read something like this: Steer prices ranged from $590 to $825 per head with the bulk of heavier cattle selling in the $700 to $825 range. With standardization, your report the same day might read like this: The bulk of mostly Choice steers of 1,025 to 1,150 pounds and 2 to 3 yield grade sold at $71 to $71.50 per hundredweight (cwt); most mixed Select and Choice steers 2 to 4 weighing 975 to 1,200 pounds sold at $69 to $70, and most Select (including Holsteins) weighing 900 to 1,150 pounds sold at $67 to $69.50.

The provisions for standardization and for market intelligence are provided largely, but not exclusively, by the federal government. Both agribusinesses and farmers and, in recent years, consumers are involved in negotiating with government over the details of these services.

Both farmers and agribusinesses also cooperate with government and private agencies on a voluntary basis in the gathering of market data. Crop farmers fill out numerous reports indicating such information as their crop yields, acreage, and planting intentions for next season. Hog producers provide data on recent production, inventories, and farrowing intentions. Cattle feeders indicate the number of cattle on feed by weight groups. Processors report their current rates of processing, inventories, prices of recent transactions, and other information. Retailers provide information on prices paid as well as on selling prices and major cost items.

The U. S. Department of Agriculture also gathers data worldwide on crop production and utilization. Why? Because the size of the soybean crop in Brazil and China's soybean demand affect soybean prices here as well as in Brazil and China.

Government and other intelligence agencies provide a great array of reports. Prices are reported the same day so that market participants know the going market prices. You have probably seen one of the private news services that reports all day long on prices gathered a few hours or even a few minutes earlier. Price data are available instantly via the Internet. Data on production and production intentions are gathered less frequently but are also compiled and disseminated rapidly. Government reports are usually specialized by commodity (meat and livestock, poultry and eggs, dairy, fruit and vegetables, and so on).

Private firms sell market intelligence reports such as the Yellow Sheet (wholesale prices of meats), Urner-Barry Report (wholesale prices of eggs), and Brock Report (crop estimates and marketing recommendations). Commodity and trade associations may provide market intelligence to their members.

There is an important difference between *data* and *information*. Farmers and agribusinesses operate in an uncertain world. They do not know all that is happening to current prices and rates of sale. They do not know how much will be produced next period or how it will impact on their selling prices. Market intelligence agencies gather and disseminate data that relate to what is going on and what is planned. The ability of a receiver to analyze and interpret market data influences the amount of information he obtains. To the extent that a receiver can use it to reduce his uncertainty (to increase the probabilities of achieving desired outcomes), he has obtained information. If public market news were not provided, most market participants would find it necessary to subscribe to private news services.

Financing and Risk Bearing

Two other related and vital functions are financing and **risk bearing.** In the latter, a firm is in a position to experience gain or loss as a result of external-ly controlled changes in the amount or price of its holdings of commodities or other assets. The value of food, fuel, and fiber going through the market system swells to more than one trillion dollars annually. At every stage in the marketing channel, someone (usually an agribusiness) owns these products and arranges a part of the enormous financing involved. The large risks of product deterioration and spoilage are assumed by the agribusiness owners and their insurance companies. Then there are financial risks. For example, a change in value of only 10% applied to a $400 billion value would mean a value change of $40 billion. Again, agribusiness usually bears these risks or provides for their transfer to others willing to bear them. The role of the futures markets in facilitating the bearing of financial risks and the financing of inventory values is one of the many fascinating aspects of the marketing story. Futures markets will be discussed in Chapter 10.

Because the farm-level supply curve is typically highly inelastic (nearly vertical) and the consumer-level demand curve is typically highly elastic (nearly horizontal), economics implies that agribusinesses can push price changes (with uncertainty) back on farmers more easily than they can change consumer prices. The farm-level supply curve is highly inelastic (Exhibit 3.1a) due to the biological lag factor limiting how fast producers can respond to price signals. The consumer-level demand curve is highly elastic (Exhibit 3.1b) because consumers have many substitutes to choose from. If the price of one good changes, the consumer can easily shift to an alternative good.

EXHIBIT

3.1   Supply–demand relationship at the farm and consumer levels.

Farm Level

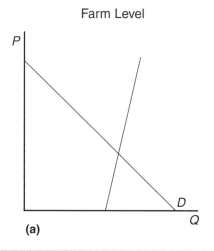

(a)

Consumer Level

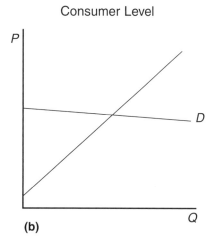

(b)

LOCATION OF AGRIBUSINESSES

Many factors affect the location of a particular business firm or plant. These include the location and availability of inputs; location of markets; transportation costs; comparative costs and skills of the labor force; community factors such as schools, taxes, housing, and climate; availability of specialized services such as government inspection and repair services for equipment; waste disposal regulations; and familiar lending agencies. Complex models that estimate least-cost locations are often used by firms deciding where to put a new plant.

We will try to explain the general locations of various categories of agribusiness rather than discuss the location of specific firms or plants. A few simple factors are sufficient to explain why various categories of agribusiness locate in particular areas and how these businesses are dispersed or concentrated within these areas.

Locations of Agribusiness Categories

Agribusiness firms generally are involved in moving agricultural commodities from production areas to consumption areas. Those firms at the beginning of the market channel—assemblers and the first-stage processors—are usually located in the production areas. That is where we find country elevators. Those firms at the consumer end of the market channel—wholesalers, retailers, restaurants, and some processors—are usually located in the consumption areas.

The interesting problems, then, are largely in the location of processors. Because unprocessed agricultural commodities are often bulky and sometimes perishable, many processing activities must be geared to the economics of transportation. A canner of perishables such as most fruits and vegetables will be located in the center of a production area to keep the costs of transporting the bulky, perishable commodity to a minimum. Its location is *supply oriented*. Similarly, because it is cheaper to move meat than the livestock from which it is derived, meat packing plants tend to be located in the heart of livestock production areas. We used the qualifier *tend* because a packing plant, once built, tends to stay in business for several decades even though its ownership may change. In some cases, production areas have shifted away from packing plants and the latter have continued to operate, albeit at a real transportation cost disadvantage. Thus, numerous East Coast packers now must ship livestock long distances because local supplies are no longer adequate. Processing plants left in uneconomic locations are eventually depreciated out and closed down.

Other examples of commodities that can be transported and stored more cheaply after processing include baled vs. loose cotton, dehydrated vs. fresh potatoes, and cheese (and most other manufactured dairy products) vs. milk. Thus, cotton ginning, livestock slaughtering, most potato processing, and dairy manufacturing tend to be located in the production areas.

Certain kinds of processing are *market oriented*. Bread baking is a good example. Bread is bulky and perishable, so it is not baked in one giant bakery in the wheat area and transported all over the United States. Instead, bread is baked in every large metropolitan area. Note, however, that bread is not baked in every small city and village. The economics of scale in this processing activity and the merchandising advantages of larger firms combine to eliminate most small bakeries.

Some products are not particularly perishable and their storage and transportation costs not significantly affected by processing, such as baled cotton vs. textiles. In these instances, other locational factors come into play, including the structure of transportation rates; duties of some foreign countries that are higher on textiles and flour or soybean oil and meal than on cotton, wheat, and soybeans; and labor costs.

Processors of many of the highly differentiated products whose transportation costs are relatively low in relation to their value may be located almost anywhere. Examples are the makers of breakfast cereals, crackers, cake mixes, and frozen entrees. Wage rates and minimization of total transportation costs may affect the location of a network of factories and distribution points by a national manufacturer.

Geographical Dispersion

Granted that soybean crushers or cattle packing plants will be located within a given area, how many will there be, and will they be located together or dispersed over the area? These first-stage processors are frequently dispersed. The number of plants depends on a trade-off between the economics of plant size and the costs of assembly. Depending on the complexities of the equipment and processes involved, the average per unit operating costs of a plant often decrease as output increases through a wide range of output. However, assembly costs generally rise as commodities are hauled greater distances to the plant (Exhibit 3.2). The balance between the two affects the number and spacing of plants over a production area. The balance has been shifting slowly toward fewer and larger plants in most kinds of food processing as hauling costs fall relative to loading and unloading costs.

The foregoing explanation must be modified, however. It would apply very neatly if a single buyer were carefully spacing her plants over a

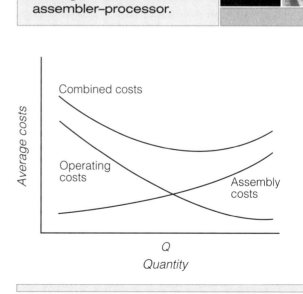

EXHIBIT 3.2

Average costs of an assembler–processor.

Combined costs

Operating costs

Assembly costs

Average costs

Q
Quantity

production area. What happens when there are competitive buyers? Then the spacing usually is not so uniform, and there will likely be more plants than a single buyer would have. In other words, competition among processors increases the number of plants.

The location of supermarkets in a big city is affected by the same forces just described. Supermarkets tend to be dispersed so that each store has the advantage of a particular group of customers who find it convenient. Studies show that a sizable proportion of consumers shop in the supermarket nearest them. As personal transportation became more convenient during the twentieth century (reducing assembly costs), grocery stores grew much larger and fewer in number relative to population. Occasionally, competition leads to two or three stores being located close together as firms compete for customers.

There are some advantages to processing plants being close together that may offset the transportation advantages of dispersion. These "agglomeration economies" may include the availability of skilled labor, better transportation facilities, special equipment and repair services, and availability of financial institutions familiar with the industry.

THE STRUCTURE OF AGRIBUSINESS MARKETS

Recall that the structure of a market indicates much about the competitive environment of its participants. Dimensions of market structure include the number of sellers and buyers, their relative size, degree of product differentiation, and ease of entry. Obviously, we cannot examine the detailed competitive structure in which each kind of agribusiness firm operates. Instead we will generalize about the structure of certain levels in the marketplace and then examine some structural data at the food processing level.

One sweeping generalization: There is likely to be no agribusiness market structure that precisely fits either the perfect competition model or any of the models described in Chapter 2. Agribusiness firms operate in market structures that deviate from the competitive model for one or more of the following reasons:

1. Some firms are large enough to influence the markets in which they buy or sell.
2. Significant aspects of product or service differentiation influence volumes traded and prices paid or received by various firms.
3. Entry is less than completely open.

A caution: Recall from Chapter 2 that competition may be intense in market structures that are not perfectly competitive. Even though many agribusinesses may have some influence on markets, they are still likely to be operating in highly competitive environments.

These structural deviations from perfect competition are a matter of degree. A firm that typically buys one-third or more of the livestock in a local market is likely to influence market price when it materially changes its

rate of purchasing. Even a firm buying 10% in a market may have an influence on the market price but likely less of an influence than that of a larger
firm. A firm with a highly regarded brand name may achieve some latitude
in pricing by means of its product differentiation. Another firm may find
that its poorly established brand name gives it very little latitude in pricing.

In many parts of agribusiness, entry by a new firm is relatively easy:
capital requirements are low, product differentiation is not very important,
and/or there are no patents, secret processes, or government licenses that
advantage existing firms. On the other hand, in some markets potential
entrants frequently find more discouraging prospects. For example, elevator A is doing well in a certain town, but there is clearly not enough
business for a second firm. If elevator B were to enter such a market, it
might eventually force out elevator A by paying higher prices to farmers
and cause financial losses not only to A but also to itself by raising grain
acquisition costs. In such cases, the sum of the anticipated losses to B may
be such a large entry cost that B does not enter that market. In a national
market, the sales of the large manufacturers of cookies and breakfast cereals are based on well-known brands; heavy advertising; and large,
sophisticated sales organizations. An entrant may have to spend many millions to gain market acceptance for a similar brand. There is considerable
risk that spending those millions will result in a less than acceptable share
of the market for the entrant. Entry, therefore, is difficult and risky enough
that it may not occur in some markets, depending on structure.

Assembly–Procurement Structure

Food processors often do much of their own assembly–procurement. More
accurately, for some commodities processors do virtually all of the assembly job involved in procurement—they may buy much or all of their farm
products from specialized assemblers. Packer procurement persons, for
example, usually do much of the livestock assembly job. A group of cell
phone-directed packer–buyers will visit farms and feedlots and bid on
slaughter livestock, and purchased livestock move directly to the plant.
Buyers employed by this packer may also buy at auctions and terminal markets where much of the assembly function is done by farmers and by the
auctions involved. Processor purchases frequently may be made from dealers and cooperatives who have assembled commodities at various buying
points. For example, Blue Diamond assembles almonds from its hundreds
of member–owners and markets the bulk almonds.

At first glance, it may appear that there are "many" firms buying from
farmers, and certainly national lists of livestock buyers, cotton gins, canneries, or local grain elevators would each number in the hundreds of
thousands. But farm products are fairly bulky in relation to their value. The
distance to the first buyer is limited by transport costs, including the product deterioration or shrink that occurs in perishable crops, livestock, and
poultry. Although we can seldom draw lines on a map and say this is a local

market area, it is true that the economically available markets for farmers are local areas. Within any such area, there are typically only a few assemblers competing for the particular farm products of that area.

Generalizations about the consequences of this noncompetitive market structure must be phrased cautiously. In some situations, price competition appears to be very keen, whereas in others it does not. The entry of another packer–buyer of livestock into an area where price competition is not keen may raise average buying prices for the next year by 50¢ per hundredweight. In some areas, the entry of an ethanol plant may raise buying prices for corn by 10¢ per bushel. The point is that the margins and profits experienced by agribusinesses in a given market often depend on how their managers play the competitive game. If each manager takes a live-and-let-live approach, then each may obtain adequate margins. For the case of ethanol, it may be that elevators are a necessary partner to enable adequate supplies to be available on an annual basis (i.e., as a result of convenience yield).

It is often true that the more concentrated areas of production have the most active competition among assemblers, whereas the areas of sparse production have less active competition. For example, it is occasionally found that an area of deficit pork production, to which hogs are regularly shipped from the Corn Belt, has local hog prices *below* the Corn Belt price level rather than *above* it. However, entry by a firm into assembly is usually not too difficult, and alert entrants are likely to be attracted to situations where oligopsonistic buying produces a good deal for assemblers.

Concentration Ratios

When economists look at the number of firms in an industry, they are interested in the total number and also the total market share of the largest few firms. The reasoning is that if a handful of firms have most of the market, these firms must necessarily recognize their interdependence in their marketing strategies. Thus, economists compute **concentration ratios,** which indicate the percentage of industry sales (or purchases) controlled by the few (customarily, four) largest firms. A four-firm concentration ratio (CR_4) above 50% is customarily regarded as evidence of a concentrated industry—one to which an oligopolistic model best applies. There are enough firms in food processing industries that low concentration is a possibility. For example, suppose there are 33 breakfast cereal companies that each have an equal 3% share of the market. In this case, the CR_4 would be 12.

Measurements of concentration are provided by the Census Bureau. In recent years, more than one-half of the food processing industries identified by the census have a CR_4 over 50%. Concentration ratios for 14 industries are reported in Exhibit 3.3. Obviously, there are great differences in the structures of the many food processing industries, but it is also apparent that a relatively high degree of concentration is not unusual.

Although most consumers are not aware of industry structure, they may not be surprised to learn that breakfast cereals are one of the most concentrat-

EXHIBIT

3.3   Concentration ratios in 14 food manufacturing industries.

NAICS Code	Industry	Four Largest Companies	
		1997	2002
LESS CONCENTRATED			
311520	Ice cream and frozen dessert mfg.	32.2	48
311511	Fluid milk mfg.	21.3	42.6
311421	Fruits and vegetable canning	24.9	23.7
311513	Cheese mfg.	34.6	34.6
311920	Coffee and tea mfg.	52.5	51.2
311812	Commercial bakeries	33.3	46.1
MORE CONCENTRATED			
311211	Flour mills	48.4	53.6
311611	Animal slaughter (except poultry)	57	58.7
311230	Breakfast cereal mfg.	82.9	78.4
311111	Dog and cat food mfg.	58.4	64.2
311821	Cookies and crackers mfg.	59.9	66.6
311311	Sugar cane milling	56.6	51.4
311222	Soybean processing	79.6	79.9
312120	Breweries	89.7	90.8

Source: U.S. Census Bureau, "Concentration Ratios in Manufacturing," 2001, 2006. Census of Manufacturers.

ed food industries. Breakfast cereals display all the attributes of a concentrated, differentiated oligopoly: market domination by a few firms, large advertising budgets, and all sorts of nonprice competition including emphasis on packaging and gimmicks. Entry is relatively difficult because large promotion and advertising programs are needed to "buy" a market share.

A sizable minority of the food processing industries are "unconcentrated" by our definition. A look at one such industry, canned fruits and vegetables, will show, however, that it does not fit the competitive model. Although about 660 firms can and freeze fruits and vegetables, the top four firms in 1997 had 25% of the market. About one-half of the total output is marketed under packer brands. The largest operations spend considerable sums on consumer advertising. Because firm brands and advertising make no sense in perfect competition, these firms are obviously operating in a noncompetitive environment.

Rising Concentration

Concentration in food processing has been rising gradually. Since World War II, concentration has tended to rise in those industries where there is effective product differentiation and lots of advertising. Breakfast cereals are a prime example. One possible explanation is that the relative growth in the largest firms leading to increased concentration has resulted from their advantages of size. However, concentration did increase in several commodity-type industries during the 1990s, including meat packing, wet corn milling, and vegetable oil milling.

Generally, food manufacturers are more concentrated than most other manufacturing, and they spend a higher proportion of each sales dollar on promotion than do most other manufacturers.[1]

The trend toward **conglomerate** food processors has been as important as the postwar trend toward concentration. A conglomerate is defined as a firm doing business in several unrelated markets. ConAgra is a giant conglomerate that processes hogs, cattle, and poultry and manufactures many brands of food ranging from Healthy Choice frozen meals to Swiss Miss puddings and Peter Pan peanut butter. Many conglomerates are also deeply involved in nonfood lines. For example, Procter & Gamble, with $3.14 billion of annual sales in such foods as Folgers coffee and Pringles potato chips, has 95% of its sales in nonfoods.

Many debate the full significance of conglomeration in the American economy. It would appear that the management of a packing plant that is part of a huge conglomerate, with access to its great financial, managerial, and merchandising resources, might view its managerial options somewhat differently than would an independently owned competitor. Likewise, the entry of a huge conglomerate into a new food processing industry is likely to be viewed differently by its competitors than entry by a new, small firm.

Concentration in Procurement

We generally have more structural data on processor sales than procurement. However, it is usually true that their buying is more concentrated than their selling. Why? Because food processors tend to sell in larger market areas than those in which they procure their raw materials. Thus, there are usually more firms competing in any sales market than in any purchase market.

Pork packing is one area in which there are sufficient data to document the greater concentration in procurement than in selling. Modern hog packing plants are so large that building one in a state automatically increases concentration there. Because a hog plant obtains most of its hogs within a radius of 100 miles, concentration in the *procurement* of hogs is greater than in the *marketing* of pork.

What is the significance to a hog packing company management of the greater concentration in procurement than in marketing? Simply that they must more carefully consider possible reactions of competitors in their buying than in their selling. The packer has a little more latitude in setting or negotiating purchase prices for hogs than in setting sales prices for fresh pork, although latitude is quite limited in both cases. Consequently, the setting or negotiating of purchase prices must be approached with more thought. Locating new packing plants near older, higher-cost competitors has been an important strategy in procurement of both cattle and hogs. A higher-cost firm may be able to compete for a long time in the national beef or pork market, but it can seldom last long if a low-cost competitor begins competing directly in its procurement area.

MARKET ALTERNATIVES OF AGRIBUSINESS

In 1869, Charles Pillsbury began a flour mill at a place with good water power and near a wheat production area. Like most firms of the day, it was a production-oriented firm. By the 1930s, Pillsbury realized that its limitation was in sales, not production, so it developed into a sales-oriented firm devoted to consumer research, advertising, and sales. Since then, Pillsbury has evolved into a marketing-oriented firm, focusing on determining and serving consumer needs. Selling becomes much easier when the seller knows the wants and needs of its customers and designs products and services to meet them.[2]

Management takes a very important step when it decides to look for opportunities to satisfy potential customers rather than trying to market more of whatever the company has been marketing. In the case of Pillsbury, it meant becoming a food firm rather than a flour miller. Sometimes managers lose their moorings—they lose their expertise as flour millers, meat packers, or cheese makers while failing to replace it with expertise in some broader area. Generally, however, the trend of the past half century has been a swing from a sales-oriented product orientation to a marketing orientation.

Most agribusinesses are sales-oriented firms, a few are production oriented, and a growing number are marketing oriented. Farmers are generally production oriented. The differences between farmers and agribusinesses stem mainly from differences in market structure. Agribusinesses have many more opportunities than do farmers by which to profit from a marketing orientation.

In addition, most agribusiness firms have price-making (usually margin making) options not open to farmers. It should be clear, of course, that margin-making power (defined later in the chapter) is not automatically equivalent to profit-making power. Margin makers sometimes go broke when demand is insufficient for their revenues to catch up with their costs. Many agribusiness firms enhance their market security and profits by engaging in various promotional activities (promotion, personal selling, and advertising) not available to farmers. Again, one must be realistic about these additional market options. Some advertising is money down the drain. A sales force on the road is a mixed blessing. But these activities provide marketing opportunities that aggressive managements use to build big firms—firms far bigger than are ever built by price takers.

Although agribusiness firms generally have *more* market alternatives than do farmers, they share certain alternatives with farmers. Firms that hold product inventories face the same chances of making money when prices rise and of losing it when they fall. Like some farmers, they may engage in a set of actions to try to outguess the market and gain from price movements. Or, like other farmers, they may engage in hedging (see Chapter 10) or other contractual actions to limit their exposure to price risks.

Advertising and Product Differentiation

Advertising is one of the chief competitive techniques by which non–perfect competition firms jockey for market shares. These impersonal, mass-selling techniques are the principal method by which sellers try to inform and influence present and potential buyers. Retailers and food processors spend large amounts on advertising.

From a firm's point of view, effective advertising must accomplish particular objectives in reaching buyers. These objectives may vary from creating awareness of a new product (e.g., announcing a new breakfast cereal) to emphasizing the special features of an existing product ("Brand X painkiller reaches the pain area in 30 seconds"). "Reminder advertising" keeps the brand name continually before buyers. Most advertising is aimed at buyers, although some is aimed by buyers at sellers. (For example, livestock buying stations advertise to livestock producers.)

The chief objective of much advertising by food processors is to build consumer demand for its brands to pull the product through the distribution channel. Retailers must be convinced to handle the processor's products. One of the most convincing selling points to a retailer is to see a consumer advertising campaign get under way and then to field customer requests for that processor's products. Retailers generally want items on their shelves that are presold—that will move promptly and profitably. Such preselling is what much processor advertising tries to accomplish. It is easy to think of food products such as cereals, coffee, soft drinks, beer, cookies, cake mixes, potato chips, pork, bread, and lettuce with highly advertised processor brand names.

Price Makers vs. Margin Makers

Agribusinesses have a much more active role than farmers do in pricing. Agribusinesses, in both their buying and their selling, typically either "set" prices or negotiate them. The latitude of agribusiness firms in pricing, however, varies considerably. The range of freedom is determined by two sets of influences:

1. The extent to which the firm's product is independent of the ebb and flow of the farm commodities from which it is derived.
2. The degree of competition from rivals in the market, especially the degree of product differentiation.

Agribusinesses typically have limited influence over the prices they pay for raw farm products. The major determinants of those prices are supply-and-demand forces that are largely outside the influence of agribusiness. True, a local buyer with oligopsonistic power may be able to bid, say, 2% cheaper than if there were more competition. That pricing ability is important to both the buyer and the seller. But it should be kept in perspective. When the average price of slaughter hogs in Missouri fell from $46 for September 2005 to $41 for March 2006, the causes were shifts in supply and demand rather than shifts in the market power of pork packers. The structure of agribusiness and the degree of competition within it is only a small force determining farm prices.

In contrast to their generally uniform and limited influence on procurement prices, agribusinesses vary considerably in their influence over selling prices. To highlight those differences, we shall oversimplify and say that there are two types of agribusiness firms employing two kinds of pricing: those that handle commodities, which set the margins received for their services, and those that market products, which set the prices of their products.

The greater part of agribusiness is engaged in handling commodities and selling services. As such, it has little control over the final consumer prices of foods. Variations in supply and demand are the main determinants of those prices. Instead, the agribusiness firm's concern is for its *margin*—the difference between, for example, the elevator's buying and selling price for wheat, or the difference between the miller's selling price for flour and its buying price for the equivalent amount of wheat. In a purely competitive market, that margin would tend to equal the marketing firm's costs of doing business, including labor, utilities, fuel, depreciation, fees, and so on. This tendency holds in real-life markets. If competition is not too intense, some profits get included.

It follows that the typical commodity-handling agribusiness is more of a margin maker than a price maker. **Margin makers** are those commodity handlers that have little or no power to set their sale prices and that focus instead on maintaining a margin, or specific differential, between sales prices and purchase prices for the commodity. When a miller is negotiating the price at which she buys wheat and the price at which she sells flour, she also is negotiating her margin. Similarly, it is much closer to the truth to say that packers set or negotiate their processing margin than to say that they set or negotiate the price of livestock or meat. We are not contradicting our earlier statement that a packer in a noncompetitive situation in a deficit area may set the price of hogs 50¢ lower than it would otherwise be. Instead, we are emphasizing that whether hogs are $30 or $60 depends on farmers' supply function for hogs and consumers' demand for pork rather than on the packers' powers as price makers.

The ability of agribusiness firms to maintain profitable margins depends on the type of competition among those supplying particular agribusiness services and the demand for those services. Thus, we would expect firms in a highly concentrated industry to obtain more profitable average margins than those in an unconcentrated industry. However, it is most important to understand that a highly concentrated meat packing industry would have no more control over the hog cycle and the rise and fall of hog prices than the currently unconcentrated industry has. We would expect, however, that the concentrated meat packers would take a little higher margin and profits on the average than do the unconcentrated packers.

Daily and weekly margins of many agribusinesses fluctuate considerably. A margin maker may accept low margins in the short term rather than shut down operations. Similarly, he will sometimes obtain much higher short-term margins than he expects to achieve on the average. Both instances reflect the fact that he has limited control over short-term swings in farm and commodity prices. It is not surprising that many marketing-oriented firms seek to reduce uncertainty by developing differentiated products and opting out of commodities.

In contrast, the processor with a successfully branded item such as Wheaties or Campbell's Soup sells products. Price fluctuations in the wheat market are of little concern to the Wheaties manufacturer. The prices charged for Wheaties and the volume sold have no relation to the size of the last wheat harvest.

Generally, two conditions must be met for a processor's product pricing to be almost entirely independent of the supplies and prices of the relevant farm product: (1) successful product branding and (2) that the cost of the farm ingredients be only a small part of the processor's product costs. Breakfast cereals, cookies, soups, and baby foods are examples.

SUMMARY

1. Farm output may appear to be very unresponsive to price changes, but farmers do respond as suggested by the law of supply. Their output responses to prices are delayed because of the necessary biological lag between a decision to produce and the actual output. Given all the difficulties caused by biological lags and the unavoidable lack of information when farmers make planting and breeding decisions, they do a good job of decision making.

2. Because processors and assemblers are typically much larger businesses than farmers, they usually organize the system of markets and institutions in which farmers sell. Some farmers face much more local competition to buy their commodities than do others.

3. Most micro marketing is organized and carried out by agribusiness intermediaries. Most handle commodities, but many large firms are able to market differentiated products.

4. Transportation (adding place utility) and storage (adding time utility) are performed by agribusinesses in response to price incentives.

5. Processing, which adds form utility, provides opportunities for agribusinesses to implement micro marketing concepts.

6. Standardization and market intelligence are especially significant to commodity handling.

7. Numerous factors affect the location of agribusinesses. Perishability and ease of commodity transport and storage before (vs. after) processing affect the location of processors. Economies of size of processing plants (vs. assembly costs) affect the number and size of processing plants.

8. Generally, most marketing industries (assembly, processing, and retailing) do not fit the perfect competition model well. This deviation does not mean that competition may not be intense.

9. The four-firm concentration ratios in numerous food processing industries, such as breakfast cereals, indicate a high degree of concentration of the type assumed by oligopoly models.

10. Procurement by agribusinesses is usually more concentrated than their marketing.

11. Industries that market products tend to be more concentrated than those that handle commodities.

12. Some large, well-known firms, including some conglomerates, are food processors.

13. Agribusiness firms, especially product marketers, have a large range of marketing options. Food processors spend enormous amounts on advertising. By appealing to consumers, they also motivate retailers to handle their products.

14. Commodity handlers can generally influence their margins but have little power to influence the prices of commodities. Product marketers can determine, within limits, the prices of their differentiated products. Marketers whose farm input costs are lower in proportion to their total costs can be more independent in setting product prices.

 STUDY QUESTIONS

1. What factors affect a producer's set of marketing decisions?

2. Why doesn't the farmer advertise in the same manner as the manufacturer? Is it sensible for farmers to advertise at all?

3. Agribusinesses engage in two different types of marketing. Discuss each and their relationship to each other. Discuss differentiated and undifferentiated products as they affect the activities of each of these two types of firms.

4. Why are agricultural transportation costs significant? Are they necessary or unnecessary? Why?

5. Give two examples of processors that are market oriented as to the places they locate plants. Give two examples of supply-oriented processors.

6. Describe concentration, diversification, and conglomeration in the food processing industry.

7. What is the difference between a price maker and a margin maker? What are the conditions a processor must meet to enable her to price her products independently of the supplies and prices of relevant farm products? What constraints does a margin maker face? Why does a firm handling commodities often have more influence on its buying prices than its selling prices?

8. What is a concentration ratio (CR)? Would a CR_4 of 10 suggest a perfectly competitive or an oligopolistic industry? Explain.

9. Do food processors spend much money on advertising? As a percentage of sales, do product marketers or commodity handlers spend more? What is meant by the statement that processors often advertise in order to pull their products?

10. As a wheat trader, you have just heard an official projection of the U. S. average yield at 30 bushels for the upcoming crop. What else do you need to know for that information to become helpful?

11. Think about an agribusiness that you know something about. Which marketing functions does it perform? Where is it located? Is it a commodity handler or a product marketer? Is it marketing oriented? Does it do a lot of advertising? Do you now understand better how and why that business performs as it does?

CLASS EXERCISE

In your commodity group, use the agricultural commodity assigned in Chapter 1 and select a consumer food product from this commodity.

1. Go to two local grocery stores and compare and contrast the pricing, advertising, and branding of that product.

2. Using the USDA values for the breakdown of the food-marketing bill (see Exhibit 4.11) and the price from one of the grocery stores, show how much each segment will receive.

Prepare to lead a class discussion about your findings.

NOTES

1. USDA, *Food Marketing Review 1989–90,* pp. 17, 63.

2. R. T. Shaw, R. J. Semenik, and R. H. Williams, *Marketing: An Integrated Analytical Approach* (Cincinnati: South-Western Publishing, 1981), pp. 10–12.

4

PRICE DETERMINATION
MATCHING QUANTITIES SUPPLIED AND DEMANDED

PREVIEW

- The process by which price and the quantities supplied and demanded are mutually determined is important to understand.

- Price often does not respond instantly to changes in supply and demand. Seasonal, cyclical, and institutional settings affect the adjustment process.

- There is a distinction to make between short-run market clearing and longer periods when production is variable. The price determination of annual crops varies from that of continuously produced commodities.

- Price expectations are clouded by uncertainty. Price cycles in a few commodities depend on lags and incorrect anticipations. For some other commodities, price fluctuations that are less well defined than cycles can also result. The cobweb model is used as a theoretical basis for cyclic behavior.

- There are relationships over time between retail and farm prices for a given commodity. Farm-to-retail price spreads vary by commodity and over time. There are also relationships between farm prices, wholesale prices, and retail prices. Certain forces give long-term stability to the farmer's share of the consumer's dollar.

KEY TERMS

cobweb model

disequilibrium

farm-to-retail price spread

flow commodities

food-marketing bill

market basket

market clearing

outlook information

price cycle

production lag

seasonal price pattern

A visitor from a centrally planned, socialist country would be puzzled by the millions of independent farmers and agribusinesses in America. "Who tells each one what to do?," they would ask. In general, anticipated prices guide farmers in what they do. One of the marks of a well-managed farm or agribusiness is that it does a reasonably accurate job of anticipating and responding to prices. "Reasonably accurate" does not require batting 1.000 (to use a baseball analogy) but rather batting .310 when the average competitor is batting .285.

Most farmers and many agribusiness firms have no perceptible influence on prices (the competitive model). Some firms have small but perceptible influences on prices. All firms operate within markets in which suppliers, customers, and competitors influence one another through their cumulative impact on prices. From a macro point of view, the decisions of firms influence prices (perceptibly or imperceptibly), and in turn those prices influence the decisions of firms. It is a marvelous interdependent system in which decisions about production, transportation, storage, processing, merchandising, and consumption are all *influenced* by fluctuating prices. At any given moment, existing prices are *determined* by past and current decisions of all market participants.

Let's begin to apply supply-and-demand analysis to farm-level price determination. We start with a simple but generally applicable model and then add some real-life complications.

1. Assume a given supply-and-demand situation. This situation has a market price and quantity exchanged. The market is cleared at this price because the quantity that all sellers want to sell equals what buyers want to buy.

2. Shift either demand or supply.

3. See how price shifts to equate the quantities that suppliers are willing to sell with the quantities that demanders are willing to buy.

We demonstrate these steps in Exhibit 4.1 as follows:

1. We start with D_1 and S and price P_1, with Q_1 as the quantity exchanged.

2. We shift demand up to D_2.

3. We observe that price P_2 is the price that will match at Q_2 the quantity that sellers are willing to sell and buyers are willing to buy.

EXHIBIT

4.1   Demand shifts.

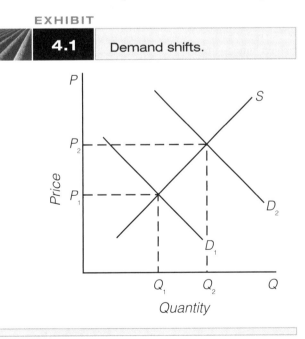

Simple but beautiful, isn't it? The important point is that market pricing is one reasonably automatic, efficient, and impersonal process by which people in the marketing system (both buyers and sellers) adjust to a new supply-and-demand situation.

High prices ration increased demand among those buyers willing to pay a "higher" price (higher than normal or higher than the last period). Obviously, we could show what happens when demand shifts down (left) instead of up (right), as in Exhibit 4.1, or when supply shifts to the right or left. But you have the picture, and you can practice by working those situations out.

Do shifts in supply and demand actually occur? If so, how large are they? Why do they occur? To answer these questions, let's think back to the discussion of domestic and foreign markets.

In general, the domestic demands for specific foods and for food in general are fairly steady, changing slowly only with changes in population, income, and tastes. In addition, these demands are divided rather evenly into weekly (or thereabouts) amounts purchased. Food consumption is daily, and consumer food buying tends to be weekly or a bit more frequent, as consumers find it inconvenient (and nearly impossible in the case of some perishables) to maintain large inventories.

Of course, some important commodities provide seasonal exceptions to the year-round consumer demands. Cranberries and turkeys are well known to be in great demand at Thanksgiving and Christmas, whereas eggs and hams do especially well at Easter. Generally, the demand for chicken is best during the summer barbecue season, whereas the demand for pork and eggs picks up in the fall. Irregular interruptions may take place in the even flow of demand. Recessions, inflation, and other significant influences on disposable personal income can change food demand overall and not necessarily evenly for all commodities. Granted the exceptions, the point is that large, unexpected shifts in domestic demand for food are unusual. One example of such a shift was the increased demand for meat due to wide adoption of low-carbohydrate diets. Such an event is very rare. Of course, the many small shifts that do occur pose real problems for the price forecaster. An example of a small shift might be decreased demand after a recall of E. coli–contaminated meat.

Foreign demand for American exports is a different matter. It is large, variable, and less predictable. Some nations buy steadily and others irregularly, and the size of each of their purchases varies tremendously. Do these variations in international demand mean that foreign consumers are much more changeable than American consumers? No. A sudden jump in foreign demand usually occurs because there was a harvest failure either in the importing nation or in a competing exporter. Other disruptions, such as war and politics, also play a role, but natural impacts of weather, fish catches, and so on are the typical causes of demand shifts. Thus, large and sudden shifts in foreign demand do occur. Supply is often more variable than demand.

The United States, like other nations, experiences large weather-induced supply variations. Moreover, major changes in input costs, such as energy prices, may shift supply curves. Government policy may affect a farmer's willingness to produce and thus may shift supply curves.

MARKET CLEARING

To understand the matching of supply and demand, one must appreciate the role of timing. Once the supply of a commodity is produced and marketed, the matching must be in terms of price alone, as quantity has already been determined. Of course, if the commodity is storable, then the quantities produced and marketed in a given year can differ. Although we consume what we produce, we do not necessarily do so for storables in the same crop year. Over a longer period, suppliers and potential suppliers, in response to expected prices, can adjust the quantities they supply. Thus, the influence of price in short-term *market clearing* is different from its influence in guiding future output. Let's look first at price as it clears the market of what has been or is being produced. **Market clearing** is the process of the market price adjusting so that all buyers and sellers currently wishing to trade at that price can do so. The more perishable the commodity, the less able sellers are to wait for a better price.

Perishable Crops

Market clearing is of maximum urgency with a highly perishable crop ready for harvesting. Let's use strawberries as an example. The supply curve of strawberry producers appears rather strange because the suppliers' alternatives are severely limited (Exhibit 4.2). Their alternatives are either to sell all they produce at whatever price is available or not even to harvest if the price is not high enough to cover harvest costs. Storage is not an alternative. The horizontal arm of this very short-term supply curve indicates the minimal price that covers harvest costs. The vertical arm of the supply curve reflects the maximum total amount available for harvest. The position of the supply curve varies from season to season as a result of natural causes such as the weather or changes in acres planted. Hence, even if demand is quite steady and predictable, the market clearing price and quantity of strawberries may vary a great deal from 1 billion pounds at $1.50 in one season to 2 billion pounds at $.50 in another season illustrated by the intersection of D with S_1 and S_2 in Exhibit 4.2.

Unfortunately, from the producer's view, this textbook example can be very real. Look, for example, at the variation in the monthly U.S. average prices for pinto beans and strawberries in Exhibit 4.3. Not only is the variation large, but these averages also mask larger, weekly price variations experienced by particular production areas. Such examples in the fresh markets are fairly common.

Nonperishable Crops

Consider wheat or soybeans as harvest time approaches. Is the supply curve really any different than for watermelons? Farmers have no alternative but to harvest if price covers harvest costs, as

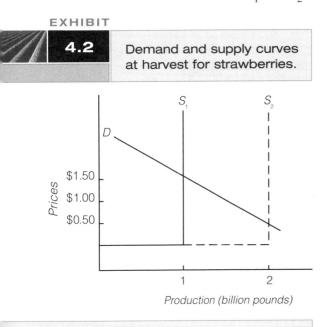

EXHIBIT

4.2   Demand and supply curves at harvest for strawberries.

S_1 S_2

D

Prices

$1.50
$1.00
$0.50

1   2

Production (billion pounds)

4.3 Variations in vegetable and fruit prices.

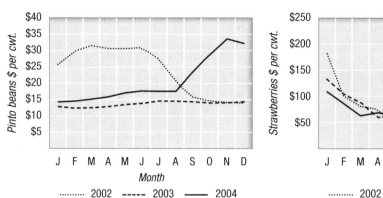

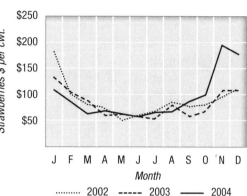

Source: USDA, Agricultural Prices, 2005.

it almost invariably does. And they can harvest only the total amount that has been produced, and no more, regardless of the price. There is an important difference, however. A producer becomes a supplier when he sells. Producers of perishables must become suppliers at harvest—they must "sell it or smell it." American grain producers, however, now have large amounts of on-farm storage as well as access to commercial storage, so that many can store all or most of their grain at harvest. The alternative open to farmers undoubtedly gives some positive slope to the supply curve, as indicated in Exhibit 4.4a. Or might

EXHIBIT

4.4 Supply for a particular crop year of a nonperishable.

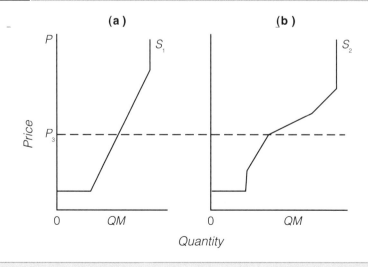

the supply curve be more like Exhibit 4.4b? That curve indicates that many farmers may wait for a certain price level, such as P_3. Large amounts will be supplied after that price level is reached.

What if demand intersects supply (either S_1 or S_2) just below P_3? Does that mean that most of this year's harvest will not be sold this year? Yes, that is correct, as long as farmers' attitudes continue to be reflected by that supply curve. However, as the marketing year progresses and a new crop is underway, farmers might reconsider their attitude about price, and their supply curve may shift downward to the right due to supply now being a combination of last year's and this year's supply. As a result, eventually much or all of the crop is sold.

Let's examine a normal **seasonal price pattern** in a storable commodity like wheat. (A seasonal price pattern is a set of prices within a year that varies somewhat regularly as a result of the regular influence of the seasons on production, marketing, and demand.) Storage costs money in terms of space rental, interest on the inventory being stored, product deterioration, insurance, and other factors. Thus, a normal seasonal pattern of a once-a-year-harvested storable commodity suggests that prices will be lowest at harvest and then steadily rise to cover the month-by-month accumulation of storage costs, until price peaks just before the new harvest. Exhibit 4.5 illustrates the average seasonal pattern for Kansas City No. 1 hard red winter wheat prices for 1995 through 2004. The diamonds in the middle of the vertical lines indicate monthly average prices after adjustments for trends

EXHIBIT

4.5　Seasonal price pattern for Kansas City No. 1 hard red winter wheat, 1995–2004.

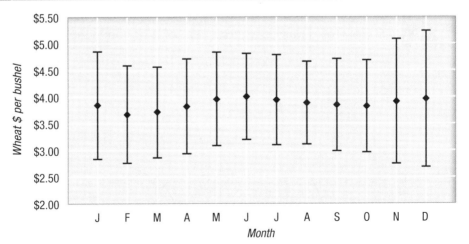

Shows one standard deviation off the mean.

Source: DTN Ag Dayta, 2005.

and irregular components. Because no two seasons' price movements are exactly alike, the vertical lines indicate the range that includes two-thirds of the monthly observations for the 1995–2004 period.

Commodities that are more expensive to store have a more distinct seasonal variation reflecting those costs (Exhibit 4.6). The price of a perishable such as apples may regularly rise 30% to 50% during a storage season, whereas the price of wheat will ordinarily rise 10% to 20%.

How, then, can we understand this normal seasonal price pattern in terms of supply and demand? During a crop year (September 1 to August 31), the domestic supply of corn steadily dwindles with domestic use and exports. The beginning stocks of corn carried over from the previous year will usually vary from 1 to 3 billion bushels. The fall corn crop will usually vary from 9 to 11.5 billion bushels. The total supply of beginning stocks plus the fall crop will usually be in the 10 to 15 billion bushels range. Whatever that total corn supply in the fall, it will dwindle steadily during the following winter, spring, and summer at a rate of about 1 billion bushels per month. Prices ordinarily rise as the amount of corn declines. But expectations about the size of the next crop soon enter the picture. Corn is planted from March through May. If a large crop is anticipated on July 1 because of big plantings and good corn growing conditions, prices may

EXHIBIT

4.6 Seasonal price patterns.

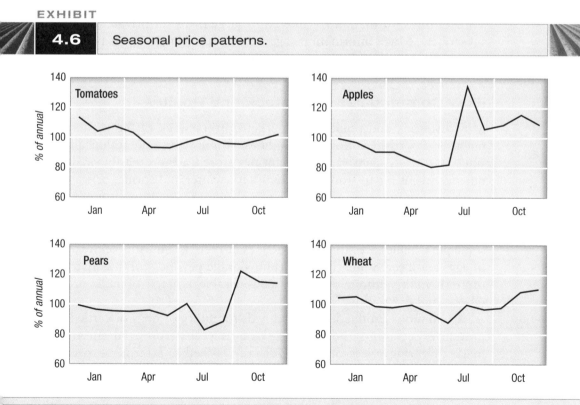

Source: USDA, Agricultural Prices, 2005.

cease their seasonal rising. However, if the weather changes and the August 1 crop report from the USDA projects a surprisingly poor harvest, then prices may rise even faster. In the latter case, many owners of corn may project that next year's corn prices will be higher, so they may pay to hold corn rather than sell now.

Suppose that in another year the world demand for corn suddenly falls in early June because the Southern Hemisphere had a very big crop and crop prospects are extremely good all over the Northern Hemisphere. Or suppose that it becomes clear by then that U. S. feed utilization and exports have both been much lower for the past three months than was expected. In both cases, the June and July prices of U. S. corn may be lower than prices in previous months, rather than higher by the amount of the storage costs.

Thus, the market price of a storable product such as corn may change almost hourly until it is transformed into a final consumer product. Corn may go through several owners after it leaves the farm. Regardless of who owns it, the owner's willingness to sell it to a final user (or to any other buyer) depends on her expectations about price developments in the future and her storage alternatives.

Obviously, information about the size of harvests around the world and about factors such as planting intentions, acres planted, and crop conditions affecting future harvests is important news to market participants. Some of this information is gathered by large firms for private use and for subscribers. Much information is gathered in the United States by a federal agency, the National Agricultural Statistical Service.

Flow Commodities—Livestock and Poultry

Most livestock and poultry are marketed every week of the year, so they might be described as **flow commodities.** Storage is usually technically possible, but it is expensive, and quantities stored are ordinarily small. It is obviously sensible to store some apples for winter and spring, or we would not have any domestic supplies during that time. But farmers will be producing bacon, eggs, beefsteaks, and milk every week, so how likely is it that next-period prices will cover storage costs? Beyond working inventories, some pork bellies are stored for bacon, but there is almost no extra storage of eggs and beef. Similarly, there is no storage beyond working inventories of fresh milk, although there is considerable storage of milk products (cheese and dry milk).

Continuous production and limited storability of hogs or cattle largely prevent expectations about the size of next year's crop from affecting the market clearing prices of this year's crop. Whether a farmer expects hog prices to be $55 or $35 next February does not change the necessity of his selling hogs this February at the going price of $45.

However, expectations about tomorrow's prices or even next month's prices can influence producers' willingness to buy or sell. A producer can

vary the timing of sale of hogs or cattle readily by a few days and less readily by a few weeks in an attempt to obtain better prices. Thus, very short-run
price expectations do influence daily pricing in some flow commodities, particularly hogs, cattle, and lambs. Temporary interruptions of supplies may
also be caused by strikes, floods, snowstorms, and even good fieldwork
weather when many farmers do not take time to market livestock.

For hogs, the daily supply-and-demand situation within a given week
can vary substantially. A small drop in prices might encourage larger shipments on the following day to avoid a feared further price drop. However,
a large drop in prices might be met by much lower shipments, motivated by
a feeling that prices will soon improve. In a similar fashion, the eagerness
of packers to buy varies depending on how many they have already purchased and their assessment of the developing market price situation.
Individual market participants almost never have accurate knowledge as to
what other participants are going to do. Therefore, they cannot predict
short-term price movements accurately.

Prices of both hogs and wholesale pork can change daily. Some of these
changes might be attributed to changes in the number of hogs supplied,
but they may also reflect the endless negotiation among farmers, packers,
and retailers.

Short-run price movements sometimes can be quite puzzling. Price may
move rather rapidly up or down by 10% to 20% for no apparent reason.
Because demand and supply in the immediate short run reflect the differing
ideas and information of many participants in the market, the results are
sometimes unpredictable.

Price equates amounts supplied and demanded, but it does not always
do so as effectively as we might like. Farmers who receive 10% less for their
livestock than for comparable livestock sold the week before or the week
after their sale are likely to question that kind of marketing system. Perhaps
the producers who become most frustrated with marketing are those who
vainly hold cattle or hogs on a declining market until they have lost greatly in price because of both the market decline and their stock's fat
condition. Marketing and the marketing system are blamed—not always
justly—for many things.

Seasonal Price Variation and Commodity Perishability

Let's summarize how the degree of storability of a commodity affects seasonal price patterns. The seasonal price pattern for most extreme
perishables is almost entirely a function of the amounts supplied through
the season. The highest prices, as a season opens, are followed by falling
prices as the harvest increases and then by rising prices as the harvest supplies dwindle. For storables harvested annually, the relative size of storage
costs and the intraseasonal supplies and demands determine the seasonal
price pattern. For semiperishable flow products, the seasonal pattern is
ordinarily influenced more by amounts supplied than by varying demands.

4.7   Average monthly prices for Canadian barrows and gilts, 1995–2004.

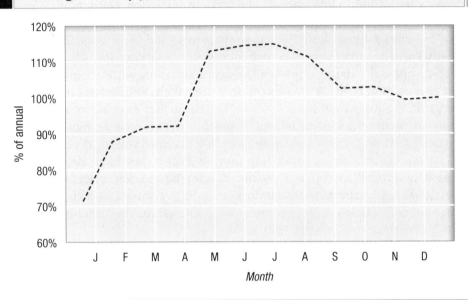

Source: USDA.

There are striking exceptions, such as the seasonal peak demand at Thanksgiving for turkeys.

As an example, Exhibit 4.7 shows seasonal price patterns for a semiperishable commodity: slaughter hogs. The price pattern reflects mainly seasonal supply fluctuations. However, price forecasters must look at more than the seasonal price pattern. One must adjust seasonal price forecasts for cyclical and trend changes, because they can overwhelm seasonal patterns. For example, when cyclical prices are falling rapidly, the high price for the year may occur in April rather than June or July. Producers and traders must become familiar with normal seasonal price patterns and with the kinds of forces that may override them.

PRICE AS A FEEDBACK SIGNAL TO PRODUCTION

We now turn from market clearing to periods long enough for production to be varied by producers' decisions. Today's prices match amounts supplied and demanded; next season's expected prices affect the amounts supplied then. On what grounds are expectations developed about the next season's prices? Many, varying clues may be used, but usually today's prices have strong influence on expectations. A large amount of **outlook information**—data and projections about market demand, supply, and prices provided by private or public agencies—is available to most farmers. Many have studied futures price movements closely; thus, their price expectations are presumably an adjusted version of today's prices. Various agencies provide predictions and advice on using these predictions, for a fee. Such predictions may be based on fundamental analysis (supply and demand), on technical analysis, or on some combination of the two. (These concepts are discussed in Chapter 10.) Price prediction is difficult, and experts are more successful than nonexperts.

It is no surprise that producers plan to increase production when they anticipate very profitable prices. Likewise, they cut production plans when expected prices are unprofitable. This response to the level of anticipated profits is the economic force behind the market aphorism, "high prices are the cure for high prices, and low prices are the cure for low prices." Certainly any participant in agricultural production and marketing should respect that rule of thumb.

Generally, the level of prices should be viewed in a relative rather than an absolute sense. Farmers consider an expected corn price in terms of prices of substitute commodities, such as food grains or soybeans, that could be grown instead. Soybeans cost more to produce per bushel (not per acre) than corn, so their price must be higher than corn to obtain much production. Anticipated relative prices and relative production costs and yields guide production decisions. Those in agricultural marketing need to understand the very important differences among farm commodities as to the magnitudes and lag times of responses to price expectations in quantities supplied.

Adjustments of amounts supplied are limited by lag times. Farmers cannot increase the output of hogs, eggs, or wheat next week by adding another shift of workers, as might be done in a factory. Because many crops are harvested once a year, increasing the amount supplied often takes a year. For some tree crops, the biological lag time to start production is up to eight years. It takes almost a year from the breeding of sows to the slaughter of their progeny; for beef cows the **production lag** (the period it takes to increase or reduce production of a commodity) is more than two years. Moreover, the lags to cutting production are usually as long as those for increasing production. Although a farmer can destroy a growing crop, cut down a producing orchard, or slaughter pregnant animals when price expectations turn lower, conditions usually must become very dismal before such drastic actions become economic.

A complication arises in supply response when an important part of the output is normally diverted to producing further output, as in livestock. For example, the retaining of heifers in the production herd reduces the number of feeder cattle that can be marketed that year. Thus, when expected prices strongly encourage increased output, the response for two years or so may be an increased retention of breeding heifers and, consequently, lower feeder cattle output. Similarly, when expected prices discourage output, the sell-off of heifers ordinarily retained may actually increase output. Therefore, what seems at first glance to be a perverse relation of price and output response is rational. The same response phenomenon occurs in hogs but to a much lesser extent because of an obvious biological difference: a sow produces 14 to 24 pigs each year, whereas a cow normally produces only one calf.

The two dimensions of price expectations—level and duration—affect the nature of supply response. If corn prices are expected to be quite good relative to prices of other crops for one year, that is a motivation for a farmer to increase corn acreage relative to other field crops and also perhaps to put on more fertilizer. If, however, the duration of those good corn prices is expected to be five years, that may be reason to plow up some pasture, acquire new equipment and more corn storage, and plant an even higher ratio of acreage in corn. The same sort of calculations affect hog producers. An expected short duration of high prices is met by keeping sows for another litter, buying feeder pigs, and feeding on pasture. An expected long duration of high hog prices results in the building of new confinement facilities.

Therefore, in the long run, the quantity supplied will adjust to a greater degree to any given price change. It is very important for both market participants and policy makers to appreciate this fact. Many bad decisions have been made on the assumption that an inelastic short-run supply (yielding high prices) will persist in the longer run. An example is the expansion of hog production just before prices fall to a cyclical low. It is painful to ignore the rule that high prices will eventually cure high prices.

The Cobweb Model

As we have seen, today's prices allocate present supplies and influence the size of future output. A few agricultural prices follow a regularly repeating pattern over time—a **price cycle,** or a long-term repetitive movement of prices. Cycles depend on a lag. Thus, high prices lead eventually to higher output, which reduces prices and leads eventually to lower output, which raises prices, and so on. We demonstrated in an earlier supply-and-demand model (see Exhibit 4.1) how the intersection of S and D produces an equilibrium price. A simple model, called the **cobweb model,** provides a theoretical description of how prices of a commodity could cycle even though its demand and supply curves are stable. This model introduces the theoretical possibility of continual **disequilibrium,** or a set of prices that keep changing over time even though the basic supply and demand schedules are stable.

We look first at the theoretical model and then ask what it means in agricultural marketing. Any economic model produces logical results based on certain assumed conditions. The cobweb model shows how it is logically possible to have cycling prices while the basic supply and demand curves remain in exactly the same place. Assume the following:

1. That production is divided into discrete periods (like annual crops)
2. That production for the next period depends entirely on the attractiveness of this period's price

3. That this period's price is a market-clearing price so therefore must be on the demand curve

4. That some random event produces a beginning disequilibrium price[1]

It is necessary to look at Exhibit 4.8 to see how these assumptions apply. Beginning with assumption 4, we assume that, somehow, there was a small output, Q_1, represented by position 1. On the basis of assumption 3, all of the output, Q_1, is consumed in period 1, at the high price, P_1, far above the supply curve. As a result of assumptions 2 and 1, output Q_2 is planned and duly occurs in period 2 because producers expect price P_1 to continue. However, in period 2, the larger output, Q_2, cannot result in price P_1 but rather results in price P_2. Thus, producers made plans to go from position 1 to EP (expected position) but in fact reached position 2. But position 2 is also a disequilibrium position from a longer-term point of view, because price P_2 is too low to sustain that output in the next period. In period 2, producers plan for output Q_1(on their supply curve at EP') in the next period. However, when output Q_1 occurs in period 3, producers arrive back at position 1. Under the same condition, the disequilibrium process could continue indefinitely with alternating periods at position 1 and 2 and alternating expectation of EP and EP', which are never fulfilled because they are not market-clearing positions (not on the demand curve).

You may have noticed an important point about the geometry of Exhibit 4.8. For the disequilibrium to repeat itself continuously, the points 1, EP, 2, and EP' must form a rectangle. If they do not, then the repetitions either converge toward a long-term equilibrium (when the supply curve is steeper than the demand curve) or explode (when the demand curve is steeper than the supply curve). In the latter case, so much would be produced eventually that price would be forced to zero, and producers might be assumed to quit in disgust. Do not take our word for it: draw the curves and prove it to yourself. In either a converging or a diverging case, a maze of lines with some rough resemblance to a cobweb is spun—thus the name of the model.

The real world is a messy place that rarely, if ever, fits any simple model. There are several reasons that we cannot present any long-term price series that fits exactly any of the three cobweb cases. None of the first three assumptions will hold consistently. Consider the first assumption, that production is divided into discrete periods. The model has often been

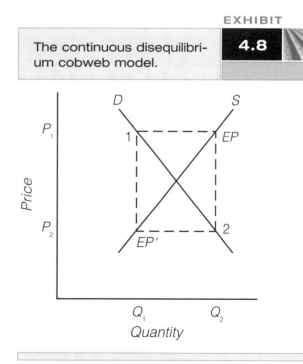

EXHIBIT

4.8

The continuous disequilibrium cobweb model.

applied to hogs with the period defined to be a year, but that is arbitrary. Although there is a lag of nearly a year from sow breeding to sale of hogs, decisions about future production are being made continuously rather than once a year.

The second assumption is probably the weakest. As already noted, producers consider more than today's price in their planning. Moreover, planned production is usually not the same as realized output because of uncontrollable factors such as weather, pests, and disease. The third assumption, market clearing, holds for perishables but not for storable commodities. Finally, we should not assume that supply-and-demand curves remain completely static over time; their erratic movement would disturb any cobweb.

Then why bother with the model? The model demonstrates how disequilibrium results may be observed in agriculture. As noted above, there are usually important lags between decision making and the resulting outputs, so that expected and realized prices are frequently different. Once a disequilibrium begins, there are tendencies in some commodities for it to continue. Exhibit 4.9 presents a modified cobweb that involves three ideas:

1. Next period's production ordinarily is high or low corresponding to last period's price.
2. Price is usually a market-clearing price.
3. There are intermittent interruptions associated with a variety of factors, such as shifts in supply or demand.

These interruptions are shown in the outputs of periods 5, 8, and 9 and in the prices of periods 6 and 9.

Certainly there are real-world interruptions associated with occasional demand shifts or occasional major effects of technology, government policy, weather, disease, and pests on output. There is also some tendency for producers to react too optimistically to currently high prices and too pessimistically to currently low prices. It is absolutely essential that producers do react to high and low price expectations, or else prices would not perform their invaluable function of guiding production. The problem arises when producers overreact. Given the short-term inelasticities of supply and

EXHIBIT

| **4.9** | A modified cyclical model. |

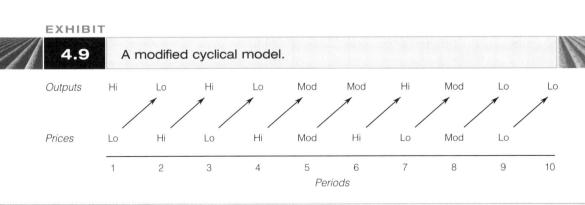

demand, small output shifts usually lead to much larger price changes. Thus, price oscillations over time are not unusual in agriculture.

Although many crops not subject to government price supports have rather severe fluctuations in price from year to year, they generally do not have well-defined cycles. The uncontrollable, stochastic impact of weather on crop yields interferes with regular cyclical patterns. Price fluctuations tend to be large because of the relatively strict inelasticities of demand at the farm level associated with most crops. These inelasticities magnify the impact of year-to-year fluctuations in output.

Although it is biologically possible for the hog cycle to be as short as two years, it has generally been longer because producers react fairly slowly to price changes. Yet changes in technology and industry consolidation have ratcheted down the time needed for a production response to prices. It is important that hog producers and marketers recognize the hog cycle. It is also important that they recognize that neither the cycle's amplitude of price variation nor its timing is usually uniform.

Biological lag times require a cattle cycle to be much longer than a hog cycle. The upswing of cattle output takes several years because of biological constraints. Downswings are more variable in length. Cattle slaughter output may increase and then remain high for three or four years after the peak in cattle prices because the attempt to reduce the on-farm cattle inventory increases sales for slaughter. Exhibit 4.10 indicates that the last six cattle

EXHIBIT

4.10 Inventory of cattle and calves by cycles in the United States.

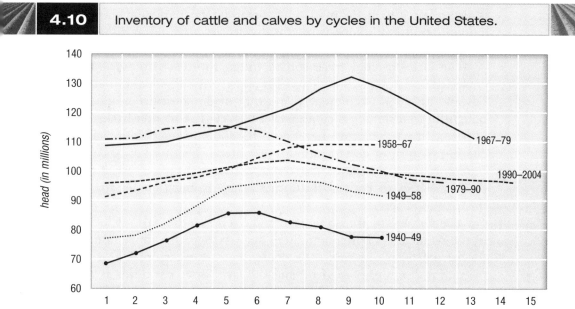

Cattle on U.S. farms January 1

Source: USDA, *National Agriculture Statistics Service.*

cyclcs, 1940 to 2004, have varied from 9 to 15 years in length. In addition to the cycle in the production of feeder animals, there are much more rapid fluctuations in beef cattle feeding that are sometimes called cycles.

One of the major inefficiencies in agricultural marketing has been cyclical production of hogs and cattle. In certain years, billions of dollars of feed have gone into hogs that more profitably should have gone into cattle and poultry or been exported. In other years, resources have been wastefully employed in cattle production. This inefficiency is not easily eliminated.

PRICES AT VARYING STAGES
OF A MARKET CHANNEL

Marketing is a flow of products through several stages of a marketing channel. How are the amounts that are supplied and demanded matched at each stage or level? For example, how are the prices of cattle, wholesale beef, and retail beef cuts determined so that there is a continuous flow through the market channel? Viewed another way, what are the relationships of prices at the various levels? The term *marketing costs and spreads* (margins) is often applied to this subject.

Farm-to-Retail Price Spread

The **farm-to-retail price spread** is the difference between the prices farmers receive and those that consumers pay for equivalent amounts of a food. It is also referred to as the marketing spread or the marketing margin. When a dollar spent at the supermarket is divided into the farmer's share and the agribusiness share, the difference is the *farm-to-retail price spread*.

The farm-to-retail price spread (often shortened to *price spread*) is compiled and published regularly for numerous individual farm commodities and also for a representative group of domestically produced foods bought in foodstores called a **market basket.** The market basket excludes imported food, fish, and beverages. Its composition represents the purchasing pattern of certain urban households. The market basket ignores food purchased in restaurants, so it understates the price spread relative to the farmer's share, because the farmer's share is much smaller for food sold through food service.

The farmer's share is the percentage representing farm value as a part of the retail price. For commodities such as eggs that move in unchanged form from farm to retail, the calculation is straightforward. If the retail price of a dozen eggs is $1.00 and the farm price per dozen is 65¢, then the farmer's share is 65%. For processed products, the calculation is more complicated. Suppose the retail price of sirloin steak is $3.79 and the price of Choice cattle is 60¢. Is the farmer's share equal to 16%? No. Many cuts of beef other than sirloin are in a carcass. There are also dressing losses and byproducts. Thus, the farmer's share is computed for a composite of all the beef cuts rather than a single steak. Moreover, the farm value is computed as the live farm price times 2.4 (which is the pounds of live animal equivalent to 1.0 pound of beef at retail), minus an allowance for nonmeat byproducts. The resulting farmer's share for Choice grade beef may be 60%.

The Long-Term Trend of Farmer's Share

For the period 1920–1990, the farmer's share of the market basket averaged 40% and varied from a high of 53% to a low of 30%. Today the farmer's share is below 20%. The high periods of farmer's share were more prosperous for farmers than the low periods. Why? Because the farmer's share has been a fairly good index of the pressure of demand on agriculture's capacity to produce. Farmer's share has been high in wartime and was also high during the export boom of the early 1970s.

Given that there have been significant variations in the farmer's share, it is impressive that the long-term trend is nearly flat. How can that be? Because the costs of producing and marketing food tend to move together, on average, over the long term. Labor costs, the biggest item, largely move together at farm and nonfarm levels. So do cost of utilities, transportation, taxes, interest, machinery, and most other items. Technology has probably advanced faster in farming than in marketing in recent decades, so the farmer's share has trended downward a bit. That same trend has been observed in the way manufacturing and retailing costs have changed.

Since 1990 the farmer's share of the retail dollar has eroded. Farm productivity has improved considerably (more output per unit of input), and cost increases beyond-the-farmgate have outpaced on-farm cost increases. Costs such as labor, transportation, and advertising have increased substantially, while firm profitability has changed little. This trend has sparked producer interest in value-added agriculture (*value added* refers to the further processing or enhancement of a commodity to gain extra value per unit). Farmers often find value-added agriculture difficult to implement because farmers have little to no comparative advantage over firms in controlling labor, transportation, and advertising.

A Theory of Price Spreads

The retail food customer generally buys neither a farm commodity nor a food marketing service but rather a retail product involving a mix of both, in varying proportions. The farmer's share statistics provide a relatively good measure of the final mix. The higher the farmer's share, the more important is the value of the commodity in the final mix. Thus, the farmer's share is generally higher for less processed than for more processed items. For example, the farmer's share for cereal products is usually low, while it is a little higher for fats and oils, and highest for eggs. Of course, the higher the farmer's share, the lower the price spread, because their sum is the retail price.

What else determines the size of the price spread? Obviously, in the long term any price spread must cover costs, including necessary profits. If the spread were lower than costs, then the service would not be provided in an open-enterprise economy. If the price spread were higher and provided excess profits, competition should arise that will reduce the profits and the price spread. Questions can be raised in the long term about the efficiency of providing the service (are the costs as low as attainable?) and the level of profits (are they excessive?). For the moment, we simply assume that the price spread in the long term for any commodity is equal to the costs of providing marketing services.

What about the size of the price spread in the short term? Marketing firms want to cover costs and make some profits. Sometimes they achieve this goal, and sometimes they do not. One important problem that marketing firms face is their inability to control volume. The meat packers can slaughter no more hogs than they are able to purchase. One year they may slaughter 80 million hogs and the next year 95 million. One week it may be 1.6 million head and another week 1.9 million. Canners have a similar problem. The amount of green beans that can be processed is affected by the size of the crop. And so it goes for many marketing agencies.

The amount supplied of a farm commodity constitutes the demand for the marketing services provided by commodity handling firms. Thus, a big wheat crop leads to a big demand for handling, storing, and buying services of country and terminal elevators and eventually of millers and bakers, whereas a small wheat crop leads to a small demand. That seems obvious, but it explains something that some farmers and many others often fail to understand. Hog producers often ask why, in the face of increased marketings and falling hog prices, the margins taken by packers do not fall nearly as much and even occasionally rise. Once we perceive that packers supply hog processing services along with pork, we understand that enlarged supplies of hogs and pork mean an increased demand for hog processing services. An increased demand does not readily yield lower prices for such services. In Chapter 2, increases in short-term demands were shown to lead to higher prices.

The real world is even more complicated than these models suggest. Neither technology nor the prices of inputs are constant over time. Prices of inputs (e.g., labor and utilities) used by processors and retailers may rise rapidly during an inflationary period. Therefore, a complex analysis is necessary when we try to explain changes in margins over time. Moreover, some studies suggest that lags of one to three months often occur. That is, if a change in output and farm prices increases or reduces a price spread, then full margin restoration may take one to three months. Another complication exists at retail. Costs of retailing cannot be readily tied to specific products; markups can vary over time for any specific product without necessarily endangering a satisfactory profit for the entire supermarket. Under these conditions, costs are not a very decisive influence on the retail part of the price spread regardless of the level of output of that commodity.

Instead, the price spread may vary more readily with the intensity of retail competition. The models of monopolistic competition and oligopoly suggest some of the influences on short-term price spreads.

Because costs are so important in determining long-term marketing price spreads, we will examine their behavior in the next section.

Costs of Marketing

Marketing costs can be categorized according to the stages of the marketing channel. In the past 60 years, food service costs have become a larger share of all marketing costs (called the marketing bill), whereas processing costs have fallen. These changes are attributed to productivity rising much more in processing than in food service and to the relative growth of the food service industry. It has been easier to substitute machinery for labor in food processing than in restaurants and food retailing.

Data on marketing costs are available by certain expense categories. The Economic Research Service of the USDA calculates the **food-marketing bill,** which is a breakdown of how the consumer dollar is allocated between farm and marketing costs (Exhibit 4.11a) and the costs of the services and materials required to market the food (Exhibit 4.11b). Direct labor cost is clearly the most significant marketing cost. In fact, it is even more important than shown because labor costs indirectly influence the costs of utilities, repairs, packaging, transportation, advertising, and perhaps other categories.

You may find it surprising that corporate profits are not a larger portion of the marketing bill. Clearly, even a decrease by half in corporate profits would not cut the overall marketing bill by more than 3%. Nevertheless, there are continued arguments about the size of profits. Presumably the most objective standard is to calculate profits as a percentage of stockholders' equity and compare them to similarly defined profit rates of other businesses.

Does It Help Farmers to Reduce the Price Spread?

Farmers have traditionally argued that marketing costs too much—that they would benefit from reducing the price spread. Would they? It depends. If the price spread can be lowered without changing the retail demand, then obviously the derived demand at the farm level must rise, and this would benefit farmers. For example, if the workers involved in transporting, processing, and selling milk would all agree to reduce their wages 10% while maintaining their productivity, then the farm value of milk would jump. A new technology that reduced total handling and processing costs by 10% could have the same effect. Or, if all the agribusinesses marketing milk were making above-normal profits and they were to cut those profits in half, then the farm value of milk would rise. The third case would give less benefit to farmers than the first two cases because many fewer dollars would be involved. You will not be surprised to hear that none of these cases is a common occurrence.

EXHIBIT

4.11 What a dollar spent for food paid for in 2000.

Farm value
$123.3 billion

Marketing bill
$537.8 billion

(a)

CONSUMER EXPENDITURES, 2000
$661.1 billion

Labor   Packaging   Transportation   Energy   Profits   Advertising   Depreciation   Rent   Interest   Repairs   Business taxes   Misc. costs

(b)

Labor	Packaging	Transportation	Energy	Profits	Advertising	Depreciation	Rent	Interest	Repairs	Business taxes	Misc. costs
38.3¢	8.1	4	3.5	4.7	3.9	3.7	4	2.6	1.5	3.6	3.5

Notes: Includes food eaten at home and away from home. Other costs include property taxes and insurance, accounting and professional services, promotion, bad debts, and many miscellaneous items.

Source: USDA Economic Research Service.

Hence, farmers do benefit when the price spread is lowered through increased efficiencies in marketing or through a reduction of monopoly profits in marketing (a much rarer case). However, farmers generally would not benefit from simplistic suggestions to eliminate the middlemen or eliminate profits through price controls. Farmers are better off to receive 40% of a $3 price than to receive 45% of a $2.50 price.

Farmers and agribusinesses are interdependent. Increasing efficiencies in farming that push the farm commodity supply curve to the right and increase sales volume will benefit not only consumers but also the handlers and processors of that commodity by providing a greater volume of business. Conversely, an increase in farming costs that moved the farm supply curve to the left would lower the output marketed and reduce the demand for marketing services.

How Farm and Retail Prices and the Price Spread Change Over Time

Prices change when demand and supply are in disequilibrium. Farm prices of most commodities change frequently. In this chapter, we discussed some of the short- and long-term factors behind those changes. It should be clear that the set of supply-and-demand factors affecting the price spread is not identical to the set influencing both retail and farm prices. Yet there must be links between all three, or else there would be shortages at one stage of the market and surpluses in the same channel at another stage.

There are varying views as to whether retail prices change first and then result in changes in farm prices or vice versa. Given the variety of different circumstances in the economy, it is doubtful that all evidence will support either explanation. First, let's consider the view that farm prices change first. Retailers use a standard markup (varied only as their input costs rise) over wholesale food prices. Suppose that there are short supplies at the farm level. As processors must bid higher prices, they raise their wholesale prices, which then leads retailers to raise prices to consumers. The price pass-through takes time—most of it is accomplished within a month, but some of it continues for another month or two. Now let's consider the situation where the initial disequilibrium is at the retail rather than the farm level. Suppose that consumer demand rises (or falls). Don't retailers respond by raising (or lowering) prices? They generally do not change their markup but instead raise (or reduce) the quantities ordered. When these changes in orders reach the farm level, they change farm product prices in obvious directions. Then, just as before, those changes in price work their way up to retail, where they finally result in price changes. Thus, an increased demand at retail, according to this model, does result in increased retail prices, but only after it first increases farm prices.

Several factors may make it difficult for us to identify the price linkages and lags. First, changes in farm supplies, retail demand, and marketing input costs may all be happening simultaneously, but not all may be detectable to an observer. Thus, prices at farm or retail may change in ways inconsistent with what an observer expects based on his understanding of where a disequilibrium has arisen. Second, there is enough concentration in some parts of the food system to introduce uncertainties as to how competitors will react to a new situation. Although a standard markup is a rather easy way for oligopolistic competitors to keep in step, situations occasionally arise in which they do not. As we will discover in the chapters on retailing, price competition can be vigorous. Finally, the concept of a constant retail markup is not entirely consistent with typical pricing tactics for many items, especially meats. A retailer may feel strongly that she must lower the price on a $1.79 meat cut by at least 10¢, or sometimes 20¢, to get any increased sales. Thus, a small reduction in wholesale meat prices of 2 to 5¢ may result in a wider retail price spread and no change in retail price. Another factor relates to the farmer's share. The smaller the farmer's share of a commodity, the less relative impact a change in farm price has on retail price. For example, a 10% change in the price of wheat has a hardly perceptible impact on the price of bread, whereas a 10% change in the price of cattle has a decided impact on the price of beef.

SUMMARY

1. We have been concerned with the operation of the pricing process as it continually matches quantities supplied and demanded. The analysis has relied heavily on supply-and-demand models. Although much can be explained and predicted about market price behavior, it is often complex and uncertain, even to those who are everyday participants in marketing processes.

2. Prices frequently fluctuate rather sharply because of sizable changes in demand or in quantities supplied. The largest short-term cause of price shifts is weather, which obviously can affect short-term supplies of crops and, through feed availability and price, the supplies of livestock and poultry. Weather in other countries has the same impacts there that, in turn, have major short-term impacts on the export demand for American farm products. Over the longer term, changes in population, incomes, and tastes are quite important demand influences. This chapter emphasized the short-term variations to which prices adjust frequently.

3. The more freedom that sellers and buyers have in timing their transactions, the more possibilities exist for unfounded expectations to enter

a market and complicate the process by which amounts supplied are equated to amounts demanded. Generally, the less perishable a farm product, the more freedom farmers and subsequent sellers have in timing their sales.

4. Seasonality of supply and demand is frequently an important cause of within-year price movements. Storable products tend to have less pronounced seasonal price swings than do perishable products, except for perishables such as milk or meat that are produced continuously.

5. In the long term, there is much truth in the aphorism that low prices cure low prices and high prices cure high prices. In other words, the presence of lower-than-normal prices generally discourages production, which in turn generally leads to higher prices.

6. The lag times in agricultural production are an especially important aspect of market-pricing problems. The lag time between a farmer's decision to increase or decrease output and the actual resulting output may vary from several weeks to several years, depending on the commodity. Thus, realized market conditions are often very different from those anticipated. Such lags in a competitive market like farming may lead to price cycles or at least price fluctuations.

7. The farm-to-retail price spread must cover the operating costs of marketing firms plus necessary long-term profits. However, in the short term, the typical price spread is considerably more variable than costs, particularly if the output of the associated farm commodity is quite variable. Generally, however, farm prices are even more variable than the marketing spread and retail prices. Also, the derived demand at the farm level for a commodity is generally less elastic than the demand at the retail level.

8. The linkages between prices at various stages of a market channel may vary from time to time and among commodities. For most commodities, evidence suggests that retail prices lag behind farm prices. Most of the lags are less than one month. Because marketing spreads do vary in the short term, and because farm prices tend to be less than one-half of retail prices, farm and retail prices do not move in lockstep, although they do tend to move together over time.

9. The farmer's share varies greatly among commodities. This variation reflects the relative importance of the farm commodity and the associated marketing services in the final mix. Thus, the farmer's share for eggs is much greater than for canned fruits and vegetables. Generally, farmers have been overly concerned about their share. The prosperity of both the egg and the vegetable producer depends on the total dollars received rather than the producer's percentage share.

STUDY QUESTIONS

1. Under what circumstances are there large variations from one month to another or one year to another in the amounts demanded of a commodity at any particular price level?

2. What, besides the vagaries of weather, influences the amount of farm commodities supplies?

3. Discuss the following statement: "Low prices cure low prices and high prices cure high prices." Explain how such prices lead to a better allocation of resources. Also explain why, for a few commodities with price cycles, price variation fails to lead to a better allocation of resources. Draw and explain the cobweb model.

4. Explain why it might be important for you as a farmer to understand whether there is any seasonality in the prices of the commodities you sell. What is the importance of any cyclicality?

5. Would a meat processor or the manufacturer of cake mixes be more interested in commodity price patterns?

6. Explain why it is that, over time, farm and retail prices have maintained about the same proportionate relation and yet seem to vary independently in the short term.

7. Is the cost of food marketing too high? Are marketing firms' profits too high or too low?

CLASS EXERCISE

In your commodity group, use the agricultural commodity assigned in Chapter 1, and complete the following tasks:

1. Collect five years of monthly price data.

2. Graph the data over the entire time period, making one graph spanning one year (according to the marketing year) with five lines representing the five years.

3. Establish whether the commodity is perishable or nonperishable.

4. Determine what caused price fluctuations observed in the graphed data.

Prepare to participate in a class discussion of the differences between the assigned commodities.

NOTE

1. A "true cycle" is said to be self-generating; the simple cobweb needs a starting event.

5

THE DOMESTIC MARKET
A DEVELOPED ECONOMY

PREVIEW

- Consumers' food purchase decisions are affected by a variety of factors.

- A marketer selects target markets and positions products to be competitive.

- American consumers are the principal market of farmers and agribusiness. That total market has grown along with growth in population and per capita income.

- The food service market has grown to be a major share of consumer spending.

- Changes in consumption are not necessarily tied to changes in demand.

- Significant changes in consumption are constantly occurring that affect prices and marketing alternatives.

KEY TERMS

at-home market

away-from-home market

consumer decision making

demand, cross-elasticities

demand, income elasticity

demand, own-price elasticity

Engel's law

farm value

market segmentation

marketing bill

Maslow's hierarchy of needs

product needs

product positioning

The world market is a series of markets. Imagine it to be an apartment building with several floors. On the ground floor, the assemblers are the market for farmers; on the second floor, the processors buy from the assemblers; next, the wholesalers and retailers are the market for the processors; finally, on the top floor, consumers are the market for retailers. The final consumer market is of utmost importance because all of the preceding markets depend on it. The demands expressed in those markets are derived from consumer demands.

A MACRO MARKET PICTURE

The U. S. food market may be considered as two large segments of consumers: an **at-home market** buying at retail and an **away-from-home** (or restaurant and fast-food) **market.** The latter market consists of public eating places and institutions (e.g., hospitals, nursing homes, schools, colleges). Tremendous numbers of people eat meals away from home, especially lunch.

Aggregate estimates of food consumption are mind-boggling for a country as large as ours. For example, if all Americans (based on an estimated population of 296 million) were to eat three meals a day for 365 days a year, they would eat approximately 324 billion meals. (Add another 1.1 billion meals per year for each additional million of population growth.)

At the most aggregate level, the domestic market is the current population (296 million in 2003) with a disposable personal income of X dollars (10.6 trillion in 2004).

FARM AND AGRIBUSINESS SHARES OF THE MARKET

I n 2002, U. S. consumers spent $709 billion for foods produced on U. S. farms. (We will ignore what they spent on imported food.) Of that $709 billion, farmers received $132 billion and agribusiness (assemblers, processors, and retailers) $577 billion. Those latter two numbers are gross measures of the size of the domestic market for farmers and agribusiness.

The share of consumer expenditures on food going to farmers is called the **farm value** and the share going to agribusiness is called the **marketing bill.** The relative shares vary from year to year; generally, the farm value in recent years has been one-fourth or less. The dollar numbers are larger in more recent years:

	1990	1994	2002
	($ in billions)		
Consumers spent	441	511	709
Agribusiness received	334	401	577
Farmers received	107	110	132

The agribusiness share has obviously grown relative to the farmer's share.

As shown in Exhibit 5.1, the agribusiness share is higher for commodities undergoing extensive processing, such as baking products, than for commodities sold in their farm-produced forms, such as poultry and eggs. These commodity data include food sold both through food stores and through eating places. The agribusiness share of consumer dollars spent in food service is much larger than the share in food stores because of the larger costs required to process and serve foods in restaurants and other eating places. Farmers in 1993 received 25¢ of every dollar spent at the supermarket but only 15¢ of every dollar consumers spent in restaurants.

Location of Markets

The final markets for food are where the people are. Although people are scattered coast to coast, the fact that there are great differences in density is important. About three of every four Americans live in a metropolitan area as defined by the U. S. Census. A metropolitan area, called an MA, includes at least one city or urbanized area of at least 50,000 people and

EXHIBIT

5.1   Farmer and agribusiness shares of food products, 2000.

Commodities	Retail price ($)	Farm value ($)	Farm value share of retail price
Apple juice, 64-oz. bottle	1.76	0.32	18%
Applesauce, 25-oz. jar	1.08	0.17	16%
Bread, 1 lb.	0.88	0.04	.5%
Dried beans, 1 lb.	0.73	0.14	19%
Eggs, grade A large, 1 doz.	0.91	0.48	53%
Grapefruit, 1 lb.	0.61	0.1	16%
Green beans, cut, #303 can	0.45	0.06	13%
Lemons, 1 lb.	1.29	0.29	22%
Oatmeal, regular, 42-oz. box	2.68	0.14	.5%
Peanut butter, 1 lb.	1.89	0.42	22%
Pork, 1 lb.	2.58	0.79	31%
Potatoes, french fried, frozen, 1 lb.	1.05	0.1	1%
Raisins, 15-oz. box	1.77	0.29	16%
Shortening, 3 lbs.	3.14	0.48	15%

Source: Food Marketing and Price Spreads, USDA Economic Research Service.

has a total population of at least 100,000 (75,000 in New England). The 20 largest metropolitan areas, called Consolidated Metropolitan Areas (CMA), each has a total population of at least 1 million, and each includes two or more Primary Metropolitan Areas (PMA). (Note that older reports may use obsolete terms, such as metropolitan statistical area or MSA instead of MA.)

MAs are heavily concentrated east of the Mississippi River and along the Gulf and West Coasts, although most states contain at least one MA. It may shock those who live in the vast interior of this country to learn that most of the population resides in counties within 50 miles of a coastal shoreline (including the shores of the Great Lakes and the St. Lawrence River).

The markets are even more concentrated from the point of view of food movement and handling than is suggested by the data on MAs. That is, most of the larger wholesalers of food are located in the larger MAs, and most of the food for the smaller urban and rural areas funnels through the larger MAs.

Agribusinesses must pay particular attention to these market locations and their changes. Americans are a mobile population. There have been massive movements in the past 100 years from farm to city, from east to west, and from the Snowbelt to the Sunbelt. Similarly, there has been a movement from central cities to the suburbs, which has hurt the markets of some retailers and created opportunities for others. There likely will be new movements in the next decade that will affect the markets for transportation firms, wholesalers, retailers, and others. Income differentials among localities are important to agribusiness as they attempt to judge the kinds of products that are likely to sell well. Commercial services provide detailed estimates of population, income distribution, and retail food sales by city and county. Thus, the food industry has access to detailed and timely estimates of where the markets are for every county and many cities in the nation.

MICRO MARKETING

What are the lessons that an agribusiness or producer group can derive from studying the global market? The chief conclusion from this quick survey of the macro market is that it is very large and growing larger but that consumer spending can vary considerably by commodity group or food delivery system. Thus, no one in marketing should assume that there will always be a good market for his particular commodity, product, or service. Note in Exhibit 5.2 that red meats have lost market share in a 20-year period, while several other commodity categories did not change. Consumers have to eat, but they do not have to eat any specific food, nor do they have to buy it in a particular form or through a certain type of retail outlet. Competition is rampant.

EXHIBIT

5.2   Consumer expenditures by food group at home.*

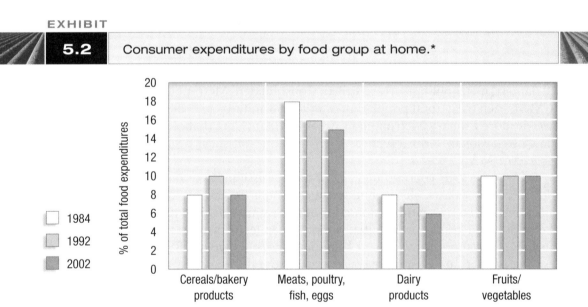

*Totals do not equal 100% because not all food categories are included here.

Source: USDA Economic Research Service.

Consumer Purchase Decisions

Why do consumers buy foods? The obvious answer is that they need them, an answer that can hardly be disproved—partly because *need* is such a vague word. We must consume food to survive. But must we consume potatoes or soft drinks or broccoli? A middle-aged couple might spend $70 for dinner and drinks at the local country club while their teenage son spends $15 for pizza at a local pizza place. Is the best explanation of those two different consumption events that the parents "needed" a country club dinner and the son "needed" a pizza?

We view consumers as people like ourselves whose desires for goods and services exceed their incomes. Budget constraints lead consumers to respond to price levels by buying less at higher prices than at lower prices and to select purchases so as to achieve the most satisfaction consistent with their individual pattern of preferences.

Most **consumer decision making**—the process of valuing the attributes of products relative to perceived costs in selecting one over another—is hardly systematic, but the process can be described as going through a series of stages. For our purposes, we describe five stages:

1. Recognition of a need
2. Search for information
3. Evaluation of product alternatives
4. Purchasing
5. Postpurchase evaluation[1]

Recognition of need can be as simple as saying, "I'm hungry," but usually it is more specific: "I'm hungry for a taco" or "I need to find some lower-calorie foods so I can lose some weight." Or, "My doctor says that I should not consume any foods that are high in fats." Or, "For the party tonight I want to serve specific foods and drinks that will impress my guests."

Maslow's hierarchy of needs—a list of physical and psychological needs that influence personal choices—ranks physiological safety first, followed by love and belonging, esteem, and self-actualization.[2] In describing physiological needs, he is going a step deeper than the product needs described in the previous paragraph. In his view, the physiological or biological needs are the most basic, and they might guide all of the expenditures of an impoverished consumer. Some basic foods, including large amounts of cabbage, beans, and flour, could safely meet the physiological need for food. However, most of the people would find such a diet hardly tolerable for four days, let alone a lifetime. A broader tie to physiological needs is the recognition that certain foods or food components are bad for long-term health. Food that is high in saturated fats is reputed to clog the arteries while swelling the waistline. Astute advertisers often remind us of the hazards of high-fat diets while suggesting that their own offerings are more healthful. Advertisers may claim that their low-fat foods are not only good for us but taste equally as good as the fatter versions. Clearly the demand for foods is more than a matter of physiology and safety. We also want variety, flavor, and other desirable characteristics.

The need that a consumer recognizes explicitly is ordinarily not one of the needs expressed by Maslow. Instead, those underlying needs influence consumers' recognition of more specific needs to which they can relate specific products and services. We refer to those more specific needs as **product needs.**

At any given moment, most of a consumer's product needs are recurring needs that she has satisfied many times before. When she is out of stock, she purchases more milk or lettuce or bagels on her way home from the office. No analysis is necessary as to how to solve most needs—she does it by force of habit.

However, these habit patterns may be disrupted as a person recognizes new product needs. These disturbances may arise from the following changes:

1. A change in the consumer's emphasis on particular psychological needs as influenced by changes in age, income, regional residence, family status, education, employment, social status, and cultural norms

2. A change in habitually consumed products, such as their availability, price, quality, and conditions of sale

3. A change in the consumer's perceptions of consumed products and competing products as influenced by advertising, promotion, attitudes of one's friends, and even chance events

It is easy to see that consumption changes with the life cycle. The child, the teenager, the young adult, the mature adult, and the senior citizen differ as to what and how much they eat, how frequently they eat, and where they eat when they are away from home. Some of the differences are purely physiological manifestations associated with the varying nutritional needs of growth, heavy activity, or sedentary living. Other important differences are related to changes in a consumer's perceptions of his or her psychological needs. A young executive may no longer find it appropriate to dine regularly on the colas, pizza, and tacos that delighted him during his early teens.

A person may decide to reexamine her consumption of a product because of changes in the product. In the extreme, it may no longer be available at the neighborhood supermarket—because of a short crop or because declining sales of a branded item led the supermarket to drop it. A more common reason is that the price has changed. A big increase in price, especially of larger budget items such as beef or milk, will prompt price-sensitive consumers to search for ways to reduce the impact on their budgets, such as partially or completely substituting a less expensive alternative. Conversely, a major drop in price will often lead to an increased rate of consumption; what had been a luxury item may become an item purchased weekly. A new, safer version of a product may gain market share because perceptions about the long-term safety of the product change. For example, many consumers have largely switched from conventional ice cream to low-fat and low-calorie frozen yogurt.

The second stage of consumer decision making is the gathering of information. Typically, any of several alternative products or services could meet our need. We compare their costs and benefits as we see them in relation to our hierarchy of psychological needs and our budget.

We make a decision, then purchase, and consume the product. But that is not the end of it. A habit is not formed instantaneously. Was it the right decision? If the product satisfies us and impresses our friends, and if we receive other information suggesting that this is the right product for us, the reassurance leads us to purchasing the product by habit. Further advertising of the product may help to reassure us. On the other hand, if something is not quite right, we may try other alternatives.

Thus a second lesson for the micro marketer is to understand consumers' decision-making process and how to influence it. Most marketers find it wise to tackle a part of the domestic market rather than all of it. Market segmentation is the subject of the next section.

Market Segmentation and Product Positioning

A *market segment* is an identifiable group or submarket within the total market. Market segments reflect differences in consumers' perceived product needs, which exist for all the reasons just discussed. **Market segmentation** is the process of identifying and focusing on target submarkets. The astute marketer seldom sells one item one way to everyone. Instead, she selects submarkets and focuses her marketing activities on the more promising ones. For example, by looking at restaurants on and near campus, you can see which firms are targeting college students.

There are various approaches to market segmentation. For a commodity group (such as beef producers) or a single product firm, one useful approach may be to identify three groups: heavy users, light users, and nonusers. A firm may go further and try to identify a product, X1, that will sell best to one group and a product variation, X2, that will sell best to another group.

Here is an example of how a commodity group identified and targeted the important food service market segment: Concerned about the relative lack of pork items available in fast-food outlets, the National Pork Producers Council helped develop the pork sandwich that McDonald's later sold as the McRib. Many millions of pounds of pork were sold as a result of that sandwich being introduced into the food service market segment. (The sandwich was later phased out of McDonald's menu, indicative of a "product life cycle" that will be discussed in a later chapter.)

Are there different market segments that spend greatly different amounts per capita on foods? Yes and no. There is a fairly small, high-income and/or high-expense-account group that provides most of the market for expensive restaurants. The demand for T-bone steaks and other particularly expensive foods has some relationship to income. There are undoubtedly some poor families who spend relatively few dollars on food. Food expenditures do not vary as much as income, but the percentage of income spent on food does vary considerably by income groups. Lower-income groups spend 34.8% of their income on food, and higher-income groups spend 8.5%.

This pattern of a declining percentage spent on food as income rises was first observed in 1857 by a German statistician named Engel. **Engel's law** concerning food expenditures and incomes has been remarkably accurate for many years and in many nations. Generally, the percentage of disposable income spent on food (in total as well as specific foods) declines in any country that has a rising per capita income. Moreover, the richer the nation, the lower the expected percentage.

Product positioning is a seller's strategy of placing a product into a target market in a desired position relative to competitors. For example, if research indicated that a macho image for beer was very important to consumption by young (and middle-aged) males, then one might aim a brand at that market with a name and promotion implying that it is the most macho beer. In the large-market segment of people concerned about meats and health, the white meats of fish and poultry usually have a better reputation than the red meats. That perception was a major motivation for the Angus Association's Certified Angus Beef (CAB) campaign.

Market segmentation and product positioning do not offer the same promise for every food and fiber product, nor are the techniques always the same. One does not try to give a macho image to bread, yet a baker may target a nutritional message at mothers raising young children or a diet-type message at a more weight-conscious submarket. For canned tomatoes, there are likely only two markets: consumers conscious of brand and those concerned with economy. Hence, a big processor may aim advertising and quality tomatoes at the first market and generic brands at the latter.

Explaining Changes in Consumption by Shifts in Supply or Demand

Many people make the error of considering any change in consumption as being necessarily a change in demand. It is not. A rise in consumption may be due to an increase in demand, supply, or some combination of both. Exhibit 5.3 illustrates the differences. The distance Q_1 to Q_2 represents a consumption increase. Note that consumption increased in all three cases, while demand increased (D_1 to D_2) in only two cases. Although we frequently do not have supply and demand curves to study, one clue to look for is what happens to price. When a consumption increase is accompanied by stable or rising prices, a demand increase (shift to the right) is probably involved—and possibly a small supply increase. A consumption increase accompanied by falling prices is more likely to represent a supply increase; it represents a change in the amount demanded but not a change in demand (not a shift in the demand curve).

The amount supplied of a farm commodity can change from one year to another because of rational responses to anticipated prices or costs or because of various surprises of nature that affect crop yields and livestock and poultry production. For example, this year's strawberry production may be lower than last year's because growers cut acreage or because of poor growing conditions.

EXHIBIT

5.3 Effects of supply or demand increases.

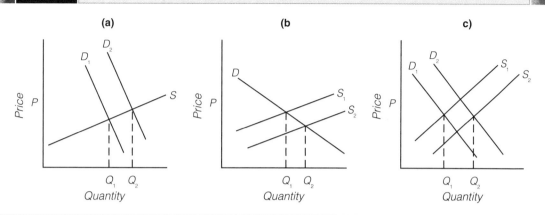

Shifts in available supplies directly affect short-term consumption. If the crop is short, consumption will go down simply because there is not more available. Likewise, when more pork is produced, consumption will go up because more meat is available and prices will fall enough to get it sold. In both cases, consumption changed while demand did not.

The idea that production—particularly of perishables—largely determines consumption in the short run is pretty elementary once we think about it. But we usually do not do that. Many people assume that all changes in consumption represent changes in demand. Often, those changes do not. However, it is true that changes in demand over the long term (several years) are important in determining up-trends or down-trends in consumption. Marketers are helped greatly by up-trends in the demand for their commodity or product.

Demand at an aggregate level is ordinarily fairly stable. Especially for a commodity, we can expect next year's demand schedule to be within a few percent of last year's. However, consistent changes of, say, 3% per year for a decade can make a big impact on the demand for a commodity. The demands faced by agribusinesses for their services and for their branded products often change more rapidly than the demand for commodities. Thus, the demand for a "natural" breakfast cereal of a certain brand might change (up or down) by 50% in a year. Similarly, a restaurant that is very popular one year may close its doors the next for lack of business.

Demand Curve Shifters

Shifts in demand curves are illustrated in Exhibit 5.3. They should not be confused with movements along the demand curve caused by shifts in supply. For example, a short crop of apples may drive the market price up $2 per bushel. That upward movement in price does not represent a rise in demand. Nor does the decline in per capita consumption of apples (resulting from the short crop) represent a fall in demand. Several factors that change the location of the demand curve of a given product may be summarized as follows:

1. Shifts in population
2. Shifts in income
3. Shifts in supplies and prices of competing products
4. Shifts in consumer perception and preferences

The first three are readily measurable, although with regard to item 3 it is often difficult to determine the exact list of products that should be regarded as competing. Measurements of consumer perceptions and preferences are difficult to obtain and frequently not directly available. The last three items represent shifts in per capita demand. As already noted, growth of population has been the biggest shifter of demand curves in the past several decades. Many food marketers have enjoyed slowly growing sales for decades simply because the number of consumers has kept growing.

Income elasticity of demand is the relationship between a percentage change in income and the quantity demanded of a commodity or specific product. Thus, where Y is income, income elasticity is

$$E_y = \frac{\Delta Q/Q}{\Delta Y/Y} = \left(\frac{\Delta Q}{\Delta Y}\right)\left(\frac{Y}{Q}\right)$$

With other factors held constant, income elasticity may be regarded as the percentage change in quantity demanded corresponding to a 1% change in income. As their incomes rise, consumers tend to buy more of certain products. The income elasticities of these commodities are positive, and a few even exceed unity. However, consumers may turn away from some products as they become more affluent; such products (e.g., rice and corn meal) have negative income elasticities. Income elasticities are sometimes measured as the ratio of dollars spent on an item (rather than quantity sold) to consumer incomes or to total consumer expenditures on all items.

By examining the income elasticities shown in Exhibit 5.4, we find some explanation of purchasing trends. We can also see the differences in groups of products and across cultures. For example, the income elasticity of U. S. fish decreased from 1980 to 1996, and it is higher in Azerbaijan than in the United States.

In a relatively high income country like the United States, consumers, as their incomes rise, are likely to increase their spending for a commodity such as beef by paying more for higher-priced cuts rather than to buy substantially more pounds of beef. Thus, the income elasticity of beef concerning *quantity* is likely near zero, and the income elasticity concerning *spending* for beef is likely to be positive but less than one. Income elasticities are likely to be larger for differentiated products than for commodities. The income elasticity (quantity) of demand for a popular brand of cellular phone is likely to be positive and may be greater than unity. That is, a 50% increase in income is associated with a more than 50% increase in sales of that brand of phone. We have noted that there is a small positive

EXHIBIT

5.4   Comparison of estimated U.S. income elasticities in 1980–81 and 1988–89 and of U. S., Azerbaijan, Egyptian, and Korean income elasticities in 1996.

Produce Group	United States 1980–81	United States 1988–89	1996 United States	1996 Azerbaijan	1996 Egypt	1996 Korea
Total food	0.347	0.318				
Food away from home	0.558	0.531				
Food at home	0.201	0.157				
Meat			0.110	0.767	0.685	0.478
Meat, poultry, fish, and eggs	0.217	0.118				
Beef	0.234	0.098				
Pork	0.160	0.040				
Other meat	0.190	0.093				
Poultry	0.105	0.126				
Fish	0.375	0.207	0.121	0.874	0.770	0.524
Eggs	0.001	0.108				
Cereals and bakery products	0.160	0.111	0.050	0.493	0.411	0.187
Dairy products	0.138	0.112	0.117	0.835	0.741	0.510
Milk and cream	0.021	−0.038				
Cheese	0.319	0.222				
Other dairy products	0.211	0.279				
Fruits and vegetables			0.086	0.621	0.550	0.374
Fruits	0.193	0.240				
Fresh	0.188	0.253				
Processed	0.222	0.225				
Vegetables	0.240	0.146				
Fresh	0.244	0.106				
Processed	0.227	0.118				
Sugars and sweeteners	0.167	0.158				
Beverages and tobacco			0.134	1.059	0.898	0.576
Nonalcoholic beverages	0.126	0.109				
Fats and oils	0.181	0.115	0.059	0.517	0.438	0.234
Butter	0.350	0.187				
Margarine	0.083	0.130				
Other	0.144	0.090				
Miscellaneous	0.251	0.210	0.109	0.764	0.683	0.477

Source: USDA Economic Research Service.

income elasticity of demand for all food in total. In recent years, as incomes have risen, consumers have spent more on eating out and have purchased slightly more expensive foods for home consumption.

The third shifter of demand for a particular commodity or product is changes in the relative prices of related items and the availability of new, competing items. The large increases during the early twenty-first century in the price of gasoline reduced dramatically the demand for large automobiles. It is difficult to find as dramatic an example in foods, but generally a fall in the price of a substitute food will contribute to a reduced demand for an item. When there is a large cyclical increase in beef prices, the demand increases for vegetable protein substitutes while the demand falls for hamburger buns. If margarine prices fall, the demand decreases for butter. Items that are associated may influence one another's demand curves. For example, when pork prices rise, the demand for barbecue sauce falls.

Cross-elasticities of demand (see appendix at the end of this chapter) can be used to measure the relationship between a change in the sales of one commodity and a change in the price of a competing commodity. The concept is a very sensible one. However, measurement of cross-elasticities is difficult.

Technology and innovation bring new products, new services, new cost-cutting methods of production and marketing, and new competition for old products. New products, such as low-fat frozen yogurt and premium, high-fat ice creams, may reduce the demand for existing products (medium-fat ice cream). A new service (fast-food restaurants) may reduce the demand for existing services (restaurants). New, cheaper methods of producing broilers shifted the supply curve to the right and helped to expand consumption.

The role of technologically developed substitutes is particularly interesting. Food technologists using cheaper vegetable materials can create a product that is very much like meats and other more expensive products. Textured vegetable proteins made from soybeans are the principal input for various imitation meats. Soybean protein has won considerable acceptance as a hamburger stretcher, as a substitute for bacon bits in salads, and so on. Such imitation products, because of their lower-cost ingredients, may provide considerable competition to livestock producers. Of course, the dairy industry has already lost many markets to margarine, nondairy coffee whiteners, and imitation ice cream and milk.

As suggested earlier, consumer's perceptions of products may change for many reasons other than growth in their incomes and changes in the relative prices or availability of competing products. Over a period of a decade or more, changes in lifestyles can alter materially the demands for particular foods. Similarly, changing concepts of health and nutrition influence demand. These concepts, which are disseminated rapidly and widely in a society with a well-developed communication system, have both positive and negative influences. That is, the demand for a product like skim milk is helped when it is perceived to be good for us, whereas demand for a product like eggs or pork may be hurt if it is perceived by some to be bad for us. Even if these perceptions may be found later to be inaccurate, they will have had their impact in the marketplace. The impact is influenced, however, by the availability of substitutes. It is much easier to find a substitute for beef than for tobacco; thus, health concerns about red meats can be expected to exert a greater impact on the demand for these foods than the much better documented health concerns about tobacco have had on the demand for cigarettes.

In surveys, many consumers indicate that they adjust their food consumption in some fashion because of concerns about health or nutrition. Leading concerns have been weight reduction, reduced fat and carbohydrate intake, and lower cholesterol.

Changing lifestyles and attitudes have led Americans to accept a great variety of new processed food products during the past four decades. Such acceptance was not present before the mid-1960s, and there are arguments as to whether it will continue into the future. Certainly, some of today's consumers are looking at processed products with a much more skeptical eye. The recent period of ready acceptance of new and imitation products is probably explained by the fact that most households are composed of city dwellers who have little concept of farm-grown foods; most families have some discretionary income with which to make an experimental purchase; processors have spent millions in promoting these new products; a growing interest in recreation and in other uses of time than in the kitchen has put a premium on convenience foods; and a general faith in science, technology, and the marketing system has led to trust in the safety of new products. However, the safety factor has been under steady attack by the "consumer movement." Skepticism has grown with regard to preservatives, flavor enhancers, emulsifiers, and other additives that are essential to a wide range of modern foods. Likewise, concern about pesticide contamination has resulted in a growing market for natural, "organic" foods.

It is impossible to make predictions about the future of trends in food purchases. We can only be confident that lifestyles and attitudes will continue to change and will continue to affect the demands for various foods and for the processing and marketing services associated with them.

To summarize this section, marketers must be prepared to deal with demand shifters that include changes in population, incomes, availability, and relative prices of competing products, as well as consumers' perceptions and attitudes.

SOME RECENT SHIFTS IN CONSUMPTION AND THEIR EXPLANATIONS

f we counted each brand name, we would find literally many thousands of food items. To the processor and retailer, each item is relevant. Here, we remark on general trends in broad categories rather than individual items.

Among livestock products, poultry meat (broilers and turkeys) has seen a strong increase and eggs a large decrease. The decline in the consumption of eggs is generally attributed to a reduction in demand associated with changing lifestyles (fewer big breakfasts) and health concerns. The increase

EXHIBIT

5.5

Per capita consumption of meat, poultry, and fish, boneless, trimmed equivalent, including skin, neck meat, and giblets, 1970–2001.

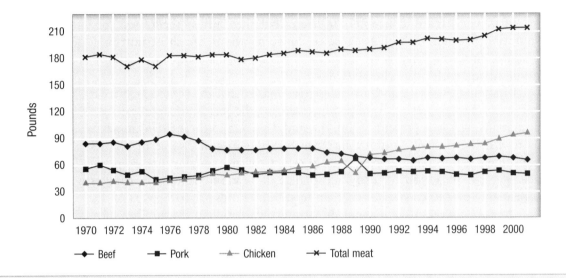

Source: USDA.

in poultry meat consumption (Exhibit 5.5) has resulted from rightward shifts in both supply and demand. Chicken meat has sold well in fast-food chains and is generally praised as being leaner than other meats. Technical gains in efficiency have reduced poultry prices relative to other meats, making it a more frequent substitute.

The short-term variations in meats mainly reflect supply factors. Production of both cattle and hogs has been subject to large cyclical swings. For example, beef consumption peaked at 96 pounds per capita in 1976 at the top of a production cycle (when it is produced, people eat it) and fell within three years to 80 pounds and eventually to 63.6 pounds in 1994. There was probably some shifting to the right of the demand for beef in the 1950s and 1960s and perhaps some shift to the left in the 1980s. Not all analysts would agree on either the nature of any demand shifts or their possible causes. Whereas beef consumption per capita fell 8% from 1988 to 2001, poultry consumption rose by about 48%. A big cause was likely the fact that poultry prices fell considerably relative to beef prices. This change resulted from the costs of poultry production falling steadily relative to the costs of beef production. More recently, per capita beef consumption has increased. Some of this consumption increase can be attributed to the popularity of the low-carbohydrate diet.

Some analysts believe that both health concerns and the fact that poultry can often be cooked (or heated) more quickly than beef have helped to increase poultry consumption so rapidly relative to beef.

In the past 50 years, the consumption of vegetable oils has increased greatly while the consumption of animal fats and oils has decreased greatly. One of the explanations is clearly a shift in demand from animal fats and oils. That demand shift is partly related to perceptions about health and some to handling characteristics. A greater variety of vegetable oils is now on grocery shelves to meet the increased demand from health concerns. It is also likely that production costs of vegetable oils have fallen relative to animal fats—a supply factor.

During the 1990s, a larger market for fat substitutes developed as food processors began to use them in such items as cheese, salad dressings, margarines, frozen desserts, frying fats, and cooking oils. Examples of such substitutes include starch-based, protein-based, and fatty acid–bases substances. Simplesse, a fat substitute made from egg whites or milk proteins, is being used in frozen desserts. Olestra, compounded fatty acids, is used in cooking oils and shortenings. The use of these substitutes will likely develop slowly; it might have a considerable impact on markets (positively for their ingredients and negatively for the traditional vegetable oils and their sources such as soybeans).[3]

Per capita consumption of purchased beverages has changed considerably over the years (Exhibit 5.6). Milk and coffee consumption have declined (although coffee has rebounded a little), whereas soft drink and bottled water consumption have gained. Coffee and soft drinks both have became somewhat more expensive relative to milk and beer. Thus, the strong growth of soft drinks and bottled water and the decline of milk probably reflect shifts in lifestyles and the power of advertising.

In these examples of consumption changes over a period of years, demand shifts have been important more frequently than supply shifts. Demand shifts seem to be fairly long term and to extend for two or three decades in some cases. Supply shifts can occur over a prolonged period when based on technological shifts (e.g., the developments in processing vegetable oils that made them superior to animal fats in many uses). However, numerous supply shifts (those due to weather) are quite short term and often last only a single season. Exhibit 5.6 shows some of the changes in per capita food consumption for a wide assortment of foods. Can you explain why some of the changes occurred and whether demand or supply was responsible for the change?

Earlier, we noted the approximate 5-to-1 allocation of the consumer's expenditures between agribusiness marketers and farmer. Obviously, both groups share a strong interest in a vigorous, growing domestic market. In many cases, both prosper together from an increase in demand. Thus, the growth of demand for vegetable oils has been good for both soybean processors and growers. The demand for services of commodity handlers generally rises or falls with similar changes in consumption of commodities. Thus, commodity handlers may benefit from a rightward shift in either demand or supply of a commodity because each can result in an increase in consumption. Leftward shifts can, of course, work the other way. A decrease in pork consumption because of either a fall in demand or a fall in

EXHIBIT

5.6 U.S. per capita consumption of major foods (in pounds or gallons).

Food	1972–76	1982–86	1992–96	2003
Red meat	128.6	122.9	113.7	118.3
Chicken and turkey	34.3	44.4	62.8	95.7
Fish and shellfish	12.5	14.0	14.9	16.3
Eggs	284	258.5	236.2	249.6
All dairy products	545.6	578.9	577.2	593.9
Cheese	14.1	21.5	26.8	30.6
Ice cream	17.8	18.1	16.0	16.7
Fluid cream products (8 oz.)	9.9	12.6	15.5	22.2
Yogurt (8 oz.)	3.0	6.4	8.5	15.2
Fats and oils	53.4	61.7	67.8	85.8
Animals	11.6	12.4	11.0	12.7
Vegetable	41.8	49.3	56.8	73.1
Tree nuts (shelled basis)	1.8	2.3	2.2	2.9
Peanuts (kernel based)	5.8	6.1	5.9	6.3
Fruits and vegetables	579.5	619.0	686.4	691.5
Fruits	241.9	270.5	282.6	274.9
Vegetables	337.6	348.5	403.7	416.6
Caloric sweeteners	122.9	124.5	146.7	141.7
Refined cane and beet sugar	96.3	66.7	65.2	61.1
Corn sweeteners	25.3	56.5	80.1	79.2
High-fructose corn syrup	3.6	37.2	56.3	60.9
Flour and cereal products	137.4	152.7	192.4	194.0
Wheat flour	113.4	120.8	143.4	137.9
Rye flour	1.1	0.7	0.6	0.5
Rice	7.2	10.2	18.6	20.1
Corn products	10.3	16.2	22.5	30.3
Oat products	4.5	3.9	6.5	4.6
Barley products	0.9	1.0	0.7	0.7
Cocoa (chocolate liquor equivalent)	3.1	3.4	4.1	4.5
Beverage milks	30.0	26.4	24.7	21.6
Whole	21.3	14.3	8.8	7.2
Lowfat (1%)	1.0	1.7	2.5	2.5
Skim	1.5	1.4	3.4	3.1
Coffee	32.8	26.8	22.7	24.3
Tea	7.5	7.0	8.1	7.6
Soft drinks	28.1	35.6	50.7	46.4
Fruit juices	6.5	7.9	8.7	8.4
Bottled water	NA	4.0	10.5	22.0
Beer	20.6	24.1	22.4	21.6
Wine	1.7	2.3	1.8	2.7
Distilled spirits	1.9	1.8	1.3	1.3

Source: Food Consumption, USDA Economic Research Service.

hog production (due, say, to higher corn prices) reduces demand for the services of hog packers.

The market situation may be a bit different for a manufacturer of a highly differentiated product. A breakfast cereal manufacturer is interested in expected population growth and in changes in lifestyle concerning the eating of breakfast. However, by product positioning and strong promotion, the manufacturer may be able to increase the market share and sales of her product regardless of overall market trends. Such processors ordinarily see more opportunities in areas of rising consumption than of declining consumption, but any change may create opportunities.

Although it may be easier for farmers and agribusinesses to follow trends than to run counter to them, many firms have succeeded in unfavorable markets. Even while the demand for bakery and cereal products has been falling, individual companies have successfully marketed new products within that category. Therefore, one must be careful in using macro developments for individual micro guidance.

SUMMARY

1. The domestic market is composed of more than 290 million consumers. It is a larger market, on average, for U.S. farmers and agribusiness than the foreign market.

2. At the most aggregate level, the domestic market consists of an ever-growing number of consumers multiplied by their per capita disposable income. Of course, only a small fraction (about 10%) of that disposable income is spent on food. Food stores and food service units compete for food dollars. In a sense, farmers and agribusinesses compete for food dollars; farmers recently have been obtaining less than 20%. Food is, of course, a joint product of the contributions of farmers and marketing firms. Consumers are purchasing more and more services and convenience combined with foods.

3. Farmers and agribusiness cannot take their market for granted, because there are substitutes for practically any specific food commodity or item. Maslow's hierarchy of needs explains some of the underlying factors affecting consumers' buying decisions. Decisions are based largely on perceptions. Perceptions are influenced by advertisers, peer groups, product labels, education, income, and the stage of the consumer's life cycle.

4. Product marketers try to identify those consumers most likely to buy their products. Sometimes such characteristics as age, income, or education help to identify target markets. The process of identifying and focusing on target markets is called market segmentation. The art of placing one's product into a target market in a favorable competitive position is called product positioning. Promoting pork as "The Other White Meat" is an example.

5. Increases in consumption arise because of rightward shifts of demand or supply. Methods of distinguishing between shifts in consumption, demand, and supply were described. Over a period of a decade or more, sizable shifts in demand or supply and in consumption can be observed. Demand shifts usually require a decade or more to have much impact on consumption.

6. Population growth has been the most important aggregate demand shifter (expander) in the postwar period. Growth in per capita income has also been important in increasing the demand for those foods with a fairly high income elasticity. Shifters of per capita demand include changes in real incomes, the relative prices and availability of substitute items, and consumer perceptions.

7. Shifters of supply include changes in the technology of production or marketing, changes in costs of production or marketing (including prices of inputs), and weather.

8. Marketers usually measure success in terms of increases in per capita consumption, which are mostly independent of changes in population and inflation. A more difficult test is to maintain a constant percentage share of consumers' income. Engel observed a "law" that the share of income ordinarily falls for most foods as incomes rise.

9. We see again the importance of the distinction made in Chapter 3 between commodity handlers and product marketers. Commodity handlers and farmers experience much the same benefits or losses from rises and falls in the demand for their commodities. On the other hand, a marketer of a differentiated product is insulated from those demand shifts to the extent that she can develop and maintain the demand for her product. She is also often fairly insulated from commodity supply shifts if she is a small user of the commodity and if it represents a small portion of her product costs.

APPENDIX: DEMAND

Quantity Response to Price

Recall the law of demand: A larger quantity is demanded at a lower price than at a higher price, all other things held constant. Thus, the quantities of a product or service that a consumer or a group of consumers demands (is willing and able to buy) vary inversely with the price.

Observation of many market situations indicates the validity of the law of demand in all but a few special situations. The logic behind the law is quite simple. Because consumers allocate their limited budgets among many competing goods, they are motivated to substitute among products as relative prices change. Thus, an increase in price of any product relative to other products leads to a substitution of other products in consumers' buying patterns and a reduced willingness to buy the higher-priced product.

In addition to this *substitution effect,* there is an *income effect.* An increased price of one product relative to all others reduces the real income of consumers and usually reduces the amount demanded of that product. For example, if gasoline prices continue to rise, you might buy less gasoline so that you have enough money left to pay your tuition bill.

Ceteris paribus ("all other things held constant") is an important part of the definition of the law of demand. Suppose you notice that per capita consumption of pork was 50 pounds in both 1991 and 2004, but the retail price of pork was nearly twice as high in 2004. Is that market observation an exception to the law of demand? Not at all. An economist would be quick to point out that any number of things could have changed during that time, and that the most obvious explanation is a big increase in all prices between 1991 and 2004. (In fact, there was a 50% increase in prices.) Demand and supply shifts over the 13-year period account for less than half the changes.

Demand Elasticities

The law of demand states an inverse relation between the price of a product and the quantity demanded. **Own-price** (or direct price) **elasticity** is a measure of "how inverse" the relation is. *Unit elasticity* refers to a relationship that is proportional: A given percentage change in price leads to the same percentage change (in the opposite direction) in the quantity demanded. *Elastic demand* refers to any situation in which a given percentage change in price is associated with a larger percent change in the quantity demanded, whereas *inelastic demand* describes any situation with a smaller percentage change in quantity. For example, a 10% fall in retail prices of milk will yield about a 3% increase in the quantity sold—an inelastic demand.

More precisely, own-price elasticity may be defined at a point on the demand curve by the following procedure. Where Δ denotes a very small change,

$$E_P = \frac{\Delta Q/Q}{\Delta P/P} = \left(\frac{\Delta Q}{\Delta P}\right)\left(\frac{P}{Q}\right)$$

Computations of elasticity often involve two points far enough apart that the change is larger than very small. The formula to handle such measurements of *arc elasticity* is

$$E_P = \left(\frac{Q_0 - Q_1}{Q_0 + Q_1}\right) = \left(\frac{P_0 - P_1}{P_0 + P_1}\right)$$

Obviously, for such a measure to have meaning, other factors (e.g., the prices of substitutes) must be held constant. Own-price elasticity may vary from zero to minus infinity. The coefficient varies along a straight-line demand curve and along almost all likely demand curves. Own-price elasticities tend to be very large at extremely high prices, such as indicated by point *A* in Exhibit 5.7 and to approach zero (be very inelastic) at extremely low

EXHIBIT

5.7   Varying elasticities on a linear demand curve.

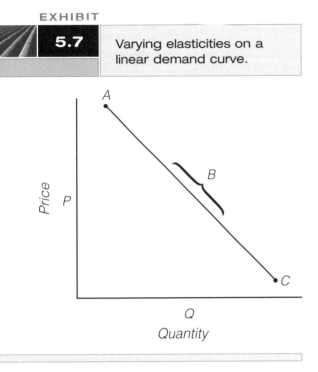

prices, such as point C. When comparisons are made among commodities as to demand elasticities, people typically are comparing the average elasticities within a fairly narrow and usual range of prices such as indicated by B.

Cross-elasticities demand measures how the quantity demanded for one commodity responds to changes in the price of another commodity. The mathematical expression is identical to own-price elasticity except that percentage changes in the price of commodity i are compared to percentage changes in the quantity demanded of commodity j. Thus,

$$E_{ij} = \frac{\Delta Q_i / Q_i}{\Delta P_j / P_j} = \left(\frac{\Delta Q_i}{\Delta P_j}\right) \left(\frac{P_1}{Q_i}\right)$$

Presumably, if we systematically compared each of 100,000 commodities with the other 99,999, we would find zero cross-elasticities for most, indicating that their demands are independent. Thus, the demand for watermelons is not affected by price changes of tennis rackets because watermelons and tennis rackets are not substitutes. Of the most interest in marketing are those close substitutes with high positive price cross-elasticities, such as corn and milo as feed grains or palm oil and soybean oil as edible oils. Also of interest are complementary products with negative cross-elasticities, such as gasoline and auto tires.

STUDY QUESTIONS

1. What is Maslow's hierarchy of needs? What relation does it have to how consumers decide which foods to purchase?

2. What sources of information do you use in making food or beverage purchases?

3. If your processing firm were going to try to market its new line of Mexican foods in Chicago's food stores, would you attempt any market segmentation? If so, what types of segmentation?

4. Do farmers or marketing agencies receive a larger share of the dollars spent for food? Are their shares the same for each commodity? Is the farmer's share of the at-home market larger or smaller than the farmer's share of the away-from-home market?

5. What is the income elasticity of demand? For each of the following pairs, suggest which one you would expect to have a higher income elasticity: eating at home vs. eating out, beef vs. broilers, frozen French fries vs. potatoes, canned condensed milk vs. cheese.

6. Suppose you observe that the consumption of apples increased sharply last year but the total consumer expenditures on apples did not change. Would you think that there had been a supply shift, a demand shift, or both?

7. If it were solely a supply shift in the last example, what would appear to be the own-price elasticity of demand for apples?

8. Name two foods that have likely had their demands expanded by the growth of fast-food chains. Name two foods that have likely had their demands decreased by consumer concerns about health.

9. The per capita consumption of broilers has increased greatly relative to the per capita consumption of beef in recent decades. Does that mean that demand for broilers necessarily increased relative to the demand for beef? What explanation is possible on the supply side? Do you think that the demand for broilers relative to beef probably increased? Why or why not?

CLASS EXERCISE

In the class exercise for Chapter 3, you selected a consumer food product derived from the commodity that you selected in Chapter 1. For this exercise, your group should perform the following steps:

1. Research and report the per capita consumption over the past 20 years for the chosen consumer food product.

2. Describe the supply–demand drivers that influenced the change in per capita consumption.

3. Prepare to lead a class discussion about your findings.

NOTES

1. This section draws on the treatment in R. T. Shaw, R. J. Semenik, and R. H. Williams, *Marketing* (Cincinnati: South-Western Publishing, 1981), pp. 41–50.

2. Abraham Maslow, *Motivation and Personality* (New York: Harper & Row, 1954).

3. R. M. Morrison, "The Market for Fat Substitutes," *National Food Review* (April–June 1990): 24–30.

THE INTERNATIONAL MARKET

PREVIEW

- Specialization and trade bring benefits both within and among nations.

- World markets are important to U.S. crop producers and other farmers in various ways.

- The growth trends and fluctuations in U.S. agricultural exports and in market shares are studied.

- Competitive and complementary food imports are discussed.

- Agricultural trade policy is explored. Reasons for opposition to free trade are analyzed.

- Trade interferences such as tariffs, nontariff barriers, export subsidies, and state trading are described.

- The WTO (GATT), NAFTA, CAFTA, and free trade issues are examined.

- International firms are becoming more involved with intracompany, intercountry transfers.

- Value-added exports represent a trend away from homogeneous commodities.

KEY TERMS

CAFTA (Central American Free Trade Agreement)

cartel

competitive imports

complementary imports

dumping

exchange rate

GATT (General Agreement on Tariffs and Trade)

infant industry argument

LDCs (less developed countries)

Most Favored Nation Clause

NAFTA (North American Free Trade Agreement)

nontariff barrier

principle of comparative advantage

Public Law (P.L.) 480

self-sufficiency

tariff

WTO (World Trade Organization)

The most important development in the markets of American farmers during the 1970s was the impressive growth in agricultural exports. Physical volume increased 50%, and dollar sales increased nearly sixfold. Exports were a dream come true for American farmers and related agribusiness. However, the 1980s were a rude shock. Physical tonnage and dollar sales of U. S. agricultural exports generally fell through the first half of the decade. There was some recovery in the second half but not to the 1981 peak. In real terms (after adjusting for inflation in the 1980s), U. S. agricultural sales abroad in 1994 were about one-third less than the $45 billion peak in 1981. Exports in 1995 reached a new high of $54.2 billion in nominal terms as export demand increased substantially. In 2004, U. S. agricultural exports reached $62.3 billion.

Exports are a major influence on farm prices and incomes and on the costs of government farm programs. As the world's largest exporter of agricultural commodities, U. S. agriculture is now an important contributor to forces of supply and demand around the world. Farmers and agribusiness are increasingly conscious that America's open economy can reap large gains and also absorb sharp shocks from its international markets. Numerous agribusinesses are either marketing in international markets or seeking ways to do so.

Although the international food market is an ever-increasing segment of the U.S. food marketing system, it is still a relatively small portion compared to the larger submarkets in the United States. Many of the issues that exist in international marketing arise from the myriad of rules and regulations involved and the cultural characteristics of the various regions throughout the world. To deal with these complexities, many firms directly invest abroad in factories and distribution networks. For example, in 2005 Cargill had more than 1,000 employees in Russia. International marketing is a major source of income for some firms. Policy changes and new multilateral trade agreements continue to make this an exciting area of business with many opportunities and pitfalls. Before the benefits and costs of trade can be assessed, the reasons for trade and the role of various institutions must be considered.

BASIS FOR TRADE

Why do firms and individuals in one nation trade with firms and individuals in other nations? Generally for the same reasons that individuals and firms within a nation trade. As individuals, we specialize and trade rather than try to operate as self-sufficient Robinson Crusoes. As buyers we try to get the best bargains, whether the commodity originates in our country or elsewhere. As sellers we try to find the most profitable markets.

We live in a large country. We accept as commonplace that the cheese we eat may be produced in Wisconsin, the frozen orange juice in Florida, the bread from wheat in Kansas, the tomato catsup in California, and the cranberries in Massachusetts.

Regardless of where we live in the United States, we would resent any attempt to restrict our purchases to hometown products. Under such restrictions, a few foods such as coffee or oranges would be unavailable at any sensible price in our area. Certainly foods would be more expensive.

You will recall from your principles course the **principle of comparative advantage.** It stated that, under free trade, people within a country specialize in producing those commodities that they can produce relatively efficiently. Price ratios guide producers as to what to produce and what to buy.

Areas such as northern Iowa or northern Illinois—with their level, fertile, and deep soils; temperate climate; and adequate summer rainfall—have advantages in producing many agricultural crops. Why then do they concentrate on corn and soybeans? Why is there not equal emphasis on wheat or strawberries? Certainly their wheat yields would exceed those of wheat in Kansas. The answer is not all that complicated. Each area produces those crops in which it has a comparative advantage. With a given set of resources and given the prices that ordinarily prevail, the typical northern Iowa or northern Illinois farmer can make more money producing corn and soybeans than wheat or strawberries. Similarly, the typical western Kansas dryland farmer makes more money producing wheat than corn. Individuals and firms around the world specialize in those activities in which they have a comparative advantage. They market the products of their specialization to people and firms that specialize in producing other products and services. Within limits, the more specialization, the more total output.

The advantages of specialization and trade extend beyond national borders. The typical Iowa farmer has a comparative advantage in producing corn compared to the typical Dutch or Japanese farmer and compared to the typical Kansas or New York farmer. For reasons that are apparently tied to politics, nationalistic pride, and strange economics, people often see transactions between producers and consumers from only the seller's side and ignore the benefits and cost of buyers. Usually, most people can see advantage in selling to the highest bidder whether he or she is American or Japanese or Arab, but they sometimes forget the advantages of buying from the best source whether it is American or Japanese or Arab.

Sometimes, laws put up tariffs, quotas, or other barriers preventing us from buying the cheapest and best products when they come across a national boundary. As we will see later, situations may exist in which some trade interference is justified. At least, citizens of most nations have tolerated or supported such laws. Although there can be no denying the economic advantages of specialization and trade, other considerations may override these advantages. It is most important, however, to understand that the economic basis of world trade is simple and straightforward. We can produce more output and have more available, in general, if individuals and firms specialize in production where comparative advantage exists.

Comparative advantage in specialized production is a matter of degree. Numerous American ranchers and farmers have a comparative advantage in raising sheep. However, the U. S. market demands more wool than is produced by these Americans, and so we buy much wool from farmers abroad. Similarly, we usually import a small fraction of our beef every year because our large affluent market consumes so much beef. Imported items that substitute directly for similar items produced domestically are called **competitive imports.** Other commodities, of course, such as tea, coffee, and bananas, can hardly be produced at all in the continental United States because of climate. Those imports are called **complementary imports.** It would be foolish to try to produce a tropical crop like bananas for which we have a cost disadvantage compared to producers in several tropical countries. Most of our foreign customers today have some capacity for producing grains or oilseeds, but their markets have grown to exceed the output of their farmers with a comparative advantage, and so they import additional amounts. The U. S. producers who have a comparative advantage in feed grains, wheat, and soybeans are so numerous that we have huge exports of those commodities.

DIMENSIONS OF THE INTERNATIONAL MARKET

The international market for U. S.-produced agricultural products is important, variable, and unpredictable. Yet much can be said about the nature of this large market.

Domestic and international markets have many similarities. Consumer demand for food is related to population and income, although the magnitude of the relationships may vary greatly from country to country. Knowledge about elasticities of demand and sales responses to advertising is essential to marketing in any country. Similarly, some of the same forces of change are affecting demand for food and agribusiness services in many countries besides the United States.

Domestic and international markets differ in important ways. First, the United States exports a very high proportion of commodities (wheat, corn, and soybeans) compared to differentiated products. Because of that commodity mix, farmers receive a larger proportion of each dollar of sales in international than in domestic markets. Second, demands for U. S. commodities abroad are more erratic than demands within the United States because they reflect such quickly changeable factors as size of harvests in other nations and political decisions both here and abroad. Most countries do not maintain large stocks, so a change in the size of a harvest quickly affects trade.

Third, governments—ours and theirs—play a much more important role in various phases of international markets. On the one hand, governments erect barriers and hindrances to trade, especially to imports and occasionally to exports. On the other hand, government agencies often attempt to encourage and develop markets abroad. The USDA often works with American wheat growers, corn growers, the livestock and meat industry, and so on in introducing and promoting commodities in new markets. The U. S. government collects data worldwide on crop production and consumption to facilitate the anticipation of foreign demands, and it has often subsidized exports to certain nations.

Fourth, changes in the value of foreign currencies greatly affect American producers' ability to sell abroad. The rate of trading euros for dollars (say, 0.83 euros per dollar, up from 0.74 in 2005) is called an **exchange rate,** which is the price of one nation's currency in terms of another's. There are as many exchange rates as there are currencies: dollars/euros, dollars/pounds sterling, dollars/yen, euros/pounds sterling, euros/yen, and so on. Moreover, these rates typically change daily as the demand and supply of the various currencies change. For instance, the Japan/U. S. exchange rate has fluctuated considerably the last 15 years (Exhibit 6.1). As you will learn in Chapter 10, the exchange rate could be hedged to reduce exchange rate variability. Buyers prefer exchange rates that favor their transactions.

EXHIBIT

6.1   Japanese yen/U. S. dollar foreign exchange rate.

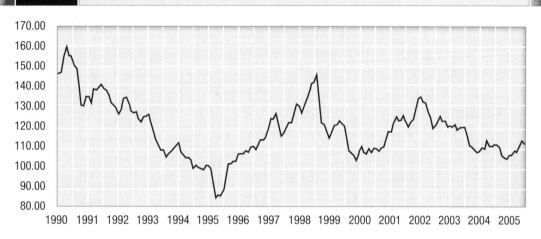

Source: Board of Governors of the Federal Reserve System.

Imagine yourself as a Japanese importer: you will clearly prefer the yen/dollar exchange rate to be low because you will have to pay less in Japanese yen for each $1 of U. S. product imported. This is good for U. S. producers because it allows for more domestic products to be sold. Thus, the four distinctive features of international markets are as follows:

1. A high proportion of commodities
2. Large and often unpredictable demand shifts
3. The strong influence of government policies
4. The strong influence of exchange rates

   If the world were an open and perfectly competitive market, one would find the wholesale price of any food, such as wheat, in every country linked by transportation costs. Wheat in a deficit country (Japan or the United Kingdom) would differ in price from that in surplus countries (United States, Canada, or Australia) only by the transfer costs (transportation, storage, and transaction costs).

   The various nations of the world have never simultaneously been willing and able to turn the world into an open and perfectly competitive market for wheat or for anything else. However rational or irrational the opposition to free trade, it is sufficient for many countries to erect barriers. In fact, no important nation, including America, allows completely free trade. Thus, any marketer seeking sales abroad must deal with a maze of regulations (quotas, tariffs, export controls and subsidies, state trading, and safety inspections) in both the potential exporting and importing nations. Add to that differences in languages, legal systems, commercial codes, and currencies, and it is easy to see why international markets are not a place for amateurs.

Crops, not livestock, are the predominant food of the world. Grains, oilseeds, and garden crops provide most of the nutrients to the billions of people on earth. The most important group of food commodities is the major grains (rice, wheat, corn, and so on). In poorer countries, grain eaten directly provides one-half or more of total calories. In most of the more developed countries, per capita grain consumption, direct plus indirect, is double or quadruple that of the poorer countries because of the large amounts fed to livestock and poultry. Meat consumption rises along with incomes. Rising populations in poorer countries increase their consumption of food grains. Rising incomes in developing and richer countries increase greatly the use of feed grains for livestock. China is important because its huge population and rising income levels are increasing its consumption of meats and consequently increasing the demand for feed grains.

U. S. exports reflect these world consumption patterns. More than 80% of U. S. agricultural exports, in dollar terms, are crops rather than livestock and livestock products. Grains and oilseeds are usually more than 50% of U. S. exports. The United States has a dominant market share of world trade in coarse grains (corn, milo, barley, and rye) and soybeans. It is a major exporter of wheat (usually more than a one-third share of world exports) and of rice (nearly one-fifth of world exports). The United States is also an important exporter of cotton and tobacco. In addition, it has a large market share of world exports of tallows and greases, and a significant market in certain fruits, vegetables, and nuts as well as in various livestock byproducts. There is a trend toward larger sales of more processed and higher-value products. Obviously, the international market has become very important to U. S. farmers.

This is not to say that foreign markets are of little interest to agribusiness. Trade in grains, soybeans, cotton, and rice is largely in the hands of big companies. The larger trading companies typically operate in many nations, and a firm's sale of grain to Russia, for example, may be met by grain shipments from two or more countries.

Firms in the United States, especially the larger ones, have found markets for their services abroad by establishing foreign subsidiaries. Soft drinks have worldwide markets; some fast-food chains have done very well abroad. Most such investments are concentrated in Canada, Europe, and Asia. Efforts to do business internationally are increasing as income levels rise and some barriers to trade are eased worldwide. Even some commodity organizations have integrated the sale of value-added products abroad.

DEMAND AND SUPPLY SHIFTS

Markets are ever changing. Markets change because of growth in population and income and gradual shifts in comparative advantage. The shifts in comparative advantage result from many factors. Falling costs of transportation encouraged trade in the last half of the twentieth century. Technological improvements affecting costs and yields of certain crops in one country more than another change comparative advantage. Government policies may raise or lower certain input costs and thus discourage or encourage production of a particular commodity in a particular country. Similarly, the increased agricultural protection afforded farmers in the European Union has artificially increased these farmers' comparative advantage in grain production and has reduced the markets for U. S.-produced grain.

The variability of agricultural exports since 1972 complicates an evaluation of trends. During the 1950s and 1960s, agricultural exports were generally low, and they rose and fell by small amounts with only a small net growth. Agricultural exports then rose at an incredible average rate of 8% a year during the 1970s. Exports fluctuated during the 1980s and 1990s, reaching $54.2 billion in 1995. Agricultural imports relative to agricultural exports have been increasing since 1990 (Exhibit 6.2).

Why did international sales rise so rapidly in the 1970s? Because of a rapid shift to the right in demand and the ability of U. S. producers to respond on the supply side. The 1970s saw a rapid increase in world demand for foods and for feed grains; a slower increase took place in the 1980s (a worldwide recession occurred in the early 1980s). The increased demand reflected a rising population and rising incomes in much of the world. World food consumption continues to rise rapidly. Food producers in numerous countries began to fall behind this strong growth, and those countries began to rely more heavily on imported food and feed grains. Growing markets for feed grains result from positive income elasticities for animal products. For example, China bought $2.25 billion of

EXHIBIT

6.2 U. S. agricultural exports and imports.

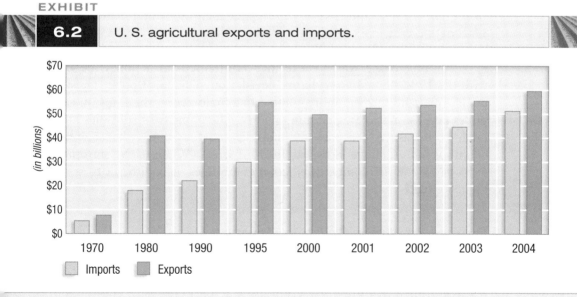

Source: USDA Economic Research Service.

soybeans in 2005 compared with $1.01 billion in 1995. Even the poorer **less developed countries (LDCs)** were able to borrow readily from foreign lenders, so they expanded their food imports. Another important cause of this major increase in demand for U. S. agricultural goods was the decreasing value of the dollar in the 1970s. A similar situation existed again during the late 1980s and throughout the 1990s as the world economy was generally growing. Beginning in 2004 and through 2005, the dollar weakened even further, boosting agricultural exports and limiting growth in agricultural imports.

During the 1970s, the United States had the capacity in terms of agricultural production, elevators, and grain transportation to respond rapidly to increased demand. It also had substantial amounts of stored grain. Other food producers around the world tended to respond more slowly. The USSR's grain output was cut by major droughts in the 1970s. Thus, U. S. exports rose rapidly in the 1970s. At the turn of the twenty-first century, China's economy was booming and demand for U. S. protein to feed the Chinese population was very strong.

By the 1980s food production had more than caught up with demand in most parts of the world. Other events hurt U. S. exports. A worldwide recession in the early 1980s slowed demand. Around 1981 further loans were cut off to numerous LDCs that had been using them to finance food imports. The rising value of the dollar in the early 1980s encouraged foreign buyers to buy at home or from competing exporters. The U. S. farm law of 1981 discouraged the growth of production and caused accumulation of large stocks of unsold grains. The U. S. shares of world production and of world exports of grain by the mid-1980s fell to levels more like the 1960s than the late 1970s.

Agricultural exports by the United States bottomed out in 1986, rose in 1990, fell in 1991, and rose in 1995. Since then the United States has seen a steady increase in exports. Part of the credit must go to the dollar ending its rise and beginning to fall in terms of many foreign currencies (Exhibit 6.3). Another cause was a more market-oriented farm policy, beginning with the 1996 "Freedom to Farm" legislation. This farm policy legislation made American farmers more competitive by lowering the floor on export prices and by subsidizing certain exports. The impacts of subsidies are difficult to measure because any analysis must assume what competing countries would have done in their absence. When U. S. subsidies of exports are met by competitors' countersubsidies, it is difficult to sort out the net effects.

Causes of Major Shifts in Demand

The major shifts in demand for U. S. exports since the 1970s resulted from several causes. Two causes—exchange rates and weather—warrant further discussion here. A third—reduction of trade barriers—is discussed later in the chapter.

6.3   Exchange value of the U. S. dollar and U. S. agricultural exports, 1970–2004.

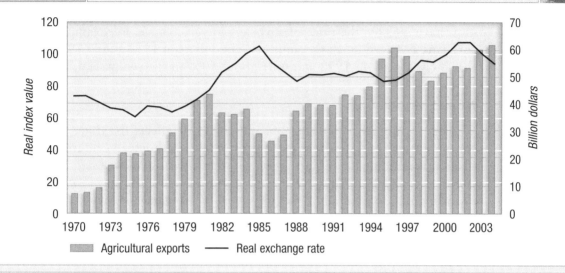

Agricultural exports   —— Real exchange rate

Source: USDA Economic Research Service.

Effect of Exchange Rates

American wheat or soybeans, when sold to the Germans or Japanese, must ultimately be paid for in American dollars, not in German euros or Japanese yen. How can a German importer obtain U. S. dollars to pay for U. S. wheat? He or she buys them from a banker at a price of so many euros per U. S. dollar. The dollar has traditionally been the favorite international currency, and many exchange rates are expressed in terms of dollars.

Generally, an increase in U. S. exports (commodities and services) to Japan, while other things remain the same, will increase the demand for U. S. dollars and will raise the price of dollars in terms of yen. However, an increase in U. S. imports of Japanese autos (other things remaining the same) will reduce the price of dollars in terms of yen. Many foreign investors have decided to invest in U. S. real estate, the stocks and bonds of U. S. corporations, or the debt of the U. S. government. Their decisions have been based on the perceived political safety of American investments, the expected growth of the U. S. economy, and the higher rates of interest often available here. A Japanese investor, like a Japanese importer of wheat, trades yen for U. S. dollars to invest in U. S. property. Conversely, a U. S. company investing abroad trades dollars for the appropriate foreign currency. Thus, in the markets for currencies, all of the worldwide activities of importers, exporters, investors, and even tourists affect exchange rates.

A German crusher considers U. S. and Brazilian soybeans in terms of the price of each in euros. Those prices can change daily because of varying exchange rates, even if the "home" prices of soybeans are stable in the countries mentioned. That fact is the basis for the frequent comment that U. S. exports and imports are affected by the "value of the dollar"—that is, by exchange rates. A "strong," or expensive, dollar in terms of foreign currency hurts our exports. Exhibit 6.4 illustrates how changing exchange rates have affected the price of soybeans in yen. Notice, for example, that soybeans averaged much the same price in dollars in 1982 and in 1992, but that the yen price in 1992 was only about 50% of the yen price in 1982.

Effect of Weather

Weather is another significant demand shifter. It affects the trade flow to various nations and sometimes affects total flow. Although world food production is trending upward, it grows unevenly because of weather. Bad (or good) crops of a commodity in an importing nation or in a competing exporting nation generally raise (or lower) the demand for that U. S. commodity. Substitution occurs among commodities. An increase in Russian sunflower or Asian palm oil production can reduce the demand for U. S. soybean oil.

Major Customers and Competitors

Customers for American agricultural products are almost everywhere, and American producers sell to almost every nation. The developed (industrialized) countries, and particularly Japan, Canada, and western Europe, have been major customers. Whereas the developed countries are still about one-half of the international market, the market shares of emerging economies have grown considerably. Asia is the largest continental market. American

EXHIBIT

6.4   Average annual prices of U. S. soybeans at farm level in terms of dollars and yen.

Year	Average Price Received by U. S. Farmers	Average Number of Yen to Buy 1 U. S. Dollar	Average U. S. Soybean Price in Yen
1982	$5.71	249.10	1422
1987	5.88	144.60	850
1992	5.56	126.70	704
1997	7.40	121.09	896
2004	7.56	108.16	818

Note: Column 3 is the product of columns 1 and 2.

producers have very large sales to Japan and large sales to South Korea and Taiwan. Europe is the second-largest continental market. Latin America is the third market in size.

What do major customers have in common that makes them major markets for grains, soybeans, cotton, and tobacco? Large concentrations of people in relation to agricultural resources, plus the money to buy, is perhaps the most inclusive commonality that fits Japan and western Europe. Climate is also important. Several major customers lie to the north of the United States and lack the warm climate in which cotton, corn, soybeans, and citrus fruits prosper.

People alone do not a market make. People are a necessary but not a sufficient condition for a market. The capability to pay is also necessary. Parts of Africa are a prime example of a population mass that needs food but has been a relatively small market because of its limited ability to pay. The poorer underdeveloped nations furnish a small but growing cash market. In addition, through U. S. government aid programs of various sorts, food shipments to such areas have sometimes been considerable. In the 1980s and 1990s, however, such aid was minimal, and although U. S. food aid spiked in 1999, it has decreased every year since then.

Producers in the United States face tough competitors in other nations for world markets. There are many places around the world in which most commodities can be produced. Although American producers have a strong comparative advantage in their major exports, and especially coarse grains, they can lose market shares by market restrictions of various sorts, such as embargoes, production controls, or too-high price supports. Because of large market shares, the United States influences the global market in grains and oilseeds. Grain and oilseed prices of any exporter are not going to differ much from the U. S. prices.

Agricultural Imports

Food imports compete directly or indirectly for consumers' food dollars. Direct competitors are items such as beef, sugar, oilseeds, pork, tobacco, wool, fruits, vegetables, cut flowers, and wine. Complementary imports, which compete indirectly, include coffee, tea, cocoa, bananas, and spices. In total, agricultural imports run about one-half the level of agricultural exports, leaving a small agricultural trade surplus (Exhibit 6.2).

AGRICULTURAL TRADE POLICY

Free trade permits maximum competition worldwide. Although many individuals accept in principle the virtues of competition and thus of world trade, in private, they often tend to oppose painful competition. A town's retailers complain when a new store in town cuts prices. Lawyers condemn a lawyer who advertises cut rates. These examples of reaction to the pains of competition could be extended to every industry and group, including college students and professors. It is even easier to complain about foreign competitors.

There is no question that increased competition can be harmful to a particular group in the short run. European grain farmers were hurt in the late nineteenth century when cheap American wheat, which had been hauled efficiently by the new railroads and steamships, flooded European markets. Suppose that you are a dairy farmer and a sudden increase of imported dairy products reduces your milk price by 5% and your net income by considerably more. Would it be surprising if you resented that foreign competition and sought protection from it? Naturally, you would still be in favor of free trade "in general" so that you could continue to buy autos and stereos made abroad! However, it is seldom possible to "have your cake and eat it, too." A nation cannot be largely protectionist without encountering similar barriers to its exports. As a dairy farmer, you may not know that, or you may prefer to ignore it. Moreover, you will likely resist arguments that the import damage is only short term and will diminish as soon as there is a compensating shift in consumption or supply.

Reasons Given for Trade Barriers

Trade barriers may be justified in some cases if they are not pushed too far and if the protection is administered very carefully. Economists who feel that those provisions are seldom met may deny the usual validity of most or all of these arguments. Below we discuss the more common reasons given for instituting trade barriers.

To stop "dumping." First, we must acknowledge that the nation has some responsibility toward producer groups hurt by import competition. Generally, the remedy should be adjustment aid rather than trade barriers. Under the Trade Reform Act of 1974, firms and their workers hurt by imports because of reduction in a U. S. tariff may obtain adjustment assistance when certain administrative requirements are met. If the import injury is due to **dumping** (a form of price discrimination in international trade in which products are sold on the world market at prices below the cost of production and below normal domestic prices), then special measures may be taken to stop the dumping. Dumping can be disruptive, and actions against it have some justification. However, complaints about dumping are often merely attempts to avoid normal competition.

To support farm incomes. Most developed nations try to stabilize and support farm incomes. Importing countries frequently use **tariffs**—taxes levied on imports to hamper or even stop them from coming into the county—to support farm prices and farm incomes. Exporting countries often use farm support prices, export subsidies, tariffs, and other devices that interfere with a free market. The political reality of support for farm incomes is a powerful impediment to free trade in agricultural commodities.

ARGUMENTS FOR TRADE BARRIERS   BOX 6.1

- To stop "dumping"
- To support farm income
- To promote self-sufficiency
- To manage the national economy
- To stabilize an industry
- To protect an infant industry
- To use as a political weapon

To promote self-sufficiency. Most countries want to produce enough food to feed their own people. Countries are naturally concerned about being dependent on some other nation or on sea lanes for something as basic as food. Such dependence in case of war, or the threat of war, could notably constrain the diplomatic options of the importer. Thus, numerous nations justify a subsidized agriculture to keep home production at a certain minimal level. Such arguments can cloak the selfish interests of home producers or simply nationalistic pride. But it would be easy for Americans, who have never faced such concerns, to underestimate the strength of these motives in some other countries. Markets in several nations would be larger for U. S.-produced grains if their self-sufficiency policies were dropped.

To manage the national economy. The governments of many countries accept responsibility for maintaining full employment, stable prices, and a desired level of growth in their economies. As they attempt to fulfill these commendable but difficult objectives, free trade may be made subordinate. Some governments undertake to hold retail food prices at "reasonable" levels. Some countries resort to control of foreign exchange, lending, and borrowing as part of an attempt to manage their national economies. Governments desperately short of foreign exchange with which to buy abroad may assert their purchase priorities rather than allow free market allocation. The high price of imported oil and huge foreign debts have caused numerous poorer nations to limit nonessential imports. By licensing imports through a governmental state trading agency, a government allocates foreign purchases according to its priorities. In fact, a government may find that its state trading agency can bargain more effectively in the international market than can its many private demanders bidding against one another. Such state trading has been common in grains. Many of these government programs have been heavily criticized, and sometimes eliminated, because they have been judged to be counterproductive.

To stabilize an industry. Closely allied to the previous argument is the use of barriers to stabilize a particular industry. For example, the U. S. import quotas on beef adjust the size of imports counter to the beef cycle (larger imports when U. S. slaughter is lower and smaller imports when it is larger). This technique should help to reduce troublesome fluctuations in beef production and prices.

To protect an infant industry. The **infant industry argument** is one of the oldest claims for protection. New industries—in agriculture perhaps, but especially in manufacturing—tend to have higher costs because they are small in scale and because many cost-saving devices and methods are discovered only through the experience of production. The argument is to protect the industry until it becomes able to survive on its own and to compete. Whether the argument is sensible depends on the particular situation, and one should look very carefully at the prospects of any industry before accepting the argument.

To use as a political weapon. Trade barriers sometimes are used to attempt to help a nation's friends and punish its enemies. If the United States has a tariff on an item, it is generally the same tariff for every exporting nation (the **Most Favored Nation Clause** is a promise to a nation that the trade regulations and tariffs applied to it will be as favorable as those applied to any other nation). The much publicized restriction in 1980 on the size of grain exports to the USSR was placed for geopolitical reasons. Such trade warfare may be costly to the United States economically and may cost more than it costs the enemy. Whether it is a sensible action must be decided within a costs–benefits context that includes more than the economies of trade. The use of trade as a weapon is disruptive. Farmers and agribusiness in the United States have opposed the practice. Nevertheless, trade warfare by the United States and others remains a possibility.

Numerous reasons are given for trade barriers, and these justifications are sometimes persuasive to the governments concerned. Although we believe strongly in the overall benefits of free trade, it would be unrealistic to overlook the circumstances and arguments that have discouraged it and that are likely to continue to do so.

Regulations Affecting the Flow of Trade

There are many ways for a nation to discourage imports or exports. Direct prohibitions of trade and extremely high tariffs (taxes on imports) are the most obvious techniques. (For brief explanations of several regulations, see Box 6.2.) There are still other possibilities. For example, a potential importing nation could heavily subsidize its farm production and thereby achieve self-sufficiency and prevent food imports. Literally hundreds of **nontariff barriers** have been developed to hinder or stop trade. One classification scheme lists five major categories, as follows:

1. Government participation in trade, including the production subsidies mentioned

2. Burdensome customs procedures for unwanted imports

DEFINING SOME REGULATIONS USED TO AFFECT THE FLOW OF WORLD TRADE   BOX 6.2

State trading—government control over importation and exportation, through either a government monopoly or control of private firms.

Support prices (intervention prices in EU)—prices at which the government will buy domestically produced products.

Variable levy—used by the EU as an import restriction. The levy is adjusted regularly to be the difference between import prices of products delivered and an "orientation or threshold price" (in effect, a minimum price goal for domestic production).

Export subsidy—a government grant to private trade to facilitate or expand exports. The United States has frequently used them to eliminate the differential between domestic prices of price-supported commodities and lower foreign or world prices.

Import quota—a specific limitation of imports concerning total tonnage or value per year.

Tariff or customs duty—a charge (absolute or percentage of value) levied on imports. The usual intent is that the tariff will protect domestic producers either by being so high as to prevent imports or by increasing domestic prices by the amount of the tariff.

Export controls—quantity limits, or embargoes, put on exports to hold down domestic prices or as part of an agreement with an importer to prevent shipments to certain enemy countries.

International commodity agreement—an undertaking between two or more countries, involving both the exporting and the importing sides, to do a variety of things. Usually there is some attempt to give longer-term stability to a commodity market by specifying minimum and maximum quantities traded for minimum and maximum prices.

Preferential trade arrangements—various agreements such as those used by the EU that favor EU associate members in Europe and Africa by reduced levies, and so on.

Source: Most of these definitions are updated from USDA-ERS Agriculture Handbook No. 411, *Dictionary of International Agriculture Trade.*

3. Industrial, health, and safety standards, including packaging and labeling regulations
4. Specific limitations on trade, including embargoes, bilateral agreements, voluntary restraints, and others
5. Restraints by the price mechanism, including special duties and credit restrictions[1]

World agricultural trade, including U. S. exports and imports, would be considerably larger if trade barriers were eliminated. Much has been done by many nations to reduce tariffs. In various forms, however, tariffs and variable levies are still important barriers for certain commodities in certain countries. These barriers may be even more important in holding down agricultural trade. Nontariff barriers introduce a discouraging element of uncertainty into plans for trade. The potential trader sometimes does not know what difficulties his or her products will encounter at the border. We have space to discuss only a few of these barriers.

State trading, by which a government agency receives a monopoly to sell abroad and/or to buy from abroad, has been common in agricultural commodities. Canada has long given the Canadian Wheat Board monopoly power to export wheat. The Livestock Industry Development Corporation of Korea and the Ministry of Commerce of Greece used to buy all corn imported by these countries. Obviously, governments using state trading can restrict imports as they wish.

Bilateral agreements between importers and exporters provide for the trading of a specific commodity for a certain future period. To some extent these agreements supersede the trading that might otherwise occur and thus are a barrier. Perhaps the agreement best known to U. S. farmers has been the grain agreement with the former USSR. It provided minimum and maximum annual guarantees as to how much American farmers would sell and Soviet purchasers would buy. Prices for trades under bilateral agreements are determined in the marketplace. Although bilateral agreements have not been popular with U. S. private traders, this agreement with the USSR was motivated by a desire to avoid disruption in the U. S. market such as had been caused by the Soviet Union's sudden, massive purchases.

Normal trade can also be constrained by the excessive encouragement of exports. Most exporting nations provide some modest help to exporters in terms of special credit, information gathered by agricultural attaches, and assistance with minor promotional expenses. Some practices go much further. The United States has linked its **Public Law 480** "concessional sales" of grain to economic development objectives in the LDCs. (This law, passed in 1954, authorized U. S. export subsidies for agricultural commodities.) Some competitors argued that the United States was "dumping" grain in those LDCs. Export subsidies are used frequently by European nations to dispose of surpluses accumulated under their highly protective agricultural policies. The United States also has subsidized wheat sales through the Export Enhancement Program (EEP).

Another constraint on normal trade is an international cartel that raises prices above competitive levels. A **cartel** is an explicit agreement among sellers of a commodity to restrict their competition by various means. These means may include setting artificially high prices, dividing up sales territories, setting sales quota, or restricting members' production. OPEC is a famous international cartel that was very successful for a time. There are usually strong motivations for cartel members to cheat on compliance and also for new producers to enter the market. Consequently, many cartels have been fairly short lived. Various circumstances facilitated the early successes of OPEC, although it faced great stress in the 1980s. OPEC's dramatic raising of oil prices in the 1970s greatly reduced U. S. oil imports and stimulated greater oil production by various non-OPEC members, including the United States. Cartels for agricultural commodities rarely achieve much for those producers.

Negotiations to Increase Free Trade

Unfortunately, the enlargement and preservation of freer trade is difficult to achieve. Joint action by the major nations is necessary to enlarge free trade, but the unilateral action of any large nation can reduce free trade. The erection of trade barriers by a single country can all too easily lead to retaliation by others.

The **World Trade Organization (WTO)** is an international organization that has sponsored numerous conferences among nations on reduction of trade barriers. The WTO replaced the **GATT (General Agreement on Tariffs and Trade),** which was organized in 1948. Its conferences are called "rounds." The Uruguay Round of multilateral trade negotiations began in 1987 and lasted into the mid-1990s. The Uruguay Round included agricultural products for the first time. Its changes were small and did not have much impact.

In November 2001, the Doha Round, in Doha, Qatar, began with considerable interest in global agricultural policy. The focus was on government price support programs that some claim give certain countries an unfair advantage in production. One of the most controversial cases to date is Brazil's claim that U. S. cotton price supports are anticompetitive. The WTO ruled in favor of Brazil. While the United States is one of the 148 members of the WTO, the United States has the privilege of choosing whether or not to comply with WTO decisions. With respect to the United States, the WTO is a voice and not a legal authority.

The United States, Japan, and the EU have been the major participants in WTO negotiations. From the viewpoint of agricultural merchants and farmers, the resistance of the EU to freer importation of many agricultural commodities has been very frustrating. Prices of European grains and animal products are supported by the EU's Common Agricultural Policy at levels that are typically considerably above the world market. The protective device is the variable levy, which expands or contracts to make up the difference between world prices and the EC protected prices. The European justifications vary from protecting incomes for their smaller farms to concerns about national self-sufficiency. Virtually all nations, including the United States, have protected their agriculture industry in various ways, so that negotiations are never a matter of the "good guys" against the "bad guys." The bargaining proposition is typically, "I'll do you some good (reduce our tariff on your widgets) if you will do us some good (reduce your tariff on our widgets)." In the case of the United States and the EU, the proposition must be, "We will reduce these U. S. tariffs on industrial products if you reduce EU barriers against farm commodities."

The United States, Canada, and Mexico have negotiated a free trade agreement that will reduce most barriers over a 15-year period. The **North American Free Trade Agreement (NAFTA)** helps free up trade within the bloc. (Thus, it is not as helpful as more worldwide agreements.) NAFTA has provided a mechanism to address trade disputes, and continued reduction of barriers will likely see increased trade within this North American trading bloc.[2] The **Central American Free Trade Agreement (CAFTA)** became a law in 2005. This agreement helps free up trade between the United States, Costa Rica, El Salvador, Guatemala, Honduras, and Nicaragua.

Fairly strong protectionist sentiment exists around the world, including in the United States. Strong efforts need to be made by U. S. farmers and agribusiness to protect the gains toward freer trade made in the last 50 years. It would be unfortunate if this huge market were to be cut back severely by trade protectionism, which generally benefits the few at the expense of the many.

SUMMARY

1. The international market is important to U. S. farmers and agribusiness. U. S. market shares of world trade in several crops are very large.

2. Specialization and trade would not occur unless they were mutually advantageous. People realize greater real income because of the gains from specialization and trade. Economists generally favor freer trade.

3. International markets for agricultural exports of raw and processed foods grew rapidly in volume and grew even more rapidly in dollars in the 1970s. The international demand for U. S. exports shifted rapidly to the right in the 1970s but moved back to the left in the early 1980s. Exports by the United States have recovered substantially since 1986. However, imports are growing relative to exports. These big shifts occurred for a complex set of reasons, including changes in the growth rates of agricultural production abroad, the changing value of the dollar, the rise and fall of international lending to emerging economies to finance their food purchases, changes in farm programs in the United States and other countries, and weather.

4. U. S. agricultural imports are growing relative to agricultural exports. In the aggregate, U. S. agricultural markets are greater because of international trade.

5. The volume of international trade is reduced considerably by many types of barriers. U. S. restrictions on agricultural imports sometimes lead to restrictions by other nations on their imports of U. S. agricultural commodities. The WTO is the venue for solving trade disputes.

6. Nations offer various reasons as justifications for trade restrictions. It is largely a matter of conflicting goals. Some countries encourage

uneconomic food production in order to be self-sufficient in times of war or to maintain the incomes of their farmers. Some emerging economies manipulate their exchange rates to manage investments and imports in ways that are expected to speed economic development.

7. There are many ways that governments can restrict and redirect trade. Various sorts of import taxes such as tariffs and variable levies are common. Nontariff barriers are even more common.

8. Persistent efforts of the big industrial countries have reduced many tariffs. These reductions have been negotiated in the various multinational negotiations under GATT and now the WTO. Efforts to reduce nontariff barriers continue. The Uruguay Round of GATT established the WTO but created only small gains toward freer trade. The WTO is now in the Doha Round, with greater emphasis on agriculture.

STUDY QUESTIONS

1. Look around at your fellow students. In a few years, some will be businesspeople, some farmers, one or two may be professors, and one may be a professional athlete. Do you suppose that most will make choices on the basis of what they perceive to be their comparative advantage?

2. Describe the similarities and the differences of domestic and international markets. What factors explain the growth in each?

3. Why are international markets much bigger for U. S. crops than for livestock?

4. Draw a domestic supply-and-demand curve for a commodity such as wool or sugar that is both imported and produced in this nation. Show how a protective tariff would increase domestic prices and reduce imports. How would it affect domestic production?

5. What do you feel are the two best arguments for some restriction of free trade?

6. Identify emerging economies. What role do these emerging economies play in the WTO?

7. Briefly define dumping, state trading, variable levies, export subsidies, and exchange rate.

8. Some U. S. farmers and agribusinesses would like to sell meat, eggs, and dairy products abroad rather than so much feed grains. Why doesn't the U. S. government require major foreign customers to buy livestock rather than feed grains?

9. What kinds of agribusiness firms sell in international markets? Can you think of any foreign firms that sell processed foods in the United States? Can you explain how a country's tariff against a firm's products might encourage the firm to locate a plant in that country?

10. Has NAFTA increased trade among the participating nations? Is the United States better off because of this trade agreement? How does NAFTA differ from WTO?

 **CLASS EXERCISE**

For the product your group selected in Chapter 3, choose a foreign country and research product trends and the causes for these trends. Consider the following possible influences on trends:

- Population
- Income
- Preferences
- Substitutes
- Others

Your group should then prepare to lead a class discussion about the changes in consumption trends that you found and why they occurred.

 **NOTES**

1. Jimmye S. Hillman, "Nontariff Barriers: Major Problems in Agricultural Trade," *American Journal of Agricultural Economics* (August 1978): 495.
2. August Schumacher, Jr., "Building Prosperity with U.S. Trade Partners," *Agricultural Outlook*, ERS, USDA (April 1996), pp. 12–13.

THE MARKETING SYSTEM

Within the marketing system a vast flow of agricultural commodities is assembled, transported, stored, processed into products, priced, and distributed to consumers. The chapters in Part II describe how the price system knits together the decisions of tens of thousands of managers into a smoothly functioning system. The markets in which prices are set or discovered and the exchanges that are made are integral to the marketing system. Organized commodity markets are gradually being replaced by other types of pricing systems that represent the specific interest of a particular marketing channel.

Numerous firms, including some large farmer cooperatives, exercise market channel leadership. We discuss joint activities of farmers, such as generic advertising and bargaining, in reference to their influence on the workings of the marketing system.

The product merchandiser and the commodity handler face different options. The commodity manager is concerned mainly with the physical efficiencies of transporting and handling and the price risks of ownership. The product manager is concerned with product development and promotion, channel development, and pricing. Part II describes the methods by which processors develop a marketing mix to implement their marketing strategies. It also develops the concept of a product life cycle and its relevance to management, and it reviews some of the ways that retailers and food service firms attract customers.

CHAPTER

7

FEDERAL RESERVE NOTE
AG58177277B
G7
THE UNITED STATES OF AMERICA
AG58177277B
ONE HUNDRED DOLLARS
100

PRICING AND EXCHANGE SYSTEMS AND ALTERNATIVES WITHIN THE MARKETING-PROCUREMENT CHANNEL

PREVIEW

- We can go behind the supply-and-demand schedules to see how a market's participants actually arrive at prices and exchange arrangements and to see how prices can be discovered and set.

- Electronic markets have revolutionized business transactions.

- There are advantages and disadvantages to mechanisms such as formula pricing and pooling.

- Decentralized, individual negotiation is becoming more important as a pricing alternative.

- Transaction costs are an important influence on the relative usage of pricing and exchange systems.

- Vertical coordination and vertical integration can take place in marketing and production contracts.

- The marketing-pricing alternatives of farmers enlarge farmers' opportunities to attempt to obtain the best prices over time for their sales while accommodating delivery to their convenience or to the perishability of their commodity.

KEY TERMS

allocation of decision rights

allocation of risk

allocation of value

contractual exchange

decentralized, individual negotiation (DIN)

electronic markets

formula pricing

marketing-pricing alternatives

marketing-procurement contract

organized markets

pooling

price discovery

pricing system

production contract

transaction costs

vertical coordination

C hapter 4 discussed prices and the competitive forces determining their levels and their variation over time. This chapter is concerned with the various systems or mechanisms by which prices are discovered or set. Even though the amounts supplied and demanded of commodity X will determine that its daily price this season will vary from about $3 to $4 per unit, how is the appropriate price arrived at for a particular day? Potential buyers and sellers certainly do not read the price off a daily supply-and-demand schedule. Farmers and agribusiness people must understand this important part of their economic environment. These pricing and exchange systems influence the ways in which market participants behave. Moreover, these systems are manmade and are subject to change. Market participants need to be aware of the impacts of alternative systems on their operations.

Naturally, sellers prefer a pricing system that provides them the best (highest) prices, whereas buyers seek the lowest prices for a given quality. A **pricing system** is a market mechanism or process (organized behavior) by which market participants discover, negotiate, or fix prices. The net costs (prices) to both buyers and sellers are influenced by the costs of making the pricing transactions. These transaction costs are more numerous and important than you might think. **Transaction costs** include all those costs incurred by sellers and buyers as they search for market opportunities and make and complete business deals, such as any fees paid (usually by sellers) to use an organized market, the transportation and shrinkage costs of transporting and transferring a commodity from seller to buyer, all the search costs (in terms of time, transportation, and telephone) of seeking both buyers and sellers, the costs of making and enforcing contracts, and the costs of collecting payment and of settling disputes. Thus, the transaction costs in a pricing system are an important determinant of its popularity with buyers and sellers.

A CLASSIFICATION OF PRICING SYSTEMS

Classification of pricing systems can help us to understand and use them. The following classification covers the more important systems in agriculture. It is possible, of course, for two or three pricing systems to be in use for a given commodity simultaneously.

PRICE DISCOVERY SYSTEMS

1. Organized markets
2. Decentralized, individual negotiation

PRICE-SETTING SYSTEMS

1. Firm price making
2. Group negotiation
3. Government price setting

Price Discovery Systems

Price discovery is the process of buyers and sellers arriving at prices for a commodity when market conditions do not permit either group to set prices. Price discovery occurs when all market participants (buyers and sellers) are individually price takers or price negotiators. The prices for many, but not all, farm commodities are discovered at the first-handler levels in which farmers often sell. The distinction between the first-handler and following levels of agricultural marketing reflects the differences in firm structure, product form, and product merchandising. Price discovery systems are usually associated with fairly equal numbers of buyers and sellers. Price discovery almost never involves differentiated products; prices are typically discovered for commodities, especially the more perishable ones.

Price discovery systems continually rediscover price. Although consecutive price discoveries may find the same price, variations—small and large—are more typical. Prices tend to change more frequently than when set in a price-setting system.

Organized Markets

Organized markets have been important in many diverse societies throughout history. Today's peasant market in an Asian, African, or Latin American town or village would not differ much from its ancient predecessor in organization and style of operation. Livestock auctions, fruit and vegetable wholesale markets, and even the sophisticated futures markets for grain, soybeans, livestock, and so on follow the same structure and function as the peasant market.

Organized markets are structured to give all potential sellers and buyers public access to one another as they discover prices. Thus, any participant's normal desire to sell high or buy low is facilitated by access to all buyers or all sellers but is tempered by competition from other participants. These markets have a set of formal rules or customs that regulate the time and place of trading, the obligations of each party, the mode of transaction, and similar matters. For example, exchange members are the only participants permitted to trade grain futures at the Chicago Board of Trade. Moreover, such transactions must occur in a certain trading pit according to a prescribed set of rules. Similarly, prices in an auction are determined by public bidding managed by an auctioneer.

Organized markets frequently are referred to as *public markets* because the operation is quite public. Prices are publicly arrived at and are usually disseminated quickly to all interested parties. Each market participant in the price discovery process is free to weigh prices recently discovered by others as he sees fit as he strives to negotiate a transaction or bids at an auction. A high level of pricing efficiency is expected in organized markets. In other words, almost every price is close or equal to the competitive equilibrium price. The organized market conditions of free and vigorous competition and a high, uniform level of immediate information generally result in a higher level of pricing efficiency than exists in decentralized markets.[1]

Electronic versions of organized markets.   Physical presence of the participants is not necessary for an organized market. A commodity may be auctioned on a conference call or through the Internet as long as participants have an understanding of and confidence in the commodity descriptions. Understanding is easier for a standardized product (corn), but it is accomplished for feeder pigs as well. The savings to buyers and sellers of personal travel time and costs and of significant commodity transportation time and costs are important reasons for interest in **electronic markets**—organized markets in which potential buyers and sellers communicate by electronic means rather than face to face. The possibility of widening the market by including more potential sellers and/or buyers on an electronic network is another reason for interest in this pricing system.

One of the most successful electronic markets has been eBay, which allows buyers and sellers from across the globe to participate at the same time making the buy or sell process a standardized transaction.

In agriculture, electronic trading has been nearly revolutionary. Commodity exchanges, such as the Chicago Board of Trade after-hours trading, Japan Tokyo Grain Exchange, and European Euronext are examples of electronic trading opening markets up to the world. For these global marketplaces, the difference in time zones was a strong reason for adopting electronic technology. On a more localized level, one can go to Missouri's Joplin Regional Stockyard website and bid in real time on cattle being sold. The firm XSAg allows persons to bid on agriculture chemical products or buy them at flat price.

Decentralized, Individual Negotiation

Decentralized, individual negotiation (DIN) is a less formalized, less public, less structured, but increasingly common pricing system in agriculture and agribusiness. This method includes any price discovery system outside of organized markets in which a buyer and seller, as individuals, negotiate a transaction. It is often referred to as *private treaty* or as *haggling*. For example, most beef cattle sales are negotiated in the feedlot or on the farm by the seller and a packer–buyer. Presumably, each party is as concerned about alternative market options and about the "going price" when she negotiates her own transaction as she would be in an organized market.

Advantages. Convenience and lower transaction costs are frequently the advantages of DIN. If the alternative is to move the commodity to an organized market, the farmer often thinks it more convenient to sell on his own farm. There are obvious physical efficiencies in moving a product only once, from farm to processor, rather than moving it to an organized market and then moving it again. A highly perishable product such as milk rarely moves through an organized market.

The farmer frequently feels that he has more control in the selling process when he sells at the farm. He can refuse a bid at the farm with little or no cost, whereas it is costly to refuse a bid received after the commodity has been shipped to a public market or buyer.

Through DIN, buyers and sellers can transact business anywhere, at any time, in contrast to the limited days and hours that some organized markets are open.

Disadvantages. Knowledge of alternate market options is usually less complete and more difficult to obtain in a decentralized, nonpublic market. Although public and private market agencies try to gather and publicize prices, this process is frequently slower, more expensive, and less satisfactory than in an organized market.

Lack of information and of negotiating skills on the part of many (but not all) farmers is a primary concern as they sell in the individual negotiation system. On the agribusiness procurement side, that situation presents certain opportunities. Meat processors and retailers may negotiate by telephone for the sale of carloads of hams or Choice grade beef carcasses with quite precise understandings as to the products involved.

An offer-acceptance system. A large buyer or large seller may organize a DIN system of price negotiation that is rather similar to an organized market. For example, a large retail chain might request that processors provide offers each Monday as to how many carloads of beef of a specified quality they are willing to provide at a specified price. The retailer each Tuesday morning compares the competing offers and accepts the most desirable. In some cases, the retailer may do a bit of negotiating to try to improve (from its point of view) one or more offers. The system appears to be a one-sided market, as several packers compete to sell to one retailer. However, to the extent that the packer can sell to other alternative retailers outside this negotiation system, it is not as one-sided as it first appears. The large size of the orders is obviously a prerequisite—large packers would not bother with a small retailer who wanted to imitate this system. This offer-acceptance pricing system is similar to that of a buying group of large farmers who request offers from competing farm suppliers for their year's fuel, fertilizer, and other needs.

As product branding becomes more prevalent, the frequency of offer-acceptance bids is decreasing. Branding can make it more difficult for a retailer to switch buyers, as consumers may become confused as to product quality. As a result, the frequency of offer-acceptance bids may be semi-annually, annually, or even every several years. Thus, much more is at stake in each bid process.

Formula pricing. One rather popular method of DIN includes **formula pricing.** It is often used at the first-handler level for meat commodities and more frequently beyond that level. A particular pair of marketing participants who often—and perhaps continuously—deal with one another may find formula pricing to be convenient. For example, a packer and a retailer may agree that a carload of beef carcasses of a certain specification will be shipped from the packer to the retailer every Wednesday; the price is to be in a certain relation to the closing Yellow Sheet price for specified beef on the day shipped. In this case, the Yellow Sheet prices are prices reported by a private news service as representative of bona fide market transactions. Both parties may agree that, at any time, they may renegotiate either the amount shipped or the pricing formula. However, such an agreement may continue to exist unchanged for many months when it meets the needs of both participants.

As a passive method of DIN price discovery, formula pricing has a limitation that sometimes becomes relevant. It depends on a base price determined in an organized market or by active individual negotiation. If a whole industry tries to use formula pricing, the base price disappears or becomes determined by so few transactions that it may not be a reliable indicator of market value. This is particularly the case for spot-market prices reported by government agencies.

Price-Setting Systems

Prices may be made or set by any of three parties: sellers, either individual-ly or collectively; buyers, individually; or government. Price-setting systems have the possibility, which is frequently realized, of failing to equate amounts supplied and demanded in the fashion of price discovery systems. To the extent that a price is set, then something new has happened to the expression of supply and demand. Sometimes people dramatize this fact by asserting that "the law of supply and demand no longer applies." That is much too sweeping a claim. But it is true that there is a difference. If the suppliers set a selling price, then they generally stand ready to supply what-ever amount buyers will take at that price (Exhibit 7.1a). Such a posture means that at any demand short of D'', some supplies will not be sold in any given time period or will be diverted to other markets. On the other hand, if buyers are able to set a buying price, then they generally stand ready to buy whatever amount will be offered at that price (Exhibit 7.1b). In this case, some demand is likely to go unfilled at any supply short of S'', just as some supplies went unsold in the previous case.

　　If the government sets a ceiling price, demanders may be prevented from obtaining quantities as large as desired at the price set and sellers from receiving prices as high as they could in a freer market (Exhibit 7.2a). If the government sets a support (minimum) price and acquires those supplies that private demanders do not take at that minimum price, then price is lim-

EXHIBIT

7.1　　Price setting by (a) sellers or (b) buyers.

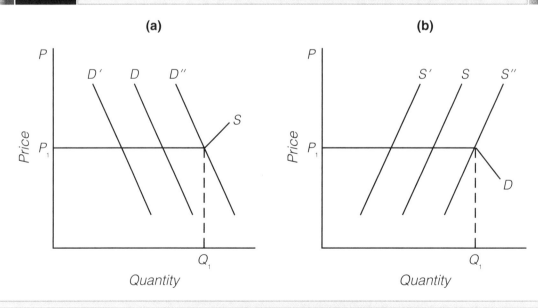

7.2   The disequilibrium effects of (a) a ceiling price or (b) a support price.

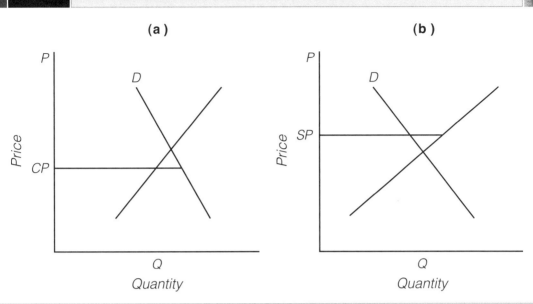

ited on the low side, and amounts supplied and demanded do not adjust adequately to clear the market (Exhibit 7.2b).

The infringement of price setting on the forces of supply and demand is significant, but its importance can be overemphasized. Private price setters would be foolish not to consider carefully the basic supply-and-demand forces in choosing the prices they set. In fact, price making in many situations is so dominated by supply-and-demand considerations that it is much like price discovery. For example, a meat processor prices her brands of bacon to retailers. But if the supply-and-demand situation changes during the week, the processor probably will have to reprice her bacon next week. Repricing has been common practice in the past, but recent trends in consumption point to pricing strategies that lock in price and quantity between wholesalers and retailers for long periods of time. This pricing method has significant implications for coordinating the value chain.

Price Making by Individual Firms

We have discussed in previous chapters the fact that many agribusiness firms are price or margin makers. Price making by a firm is much more likely for differentiated products than for commodities. The branded cereal manufacturer prices his product to retailers as does the bacon processor, the cake mix and soup manufacturers, and others. Even the country elevator sets a retail price at which it will sell feed grain to local farmers. Price behavior differs among these examples. The local elevator may reset its feed grain price almost daily, whereas the price of the branded soup or cereal may change only two or three times a year. These differences must be explained in terms of competition, the nature of the product, and the nature of basic supply-and-demand forces. Feed grains as a commodity are basically priced in a worldwide price discovery market, and the local elevators must adjust their retail prices accordingly within a relatively small range of discretion. On the other hand, a maker of a highly differentiated product has much more discretion in pricing her products as long as her costs are not linked closely to any commodity markets. Thus, we may read in the newspapers that the improved prospects for a record high wheat harvest have led to a slump in wheat prices, but nothing will be said about a slump in the prices of Wheaties.

Any agribusiness manager charged with price setting should find very quickly the degree of discretion that he can realistically exercise. He may also find it profitable to analyze carefully just where he should set price within that discretionary range.

Group Negotiation

Group-negotiated prices in agriculture involve farmers negotiating as a group with individual buyers. Such negotiation is sometimes referred to as "collective bargaining," although it differs in some important respects from industrial labor–management collective bargaining. Group negotiation is increasing in agriculture. Some kinds of group negotiation are akin to price discovery and could have been discussed in that section.

Group negotiation is employed by producers of certain fruits and vegetables for canning and high-value specialty commodities (e.g., organic soybeans, high lysine corn, organic milk). Prices and other terms of trade are typically negotiated prior to the planting of crops. A cannery tends to have considerable power in setting price because alternative markets are not usually accessible to producers. Producers have sometimes tried to countervail this power by negotiating jointly through their bargaining association with each individual buyer.

Generally, group-negotiated prices are more stable during a season than if they had been determined in a price discovery system. However, groups generally have no power to control entry or exit of producers or to control industry output. Consequently, supply-and-demand forces come to bear on interseasonal (longer-run) prices. If a group negotiates high prices, the resulting expansion of output in following seasons will force lower prices as a long-run consequence. Bargaining groups may be quite successful in disposing of an extra-large crop or in other efforts that increase the short-term stability of prices and producer incomes. However, they usually have limited effects on longer-term prices and incomes.

Government Price Setting

Price ceilings have occasionally been applied to food products in wartime in the United States but only rarely in peacetime. The disruptions of the food markets, long-term effects on farm output, administrative complexities, and ideological considerations generally discourage this type of price setting except under the extremities of war.

Price supports have been much more common. They have been used on numerous commodities since the 1930s in an effort to increase and stabilize the incomes of farmers. During much of the past 80 years, the prices of corn, wheat, cotton, peanuts, tobacco, and manufactured dairy products have been partially determined by the level of price supports. Private trading continues in organized or other markets for these price-supported commodities.

PRICE SYSTEMS IN USE

xhibit 7.3 indicates the authors' opinions concerning the pricing systems used in recent years for major commodities. On a few commodities, it could be argued as to which was a major or supplemental system. Moreover, the impact of government has varied over time from a major price determinant to a minor and sometimes negligible influence in pricing the major field crops and so does not appear on the table. Note that the table deals mainly with farmer–first-handler markets. Firm price making tends to become more important at stages closer to the end user.

EXHIBIT

7.3   Pricing systems at first-handler stage for major agricultural commodities.

Commodities

Pricing Systems	Livestock	Fresh meat	Fluid milk	Eggs	Dressed broilers	Tobacco	Cotton	Fresh fruits and vegetables	Processed fruits and vegetables	Grains and oilseeds
Organized markets	A			A		T	A	A		T
Individual negotiation	T	T		T	T		T	T	A	A
Firm price making	A	A								A
Group negotiation	A		T					A		T	A

Note: "*T*" indicates the typical or predominant system; "*A*" indicates an additional or supplemental system, but systems of minor use or influence are not indicated. Level of pricing is considered only at the first-handler stage, except for fresh meat and dressed broilers, where it is at wholesale level.

COMPARATIVE PERFORMANCE OF PRICING SYSTEMS

Whether the performer is a politician, a football team, or a pricing system, judgments about performance are rarely unanimous. Judgments made from a private participant's point of view may differ from those made from a public interest point of view.

Private views of performance may often be inferred by observing market participation. If a farmer chooses to sell his slaughter hogs at a nearby processor buying station rather than ship them to an organized market, he has expressed his view concerning the better system. But what if there is little practical choice because the nearest alternative is 250 miles away? Or, if there is a nearby organized market, would its closing affect his ability to negotiate with that processor and his degree of satisfaction?

Agribusinesses have operated in all of the price discovery and price-making systems. As buyers from farmers, agribusinesses have generally shown a preference for privately negotiated prices or for price setting, although they have sometimes strongly supported organized markets. When they sell to other agribusinesses, most dealings are by individual negotiation, frequently in an account-supplier scheme with formula pricing. As will be indicated later, agribusiness firms have shown much more interest than farmers in contractual and vertical arrangements as replacements for the spot markets being discussed here. They have generally been opposed to government price support programs.

To the extent that market participants reveal their preferences by their actions, the largest move in the past 50 years or so has been toward DIN and away from organized, terminal markets. The lower transaction costs of DIN were likely the primary motivator. As that shift occurred, the disadvantages associated with DIN became more obvious and interest increased in electronic markets. It is unlikely that farmers can activate a new pricing method such as electronic markets without the aid of a strong cooperative or government.

Thus far, the discussion has focused more on private than on public appraisal. How well do these pricing systems compare to various public standards?

1. Minimization of transaction costs. Ordinarily, shipping costs are minimized by direct shipment from the seller to the buyer. Most pricing methods, other than physical assembly markets, compare well on this standard, as they permit direct shipment. Other transaction costs involve buyer or seller travel, telephone calls, paperwork, and other related costs. Formula pricing is very economical, as are other DIN methods not involving travel of buyers and sellers. Buyer visits to farms and feedlots and to small auctions may be expensive. Group bargaining in a favorable environment may have low transaction costs.

2. Spatial pricing efficiency. The enlarged markets of an electronic system probably create the greatest potential efficiency because of the large number of potential participants. Isolated buyers or sellers probably have most to fear from a DIN system in which there is little competition on the other side of the market; in such a situation they must take whatever price is offered.

3. Level and stability of prices.   Pricing systems are generally comparable on this measure. The government pricing systems are likely the only ones that differ significantly. In fact, the main reason for using government systems is dissatisfaction with market-determined levels of prices or price instability.

4. Integrity and equity of the price-making process.   Opportunities for deceit and fraud arise occasionally in any commercial system. In recent years, formula pricing seems to have received a disproportionate amount of criticism, although that has not reduced its high level of use. The concern is the possibility of price manipulation in a thin market. Such markets exist when formula pricing becomes so widespread that the cash market is based on very few reported transactions. If the industry has confidence that the few transactions are truly representative of supply-and-demand conditions, then there is no problem. However, if some market participants fear that the base prices can be manipulated, then severe discontent can erupt. In both live hog (Exhibit 7.4) and live cattle markets, there have been complaints and congressional hearings on thin-market problems. In contrast, the wholesale cheese market has not had a crisis of confidence, even with far fewer base price transactions. Confidence is a function not only of the number of base price transactions but also of various market characteristics important to the particular group of procedures involved.

EXHIBIT

7.4   Percent of U. S. hogs sold through various pricing arrangements, January 1999–2005.[2]

	1999	2000	2001	2002	2003	2004	2005
Hog or meat market formula	44.2	47.2	54.0	44.5	41.4	41.4	39.9
Other market formula	3.4	8.5	5.7	11.8	5.7	7.2	10.3
Other purchase arrangement	14.4	16.9	22.8	8.6	19.2	20.6	15.4
Packer-sold				2.1	2.2	2.1	2.4
Packer-owned				16.4	18.1	17.1	21.4
Negotiated (spot)	35.8	25.7	17.3	16.7	13.5	11.6	10.6

Source: 2002, 2003, 2004, and 2005 data are based on USDA Mandatory Reports. 1999–2001 data are based on industry surveys by the University of Missouri.

CONTRACTUAL EXCHANGE ARRANGEMENTS AND VERTICAL INTEGRATION

Pricing is only a part of a total transaction or exchange arrangement. In fact, some exchanges do not involve commodity pricing at all. We turn now to this broader aspect of exchange arrangements.

All phases of a transaction or exchange between buyer and seller need not be completed at the same time. Delivery may be immediate or much later than the initial phase of the transaction. Price may be agreed on initially, at time of delivery, or at some other time. Transactions where the phases are not completed at the same time are referred to frequently as **contractual exchange** arrangements.

Important Definitions

Various definitions of integration and contracting have grown up among farmers, agribusiness, and marketing specialists, with the unfortunate result that the same terms sometimes mean different things to different people. The narrowest meaning of vertical integration is ownership of contiguous stages in the marketing channel. A firm owning two or more levels of production or marketing is vertically integrated. How do we distinguish between levels or stages? Each level or stage produces a marketable product or service. Thus, a feed company that feeds its own livestock rather than selling feed alone is said to be vertically integrated. Similarly, a food processor that sells retail to consumers is vertically integrated. Also, we see **vertical coordination** in the agricultural sector where firms share information to improve efficiencies.

A **marketing–procurement contract** (M–P contract) is an agreement between a seller and a buyer covering the product, time and nature of delivery, price, and other aspects of an exchange in which some of the terms do not take place at the time of the immediate transaction. Common usage allows a rather brief time to elapse before a transaction is regarded as an M–P contract. For example, the transaction in which a Texas packer takes delivery of cattle up to 10 days after purchase is generally regarded as a cash transaction rather than an M–P contract. However, a written agreement of a packer to accept a cattle delivery in 90 days at a certain price would definitely be regarded as an M–P contract. Similarly, an agreement of a cotton ginner to purchase a farmer's cotton production in two months at a set price is an M–P contract.

Farmer acceptance of procurement contracts tends to rise after a period of declining farm prices. However, a trend toward use of procurement contracts for fed cattle has been seen for several years (Exhibit 7.5). Questions have been raised about the influence of captive supplies on the overall price level. Can buyers lower acquisition cost (prices) by "locking in" a certain volume of the commodity? If the buyers secure the highest quality this way, their transactions may lower reported market prices.

A **production contract** involves the buyer in the physical production process. Thus, a farmer *(contractee)* has a production contract when she takes responsibility for rearing or caring for broilers or turkeys or for feed-

7.5 Live cattle marketed through contracted monthly cattle sales.[3]

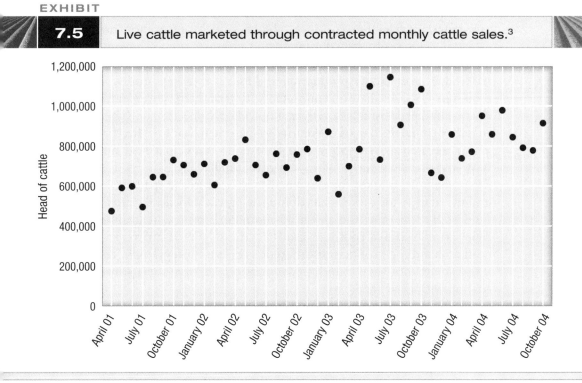

ing pigs owned by another party called a *contractor* (another producer or firm, such as a feed company or processor). Generally, her payment is in the form of a piece-wage—so much per pound of the commodity returned to the contractor. Production contracts apply to some crops. For example, often a cannery in the Midwest owns the growing crop of peas, sweet corn, or tomatoes and pays the farmer a fixed compensation per ton, which is expected to cover payment for his land, labor, and management. An M–P contract affects only the timing of the transaction between producer and buyer, whereas a production contract involves the contractor in the production process.

Motivations of Agribusiness to Integrate Vertically

Assuming that contractual or ownership integration replaces the spot markets when (and only when) buyers and sellers are motivated toward such replacement, what are the motivations? The leaders in contracting or integrating—especially of production contracts—are usually the agribusiness firms, so their motivations deserve top billing. These motivations involve some mix of seeking or controlling product quality. A fruit-and-vegetable cannery faces some very special problems of controlling the quality of its products and of scheduling an efficient flow of product through its processing lines. Rather than take chances in the marketplace, the cannery generally contracts with producers to control as much as possible all of the factors that affect the quality and quantity delivered to the cannery (factors such as variety, cultural and harvest practices, pesticide application, and planting and harvest quantities and dates). Production contracts and/or vertical integration are generally essential to the profitable coordination of production and canning.

Large contractors that began as feed companies or poultry processors have taken over broiler production and much of turkey production, gaining efficiencies of coordination connected with feed distribution and broiler production and processing. Moreover, it quickly became apparent to feed makers that they gained feed market security to the extent that they tied broiler growers to themselves by contract. Of course, an individual feed maker would have lost market security when competing mills tied growers to themselves. Thus, the open market for broilers disappeared in the space of a few years, and the market for turkeys has diminished greatly for fresh birds.

Grain companies and elevators competing to procure grain have found that various types of contracts are attractive to some farmers. Farmer cooperatives handling products as different as grain, turkeys, milk, and specialty crops sometimes have found it advantageous to have some sort of contractual tie with their members.

Farmers' and Agribusinesses' Motivations to Contract

Why do farmers contract? The motivations vary by type of contract and commodity and probably also by the kind of farmer. Her motivations in the simpler M–P contracts may involve her desire to separate the pricing decision from time of delivery, whether pricing comes before or after delivery. Another advantage is that production contracts allow price risks to be shifted to the contractor. Often, access to market is involved; one no longer can raise broilers without a production contract, and rarely would one raise a canning crop, hogs, or sugar beets without a contract. Some farmers become growers for contractors because they lack the capital to finance their own production. The desire to work together cooperatively for certain goals may motivate a farmer to contract with a cooperative to market his grain, milk, or wool.

Production contracts dominate agriculture today. According to a 2004 USDA report of 2001 data, for hogs and poultry and eggs, the portions being produced under production contracts are 53.4% and 81.3%, respectively.[4] The percentages for hogs and poultry are considerably higher than for cattle or grains and oilseeds. This difference can be attributed to the ability to coordinate genetics and inputs for large-scale poultry and hog producers. Cattle are much more difficult to produce under contract because of the lack of coordination between cow-calf producers, backgrounders, and feedlot portions of the value chain. For grains and oilseeds, identity-preserved crops (crops with special characteristics that are segregated from general production) are sometimes grown under production contracts. The most notable example is seed corn. Because grain and oilseed specialty production involve considerable weather risk and production uncertainty, geographic dispersion of crops is necessary to mitigate these risks.

Every contract has three important characteristics: allocation of value, allocation of decision rights, and allocation of risk. If you can remember these three characteristics, then you will understand why contracting is a useful business management tool, and you will understand why contracts are often contested in a court of law. **Allocation of value** refers to how the contractee (the entity accepting the contract) and contractor (entity offering the contract) share in the value of the commodity or product being produced. For example, an Alaska blueberry farmer may have a contract with an agribusiness to deliver 15 tons of blueberries at a price of $1.50/pound. The specification of $1.50/pound sets the value of the contract. Now, suppose that the contract specifies that should the contractee deliver blueberries of which 80% meet a minimum size specification, a 5% bonus will be paid. This allocation of value indicates that the contractor has a use for blueberries meeting a minimum size, and the bonus sends a signal to the grower that there is value in managing for size.

Allocation of decision rights refers to provisions of the contract that require the grower to follow a certain protocol. For example, a hog production contract might specify that the feeder-pig grower must wash down facilities prior to receiving each new load of feeder pigs. If he does not, then the contractor is not obligated to deliver feeder pigs. Thus, the decision right to clean is established by the contractor through the contract.

Allocation of risk establishes whether the contractee or contractor bears the cost should something go wrong. For example, suppose a contractor offers a barley producer a barley contract for the delivery of barley to Orofino, Idaho. The contract terms indicate that 10,000 bushels are to be delivered. If the stated quantity is not delivered, then the contractor will probably not offer the grower a contract the following year. The contractor has a use for the amount of barley contracted, and should the contractee not deliver the stated quantity, the contractor will have to fulfill its needs elsewhere, which may be costly. Contract terms typically include an "Act of God" clause, which allows the contractee to fail to fulfill the contracted quantity due to inclement weather or natural disaster.

MARKETING–PRICING ALTERNATIVES OF FARMERS

Farmers frequently face many different **marketing–pricing alternatives**— various arrangements allowing them to time the pricing, delivery, and transfer of ownership for a commodity separately, when carrying out those phases simultaneously would not be advantageous. These alternatives form a continuum ranging from the cash market to marketing–production contracts. Many times, these contracts can be executed within the same pricing systems described earlier.

For storable commodities such as the grains, timber, cotton, and oilseeds, farmers can make choices as to the following factors:

1. Timing of pricing
2. Timing of delivery
3. Timing of sale
4. Contracting

5. Forward pricing in cash or futures markets

6. Pooling

Producers of hogs and cattle can choose among all but the second alternative. Full-fledged pooling is unusual in livestock, however.

Let's suggest first why some farmers are interested in each of those choices.

1. *Timing of pricing.* As we have seen, agricultural prices are often quite variable, so the differences between big profits and big losses may depend on which price within the year a farmer receives. Timing of pricing thus is important. By turning to devices that separate delivery from setting of price, a farmer may achieve almost complete freedom to seek the highest possible prices. His success will depend on the quality and analysis of his information and his courage in acting on numerous factors outside his control. For tax reasons, farmers sometimes do not want to receive payment until after January 1.

2. *Timing of delivery.* Delivery at harvest of a storable commodity is often time consuming and occasionally is impossible (for example, if the elevator has no empty bins). Thus, a farmer may seek arrangements that give preferential acceptance of his delivery or allow its postponement to a more convenient time (see *timing of sale*).

3. *Timing of sale.* Sale at a time other than at delivery or pricing may be convenient or may offer price security to a farmer.

4. *Contracting.* A farmer may enter into a market contract so that he has a known outlet for a particular quantity or quality of a commodity. Some producers enter into long-term marketing contracts that set the price based on some formula, offer quality premiums or discounts, set a trade amount to deliver, and set a delivery period.

5. *Forward pricing in cash or futures markets.* A farmer may time her pricing by contracting in either the cash or the futures market. Each type of contract has its attractions and its disadvantages. Generally, the cash contract is simplest, and many farmers use it because they feel uncomfortable with a futures or an option contract. The producer can set the amount for a cash contract, whereas futures contracts are available only in fixed amounts. Cash contracts do not require margins or deposits. With a cash contract, there is no uncertainty about basis—no chance to lose or to gain on a shifting basis. On the other hand, there is no way out of a cash contract, as these contracts are made to be kept, not to be canceled later. The most disastrous possibility is a widespread crop failure that prevents the farmer from having the commodity to deliver and forces her to buy it elsewhere at a higher price than she receives on delivery (per terms of the contract).

6. *Pooling.* **Pooling** is the act of consigning a commodity to be sold along with others by a cooperative or other agency, when and where it deems best. The farmer receives the average pool price for his quality and quantity. The pooled price may be better than the farmer would achieve, or it could be

worse. Much depends on the expertise with which the manager of the pool times the sales. In some situations, pooling of grain and rice has been quite successful. Pooling generally appeals to producers who are risk averse.

In addition to the methods described above, numerous other marketing alternatives have risen in popularity in recent decades. The usual tendency for prices of storable commodities to be lower at harvest than at later times in the marketing year has provided a strong incentive to farmers to consider alternatives. However, simultaneous sale, pricing, and delivery at completion of production or harvest has been the traditional marketing technique in most of agriculture and remains the most popular in several of the major commodities.

Before a farmer plants a crop, he needs to estimate the probabilities of receiving various prices and achieving various yields. By comparing the probable total revenues with the estimated total cost of raising the crop, he can estimate his chances of a profitable crop. If the chances of profit are slim, he needs to examine alternative crops. Once he selects a crop, he must develop and follow a marketing plan.

Generally, the most pricing flexibility is obtained with a marketing plan that includes a mix of pricing alternatives (e.g., pricing a fraction of the total output preharvest, another fraction at harvest, and the remainder later). The size of the fractions may vary with market circumstances and with the attitudes of the farmer. For example, if at planting time the farmer has an unusual opportunity to lock in very profitable prices, he might contract most of his probable crop, particularly if he fears lower prices later. Conversely, if prices at planting time are barely profitable, an optimistic farmer may decide not to contract anything until later, whereas a pessimistic farmer may contract most of his crop because he fears even worse prices later.

The choice of a marketing plan depends on other factors besides price expectations. Does the farmer strongly prefer cash contracts to futures contracts? What are the cash flow needs of the farm each month of the year? Does the farmer have on-farm storage? Does she worry about the financial soundness of the contractor or elevator? If grain is stored in or contracted to an elevator that goes bankrupt, the farmer may face delays and losses in recovering the grain. Is quick payment at harvest essential to placate creditors? Is the crop in such poor condition that storage seems unwise?

We suggest the following generalizations: By using a mix of cash sales, forward sales, and futures contracts, a farmer can obtain great flexibility in fixing the prices of his grain, oilseeds, cotton, and livestock. For that flexibility to be worth much, he must do his homework well. Surely, decisions so vital deserve serious study and regular attention. There is market risk in these alternatives, as there is in sales for cash at harvest, but some of these alternatives should produce returns that are less variable from year to year than entire cash sales at harvest.

Exhibit 7.6 compares various marketing–pricing alternatives. Below we briefly describe each one, using the outline and numbers given in the table. Futures contracts and basis are discussed in detail in Chapter 10.

EXHIBIT

7.6   Characteristics of marketing–pricing alternatives of farmers.

	Characteristics*			
	1	2	3	4
1. Price cash or futures preharvest				
a. M–P contract at fixed price and delivery at harvest	Y	N	N	N
b. Price fixed in futures and deliver cash at harvest	Y	Y	N	N
c. Price fixed in futures but store at harvest	N	Y	Y	D
2. Price cash at harvest				
a. Accept current cash price on delivery	Y	N	N	N
3. Price cash sometime after harvest				
a. Store on farm and wait	N	N	Y	N
b. Store at elevator and wait	N	N	Y	Y
c. Deliver and sell but defer pricing	N	N	N	Y
d. Accept current cash price on delivery but buy corresponding futures	Y	Y	N	N
4. Pool	P	N	N	Y
5. Production contract	Y	N	N	Y

*CHARACTERISTICS CODES

1. Quick payment	Y = Yes
2. Requires futures contracts	N = No
3. Involves physical storage risks	D = Depends on whether storage is on farm or at elevator
4. Involves financial risk of elevator or contractor	
	P = A quick partial payment

1a. An M–P fixed price contract made preharvest with delivery at harvest. The agreement (ordinarily written) specifies a fixed price for a certain quantity of commodity of a specified description (grade, weight, and so on), and usually includes provision for premiums or discounts for any of the shipment that deviates. It specifies a delivery period and penalties if the agreement is broken. Because it could be quite costly to contract to deliver more grain than is actually produced, crop farmers typically contract conservatively to allow for a short crop.

The aggregate use of these forward sale contracts fluctuates considerably from year to year. When sellers are pessimistic about future price levels, they are more eager to contract.

1b. Forward price in the futures market prior to harvest; sell and store after harvest. In fixing a price, the producer must allow for the local basis—the difference between a cash price and a futures price for a commodity in a given locale. If the futures price is unusually high relative to the forward contract price available at planting, futures contracts are likely preferable to forward contracts. The reason is that a seller may benefit from the narrowing of the basis. Conversely, if the basis is unusually narrow and the chances are that it may widen, then forward contracts are preferable to futures.

1c. Forward price in the futures market prior to harvest and store after harvest. If the basis is wide at harvest, then a farmer can often earn a good carrying charge because the basis normally narrows toward the delivery month. However, a basis that is unusually narrow at harvest is a market signal to sell the cash crop now rather than storing.

2a. Deliver, sell, and price at harvest. This traditional alternative has been explained.

3a. Store on farm at harvest; sell and price later. Home storage is a popular alternative among grain producers, providing pricing flexibility after harvest. If storage already exists, storage costs are low (how low depends mainly on interest rate levels). The price gain usually exceeds the storage costs. Harvesting and later delivery are more convenient. Some farmers just have trouble deciding when to sell.

3b. Deliver to elevator at harvest; store and price later. As compared to 3a, no on-farm storage facilities are needed, and responsibility for storage protection lies with the elevator or warehouse. Typically, the farmer has to sell to the warehouse at some point, because it costs too much to move the commodity to another buyer.

3c. Sell and deliver at harvest but defer pricing. The farmer delivers and passes title to the elevator. The farmer and elevator contract that payment will be made at some future date (ordinarily within a few months) selected later by the farmer. Payment will be based on the market price prevailing on the day selected, minus any specified discounts for this service. In one version of this formula pricing contract, the elevator's daily offer price is the market price; in another version, the nearby futures market closing price minus a specified basis is the offer price.

The buyer will likely hedge the purchase on the futures market, dispose of the grain, and have the use of the sales receipts, interest free, until the farmer closes the transaction. Because the farmer is in effect making an unsecured loan to the buyer, she should consider carefully the risk involved.

3d. Deliver, sell, and price at harvest, and then buy a corresponding amount of futures. This rather unusual alternative in effect postpones pricing until the futures contracts are finally sold. An open position in the cash commodity before harvest (or completion of feeding) is transformed into a speculative position in the futures market. This highly risky activity is not recommended.

4. Deliver and sell to a pool at harvest. The pooling firm typically pays immediately 75% to 85% of the expected final price and then settles accounts at the end of the marketing year.

5. Production contract. For the farmer who does not want or cannot afford any price risk, a piece-wage production contract may be the best alternative. These contracts vary somewhat as to specifics among the contractors of a commodity and to a greater extent among commodities. In general, however, production contracts specify for a particular flock of poultry or a particular acreage of vegetables the respective duties of the contractor and the farmer. For example, the contractor furnishes broilers, feed, and perhaps medications, litter, and fuel. The grower (farmer) furnishes a building and cares for and feeds the contractor's chicks according to directions furnished by the contractor. The agreement specifies a payment schedule for the grower's services. This payment is in the nature of a piece-wage, although the language of the agreement calls the farmer an independent contractor rather than an employee of the processor. The payment schedule may indicate a base payment of so many cents per pound of healthy broilers received by the contractor plus premiums or less discounts based on production efficiency.

SUMMARY

1. Although the forces of supply and demand determine the general price level of a commodity, individual buyers and sellers somehow have to set, negotiate, or otherwise discover the actual price for each transaction. Although most farm commodity prices are discovered within organized markets or by individual negotiation, some prices are set by individual firms, group negotiation, or government fiat.

2. The prices of livestock once were discovered almost exclusively in organized, public markets, such as terminals and auctions. Now, most livestock prices are discovered through decentralized individual negotiations on farms, ranches, and feedlots, although public markets are still used and are an important source of market information.

3. Prices for most fresh fruits and vegetables (and for livestock) are discovered through decentralized negotiations or in organized wholesale markets. The marketing flows of some fruits and vegetables are regulated by industry groups under the authority of government-monitored marketing orders. Regulation adds group action and negotiation to the process of matching quantities supplied and demanded.

4. Price-setting systems generally are associated with less day-to-day and week-to-week price fluctuation than price discovery systems. However, price-setting systems are still influenced—although a little differently—by basic, long-term supply-and-demand forces. Even government-set price levels must generally swing up and down over farmbills with basic changes in supply-and-demand forces.

5. The pricing efficiency of a public, organized market with equal access of buyers and sellers is rightly admired. However, as physical assembly in such markets often has high transaction costs, an electronic market without physical assembly provides a viable organized market for some commodities.

6. Marketing–procurement (M–P) contracts allow the separation of sale, delivery, and pricing dates and appeal to some agribusinesses and to certain farmers for a variety of reasons. Periods of instability of farm prices stimulate interest in the timing of the pricing of nonperishables and even of livestock. Farmers may use marketing–procurement and futures and options contracts to try to receive higher prices in the marketing period or to spread sales throughout the year in an attempt to guarantee receiving the average annual price rather than a lower harvest season price.

7. Production contracts have been initiated by agribusiness for reasons of market security and processing efficiencies. Production contracts involve agribusiness in the production process, whereas M–P contracts do not.

8. Farmers face an array of marketing–pricing alternatives varying from spot markets (settling everything now "on the spot") to M–P and production contracts. Agribusiness faces all of those alternatives plus vertical integration. The degree to which a particular marketing–pricing alternative is used varies greatly among commodities and may vary somewhat within a commodity sector from one season to another or from one region of the country to another.

STUDY QUESTIONS

1. Does price change more frequently in a price discovery system or a price-setting system? Explain.

2. What is an electronic market? What are its advantages compared to a regular livestock auction?

3. How can there be competition when there is decentralized, individual negotiation?

4. What is formula pricing? What are its pros and cons?

5. Do the forces of supply and demand have any influence on prices set by price-setting systems? Explain.

6. List several performance aspects of a pricing system. Compare the various pricing systems by their performance. How do you think they would be ranked on the basis of the transaction costs to the sellers?

7. Assuming a pork production contract, provide examples of how a contractor might ensure that allocation of risk lies with the contractee and that allocation of decision rights lies with the contractor.

CLASS EXERCISE

In your commodity group, for the commodity assigned in Chapter 1 and the agribusiness chosen in Chapter 2, discuss to what degree the agribusiness is involved with controlling the agricultural marketing system. Your group should be prepared to discuss with the class the characteristics of your agribusiness in the following areas:

1. Degree of marketing system control
2. Capital
3. Location
4. Corporate philosophy
5. Quality

NOTES

1. Steven Buccola, "Pricing Efficiency in Centralized and Noncentralized Markets," *American Journal of Agricultural Economics* (August 1985): 583–90.

2. Glenn Grimes and Ron Plain, "U.S. Hog Marketing Contract Study." Online [downloaded at www.agebb.Missouri.edu] May 2005.

3. Livestock Marketing Information Center, USDA-AMS National Daily Direct Slaughter Cattle—Committed Cattle Summary. Online [downloaded at www.lmic.info] January 2005.

4. J. MacDonald, J. Perry, M. Ahearn, D. Banker, W. Chambers, C. Dimitri, N. Key, K. Nelson, and L. Southard, "Contracts, Markets, and Prices: Organizing the Production and Use of Agricultural Commodities," USDA, *Agricultural Economic Report No. AER837*, November 2004.

CHAPTER

8

PROVIDING THE OPTIMUM VARIETIES AND QUALITIES

PREVIEW

- Grading is often an aid to communication in commodity markets. Grades may aid traders, producers, and consumers by contributing in several ways to operational and pricing efficiency.

- Trading on the basis of description reduces transaction costs and promotes competitive markets. Grades sometimes assist in trading by description, especially at farm and wholesale levels.

- In its most generic sense, grading is sorting the various qualities of a commodity. Such quality sorting is useful in any market context in which buyers perceive value differences among units of a commodity. But grading as used in this chapter is a special sorting by a third party (government) according to standardized criteria. Thus, grading usually achieves a special credibility.

- Consumer grades are a means by which the expert grader can assist the inexpert consumer. However, consumers can also benefit from many grades used solely by traders. Processors and retailers often rely on brands and labels rather than grades to communicate messages about quality to consumers.

- In the short term, grading is a sorting device—a means of sorting a diverse commodity into homogeneous bundles. In the long term, grading may be used to help redesign commodities. Such redesigns depend on the underappreciated fact that the qualities of many marketed commodities are alterable within limits.

KEY TERMS

grades
heterogeneous demand
homogeneous demand
quality
yield grades

An egg is an egg. A steak is a steak. Wheat is wheat. Ah, yes, but eggs differ in appearance, freshness, and palatability. A steak from a 12-year-old dairy cow and one from a 16-month-old fattened steer differ in appearance and eating characteristics. The wheat desired by a macaroni manufacturer is not the same as the wheat desired by a baker of white breads.

Obviously, the marketing system requires considerable communication and physical sorting. Somehow the differing varieties and qualities of already produced commodities need to move to those buyers who most desire them. Moreover, in the long run, the innumerable demands of the marketplace for all the endless variations of agricultural commodities must be communicated to producers to guide their production.

Relative prices, of course, are primary incentives to farmers and agribusiness. An increasing demand for quality A relative to quality B may be expected to increase the output of A relative to B, assuming that the relative outputs can be altered—and they usually can be. We will have more to say about this point later in the chapter.

First, let's consider how the marketing system communicates about diverse commodities and how it gets them sorted and directed to those buyers most desirous of purchasing them.

TRADING BY DESCRIPTION

Trading of commodities in the developed world is frequently done on the basis of description rather than by personal inspection of the items traded. Trading description reduces trading costs greatly and promotes competition and pricing efficiency, because both buyers and sellers can increase their area of search beyond the area where they are able to inspect the commodity. Obviously, if buyers and sellers are to make transactions without inspections, they must have descriptions that are accurate and reliable. Credit is involved in most large transactions, so the creditors also must have confidence in the descriptions.

Descriptions of commodities are provided in several ways. Many descriptive trade terms gain widespread understanding and acceptance. Such tobacco terms as *flue cured, burley,* and *Connecticut-Valley-Shade-grown* are very informative to tobacco traders. Grain merchants know much about the characteristics of wheat as soon as it is identified as red hard winter, dark northern spring, durum, soft red, or white. Produce dealers know the distinctive characteristics of Texas vs. Florida grapefruit, of Minnesota Red vs. Washington Russet potatoes, and of Jonathan vs. Winesap apples. Global dealers know the characteristics that distinguish cheese, wine, and hops.

Useful as these and many other trade terms are in describing commodities, they are seldom sufficient. One carload of Jonathan apples may be worth much less than another because the apples in one are not uniform in size and have many defects, whereas the other carload represents the peak of uniform perfection. One carload of Iowa corn may be 14% moisture, in excellent condition, with no heat damage and only 1% foreign material, while another carload may be 20% moisture with 5% foreign material. Identification of these variations in quality is essential.

A considerable diversity is inevitable in commodities marketed from agriculture. Nature is conducive to diversity. The printer of a textbook can produce 10,000 or 100,000 copies that are virtually identical. The cattle feeder or the grower of onions or apples finds it impossible to match the uniformity of the printer. Moreover, the activities involved with harvest, transportation, and storage often increase the diversity further. Perishable commodities receive varying amounts of damage and incur varying degrees of deterioration on their way to market. Grain can acquire additional foreign matter, additional breakage of kernels, and even additional moisture on the way to market.

When traders wish to trade on description, should the buyer rely on the seller to describe the condition of his eggs, apples, potatoes, or wheat? She may. If there is a continuing trade relationship between the two, they may learn to communicate well and to have confidence in one another. This is not always the case. Buyers may deal with many sellers and vice versa, so the two parties are frequently strangers. Misunderstandings and disputes about quality are much less likely to arise when there is third-party sorting, describing, and certifying. It is essential that the third party be expert and totally independent of the trading parties.

It is hardly surprising that the development and application of standardized sorting and descriptions for many farm commodities have gravitated to the federal government in the form of U. S. standards or grades. In many instances, the sorting was first instituted by an industry trade group, a chamber of commerce, or a state government. However, the need for national uniformity has usually led to federal standards applied by federal employees or under their supervision. Thus, we will discuss *grading* as the sorting of a commodity into quality classifications according to federal standards, recognizing that third parties other than the federal government sometimes develop and apply grading standards.

More recently, agribusinesses have focused on price incentives for quality. As technology allows for better assessment of quality, more commodities receive premiums for meeting certain quality requirements or discounts for not meeting quality requirements. Apples, dry-edible beans, sugar beets, chicken, corn, canola, pork, and beef are examples of commodities that have premiums and discounts associated with pricing.

QUALITY AND GRADING

We now need to define *quality*. A horticulturalist and an economist would not be likely to define the quality of tomatoes in precisely the same terms because of their differing fields of interest. Many agricultural economists would accept this definition: **quality** is the sum of the attributes of a commodity that influence its acceptability and value to many buyers and, hence, the price they are willing to pay for it.

Grading is then the dividing of a commodity such as tomatoes or wheat into classes. Each class has a distinctive acceptability to a significant group of buyers. The sorting is done according to a set of criteria called *grade standards,* and the resulting classes or groups are called **grades.** Grades are useful only when they conform to differences in demand. Whether and how much grade classes differ in market price depends on relative supply and demand.

Assume that varying qualities of a commodity are being produced and demanded. Then the task of the marketing system is one of matching supply to demand. One might imagine a system by which every unit of a commodity—say, tomatoes—is inspected by every buyer to obtain the best possible matching of qualities produced with qualities demanded. But such a system, if it were physically possible, would be fantastically expensive.

The market system has some shortcuts to reach equilibrium. Grading is one of these shortcuts. Assume that fresh tomatoes are sorted into three grades. The market system can give each buyer her opportunity for choice by providing her these three grades rather than the infinite variety of all fresh tomatoes in the market system. In this case, has the market system greatly curtailed the buyer's choices to provide an economically workable scheme? Not necessarily. Although it is probably true that no two tomatoes are biologically identical, it is entirely possible that all tomatoes in a grade are identical as far as the typical buyer is concerned. Minute differences in attributes that do not influence acceptability are not quality differences in any meaningful economic sense.

Grading Benefits Trading

Let us caution quickly that grades, as standardized descriptions, are not developed and used just for the benefit of ultimate consumers. In fact, agribusiness firms and farmers use grades much more than consumers do. Grading exists primarily for trading. This is true for several reasons. First, agribusiness firms deal more often without personal inspection. Second, credit agencies, futures markets, and even the supervisors of agribusiness employees demand independent assurance as to the quality of commodities being bought and sold in the marketing channel. Third, and most important, many commodities reach the consumer after having been processed into manufactured, branded products. Thus, in many cases they lose their original identifying characteristics. The consumer purchaser of a branded bread or cake mix may care nothing about the grade of wheat in the ingredients; if she is not satisfied with the cake mix, she shops next time for another brand. Regulated grade standards typically are not used to identify varying qualities of foods in the retail market.

Grading Is Ordinarily Voluntary

As a marketing convenience, the use of federal grades is ordinarily voluntary, and the associated costs are paid by the users. There are some exceptions. During the time of World War II price control, grading of several agricultural commodities was mandatory. Today, the federal government, as a large buyer of commodities for the armed services, often utilizes grades. Marketing orders for fruits and vegetables often use grades as part of their quality and volume controls. In several specific instances, federal grades must be used. Grains sold by grade for export must be graded by federal standards. Any cotton traded by description must use the federal grades, as must any cotton tendered on futures contracts. Tobacco also has certain specific grading requirements.

As grading is ordinarily voluntary, its use depends on acceptance at one level of a market channel, at least. For example, the widespread use of beef grades in trading among packers and retailers stems from the insistence of retail buyers; cattle producers, as sellers, have not been enthusiastic about beef grades. Although U. S. standards exist for about 400 fresh, canned, dried, or frozen agricultural products (running the gamut from anise to wool), some of these standards have virtually no use. Generally, grades are not used when buyers and sellers do not find them to be useful.

Because grades are a means of communication used voluntarily, they must be designed in reasonable accord with the desires of industry users. Because there are often conflicting interests within a market channel, a particular set of grading standards may represent a compromise.

CONSEQUENCES OF GRADING

Grading is used when its consequences are believed to be beneficial. As an aid to communication, grading contributes to both operational and pricing efficiency. It also is viewed as a safeguard for consumers. Some of the consequences often attributed to grading are really consequences of any kind of quality sorting.

Contributions to Operational Efficiency

1. *Saving time for traders.* The purchase and sale of unseen commodities by telephone or electronically is a tremendous saver of time and travel costs. Additional time and stress are saved because there is no need to haggle and fret about quality—it has been defined by the grade.
2. *Saving time for consumers.* Consumers may rely on grade labels rather than taking the time and trouble to learn how to inspect for quality and to perform such inspection prior to each purchase.
3. *Saving time for lenders.* Those who finance grain and other commodities from harvest until consumption must have assurances as to the qualities involved. Grades provide that assurance and eliminate the necessity for some inspections.
4. *Permitting mixing of separately owned commodities in storage and pooled sales.* Suppose that 100 farmers deliver wheat to a local cooperative for pooled sale. The amount and grade are recorded for each farmer at delivery. Wheat of a similar grade is stored together rather than separately. When the wheat is sold, the market receipts by grade are allocated back to each farmer.

Contributions to Pricing Efficiency

1. *Increased recognition of value differences.* Without ways to separate a commodity into different qualities, traders tend to negotiate an average price for everything. Grades help the producer of a top-quality commodity to receive a premium price. In the absence of grades or

other quality sorts, the quality that is cheapest to produce tends to drive the more expensive qualities out of the market.

2. *Better allocation according to demand.* Sorting by quality enables those who demand a particular quality to get it: those who want a top quality are not turned off by receiving average or poor quality; those who want a bargain and will accept cheap quality can buy it. Thus, quality sorting facilitates the market segmentation process. Grading is a popular way to do quality sorting, although it is not the only way.

3. *Better market news.* Price ranges for a commodity such as beef cattle are frequently so wide as to be meaningless, until they are narrowed down by quality classifications such as grades.

4. *Facilitating futures trading.* Futures prices are tied to specific grades. If there were no grade specifications, only the poorest quality of a commodity would be delivered. Such deliveries might not provide the minimum quality control that is necessary to futures trading.

5. *Broadening the market.* The ability to buy on quality description greatly increases the geographic area within which a buyer will bid. These enlarged bidding areas reduce market price imperfections. Although sellers could provide quality descriptions, buyers may prefer to rely on third-party grading.

Grades as a Consumer Aid

Consumers rarely have the time or the economic incentives to develop the expertise necessary for evaluating quality in the many commodities they buy. It is often argued that federal grade labels at retail should identify quality and eliminate the need for consumer expertise. A few commodities, such as beef and eggs, ordinarily are grade labeled at the retail level; most commodities are not. A particular retailer may have learned that her customers demand a particular quality of carrots or peaches, so that she uses grades in buying for her customers. Thus, her customers obtain the desired quality without seeing or even knowing about the grades.

CHALLENGES OF GRADING

This section presents some of the problems with grading in a question/answer format.

Do Grades Reflect Consumer Preferences?

Consumers have generally been friendly to grade standards, but they have not been a powerful force in obtaining them or in determining their design. Most grades were designed to fit wholesale trading, and many are of no direct interest to consumers. People go too far when they say there are no consumer grades. Such critics seem to assume that a consumer grade must be of consumers, by consumers, and for consumers. In this view, a grade designed by the trade is by definition not a consumer grade. Our definition of grading as the sorting into classes that have distinctive acceptability to buyers is a broader definition. If a commodity's grades are designed appropriately, they may help to satisfy certain preferences of consumers, whether or not consumers see the grade labels.

What About Subjective Judgments by Graders?

Grading often involves criteria that are not readily measurable. Subjective judgments and even subjective weightings of several judgments are often required. Grading services must consider these factors in training and supervising a staff of graders. Just as a first-base umpire must be prepared to call very close plays, graders must exercise judgment, except that the grader may call hundreds of such close decisions per week. To reduce the problems of subjectivity, standards include objective measurements whenever possible.

Are Graders Honest?

In rare cases, the integrity of graders unfortunately does become an issue. Scandals occasionally arise involving the bribing of graders. The assignment of grades to specific lots of merchandise may affect considerably the total returns to a seller. The federal grading service exercises constant supervision to minimize such malpractice.

Do the Grades Measure Quality as Perceived by Buyers?

A more fundamental problem related to accuracy is that the predictive relationships of grade standards to buyer-perceived quality may be imperfect, either because research has not determined better relationships or because research findings are not incorporated into grading standards. Most grades are probably quite accurate, but it is important to note explicitly that any generalizations about the usefulness or effects of grades depend on the tacit assumption of an accurate relationship between grades and actual qualities. The development of such relationships depends on a careful interpretation of market demands in terms of grade criteria.

What About Quality Deterioration After Grading?

A fresh fruit may be grade A in California on Monday and grade C by the time it is sold in Chicago the next Monday. Corn with 3% broken kernels in an Illinois elevator may have 10% broken kernels by the time it is hauled to the Gulf, loaded on a ship, and reloaded on a barge at Rotterdam. Traders must learn how to deal with these problems; the fault is not in the grades.

Do Grades Need to Be Identical from Farmer to Consumer?

Grades are useful insofar as they have meaning to buyers and sellers. But buyers at one market level may be interested in somewhat different qualities than buyers at the next higher level. For example, packer–buyers of slaughter cattle are quite interested in dressing percentage and yields of trimmed cuts, because these qualities directly affect the value of the fed cattle. Retail customers have no interest in either cut yields or dressing percentage but are highly interested in the eating qualities of the steaks and roasts and the proportions of edible lean to fat and bone.

Do the Grade Standards Measure Only Those Qualities That Are of Common Interest at Every Stage?

Eating qualities are important to retail and packer–buyers because they are important to the ultimate buyer—the consumer, in this case. Therefore, all of the factors that are important to buyers at any stage should be carried from the producer to that stage. Grade standards can be made multidimensional, and a particular dimension (e.g., cheese grade) can be used at early stages but be unnecessary at the consumer level.

How Do Traders Get the Grade Boundaries Changed?

Sellers want the highest possible grade assigned to their commodity. Because not all producers sell precisely the same qualities, any system of grade names and boundaries will be more acceptable to some sellers than to others. It is likely that sellers overestimate the importance of these grading factors. Economists often point to the uselessness of renaming A grade as AA in the hope of increasing market returns. But it is entirely possible that Mr. Brown's net returns are affected by a grade boundary that determines whether his cauliflower or cattle fall in the top of the B grade or the bottom of the A grade. In any case, many producers and traders believe that grade boundaries and names can be altered to their relative advantage or disadvantage. Consequently, industry pressures to change grade boundaries and grade names are common.

Moreover, such pressures occasionally obtain results. Grading is generally voluntary, and the very existence of the grading services depends on the maintenance of grades that are acceptable to the industry power structure (or a sufficient part of it). To respond adequately to these opposing pressures yet maintain standards that are of service and benefit to the industry and to the economy may require statesmanship. Sometimes, of course, grade boundaries need to be changed. Changes in production technology or in market demands may make changes in grades essential if they are to remain an effective communication device in the market.

How Much Diversity Within a Grade Should Be Allowed?

An optimum grade standard would divide the products into homogeneous groups so that all units in a given group possess an identical market value to any given buyer. There would be agreement among buyers that units within a grade were perfect substitutes in a value sense. However, for various practical reasons, the optimum is more than can be attained. If buyers are to accept a grade as a substitute for personal inspection, there must be minimal value differences within the grade. If value differences within a grade are significant, a buyer who buys a grade "blind" is likely to receive a lower-valued portion. In general, whenever a grade is so wide as to permit a sizable range of values within it, trading must depend on additional description or specifications or on personal inspection. In effect, grading is not then fully serving its intended purpose. Some specialized buyers of commodities, such as grain, may use a set of criteria in addition to or instead of grades.

What Is the Relationship Between Grading and Branding?

As we will discuss later, brands of manufactured foods serve as a communication device in a fashion somewhat similar to grades. There are important differences, however. Brands identify a product with its maker or seller; grades identify a particular quality regardless of the maker or seller. By emphasizing quality differences among sellers, brands tend to reduce price competition. Over time, brands encourage product research and development because the seller may capture gains when he achieves a better product. Grading, by placing foods into homogeneous classes, tends to increase price competition and to discourage private research and development. We think of grades for undifferentiated, bulk commodities and brands for differentiated manufactured products. But a few products at retail, such as eggs and canned fruits, may be on the borderline between those two categories. Consequently, at the retail level, there can be conflicts between brands and consumer grades.

COMPETITIVE RELATIONSHIPS AMONG GRADES

The various grades of a given commodity compete among themselves in the marketplace in much the same fashion as other products. The volume sold of one grade may gain while the volume of another falls. Relative prices of two grades may also change over time.

Whether relative supplies of the various qualities are alterable and whether buyers agree about quality are the two important variables in the competitive relationships among grades. Some of the variation in qualities is uncontrollable—it is a result of genetic and nutritional diversities in production. However, over time, genetics and nutrition can often be altered. Now that most cattle are fed grain, the percentage of cattle grading Choice has grown greatly. Moreover, some qualities are affected by harvest and marketing techniques. Inferior grade B milk results from poor sanitation, not inferior cows. Broken kernels of grain may result more from the techniques of harvesting, drying, and shipping than from the biology of corn production. The quality of most fresh fruit at retail is highly affected by refrigeration and postharvest handling. Hence, handlers have a great impact on the quality of most food products.

Demand for quality is defined as **homogeneous demand** when buyers agree on the ordinal relationships of the various qualities of a commodity. Milk is a good example. Thus, all buyers will agree that grade A is better than grade B, although some may be willing to pay 15¢ a pound more for grade A while others would only pay 10¢ more. In contrast, demand is **heterogeneous** when two or more groups of buyers give different rankings to various qualities. For example, one group might say that lean beef is best while another group says that fatter beef is best.

GRADING OF SELECTED COMMODITIES

We have emphasized that grading serves somewhat different functions for different commodities. Grains are examples of the many commodities in which grades are used strictly in the trade and do not reach through to retail consumers. The processing grades of fruits and vegetables and the grades of wool, cotton, and tobacco are not consumer grades. The most important items sold by grade on the label at the consumer level are likely to be beef, lamb, butter, poultry, eggs, milk, and a very few fresh fruits and vegetables such as potatoes. Except for milk, grading is not the same as inspection for wholesomeness. However, grading of food products in processing plants is not permitted unless the plants and the processing meet exacting inspections for sanitation and wholesomeness.

Grain Grades

Grains are a chief item of commerce in most nations. With the settlement of the rich Illinois prairie, grains became a very important item of sale for U. S. farmers and of domestic and international commerce. Traders at various market centers gradually developed their own grain grades, which differed widely among the many markets. Grain prices were frequently unsatisfactory in the latter part of the nineteenth century, and farmers often complained of unfair grading. European buyers were also quite critical of the quality of American grain. Although the need for national standardization became apparent in the latter 1800s, resistance to federal grading prevented legislation until a United States Grain Standards Act was passed in 1916. The act required federal grades and inspection for grain exported or sold in interstate commerce. The interstate commerce requirement was rescinded in 1968.

EXHIBIT

8.1   Rice grades, grade requirements, and grade designations.

Grade	Maximum limits of SEEDS AND HEAT-DAMAGED KERNELS				Maximum limits of CHALKY KERNELS			
	Total, singly or combined, number in 500 grams	Heat-damaged kernels and objectionable seeds number in 500 grams	Heat-damaged kernels number in 500 grams	Red rice and damaged kernels in percent	In long grain rice in percent	In medium or short grain rice, in percent	Other types in percent	Color requirements (minimum)
U.S. No. 1	4	3	1	0.5	1	2	1	Shall be white or creamy
U.S. No. 2	7	5	2	1.5	2	4	2	May be slightly gray
U.S. No. 3	10	8	5	2.5	4	6	3	May be light gray
U.S. No. 4	27	22	15	4	6	8	5	May be gray or slightly rosy
U.S. No. 5	37	32	25	6	10	10	10	May be dark gray or rosy
U.S. No. 6	75	75	75	15.0	15	15	10	May be dark gray or rosy

Source: USDA.

Grade standards for several specific grains were developed during the 1920s through USDA cooperation with the trade. The grading factors were measurable characteristics deemed important by the grain trade. Exhibits 8.1 and 8.2 list the USDA rice grade and soybean grade requirements. These characteristics include condition, foreign material, cracked or damaged kernels, moisture, color, and test weight. Grain quality is alterable. The amount of foreign material, moisture, cracked kernels, and condition are usually affected greatly by harvest and postharvest handling. Demand is generally homogeneous. Thus, prices and grades are correlated positively. Because grain is sold in large amounts (truckload, carload, or shipload) and because grade is a set of factors, it is possible and often profitable for a seller to blend grain purchased from various sources in such a way as to raise the average grade. On the other hand, the grade can deteriorate as the quality of grain does.

The grade of a corn shipment may decline by one or more grades during shipment overseas because of the increase in broken corn and dust resulting from loading and unloading. Buyers dislike broken corn because it handles poorly and molds more easily. Increased dust also raises the probability of dangerous dust explosions.[1]

EXHIBIT

8.2   Soybean grades, grade requirements, and grade designations.

Grade	Minimum test weight (Lb/Bu)	Heat-damaged (%)	Damaged total (%)	Foreign (%)	Splits (%)	Soybeans of other colors (%)
				Maximum		
US #1	56	0.2	2.0	1.0	10.0	1.0
US #2	54	0.5	3.0	2.0	20.0	2.0
US #3	52	1.0	5.0	3.0	30.0	5.0
US #4	49	3.0	8.0	5.0	40.0	10.0

Source: USDA.

Grain grading, like most grading, facilitates trading by description and market price reporting. Millions of tons of grain are traded solely on the basis of the grade description, although some buyers may insist on some additional specifications, such as protein level in wheat. Concerns about pesticide residues and mycotoxins may lead to further specifications. Because buyer and seller may be located half a world apart, grades are particularly useful in grain trading to minimize misunderstandings and disputes about quality. Grading also facilitates bulk storage and cooperative pooling. An elevator operator need not keep separate the grain owned by various farmers in the elevator when it is identified by grade. Futures market trading, which is very important in grains, would not be possible without some such classification as grades.

Beef and Beef Cattle Grades

The price reports of trading in beef cattle in the eighteenth and nineteenth centuries reveal a variety of nonstandardized trade terms for indicating quality. The first concrete steps of the federal government toward grades were intended to further the development of market news for carcasses and slaughter cattle during World War I.

Soon afterward, in the 1920s, the consumer grade labeling of beef carcasses was instituted on a voluntary basis because of an intense campaign of cattle breeders and feeders. As a result, a new concept of beef grades developed: the grade labels at retail were to be used to deter retailer misrepresentation of quality and to promote the consumption of fed (grain-fed) beef. In the 1920s only a small proportion of beef was fed in contrast with today's very large proportion. The large meat packers were not enthusiastic about government grade marking of carcasses, but they soon paid grading the compliment of imitation by developing similar private grades or brands.

During the 1930s, a sizable and growing fraction of top-quality beef was marked with either packer grades or federal grades. Beef in the lower qualities was seldom grade marked because a mediocre stamp of quality was regarded as a poor merchandising device. By 1940, only 8% of all beef was federally graded, which suggests the small fraction of total beef output that was top quality. The grades were marked on the carcasses in the packer coolers by federal employees.

Consumer grade labeling of beef received a powerful impetus from several developments. To reduce costs and monitor quality, federal grading of all beef was made compulsory during both World War II and the Korean conflict as an integral part of price control. All elements of the trade, and particularly retailers, became much better acquainted with grades. Demand for beef rose rapidly in the next 20 years as a result of rising postwar incomes and other factors. Feed grains were relatively cheap, and cattle feeding increased rapidly, so the proportion of beef susceptible to promotion through quality grade labels also rose rapidly. Grading standards were made leaner so that more beef fell into the Choice grade, which retailers wanted to merchandise. Retail chains began to utilize the top federal grades as both a procurement and a merchandising aid. Grades provided top retail management with an easy check that buyers were honestly obtaining the quality they claimed to be buying. Moreover, numerous smaller beef packers had gained a considerable share of the market once dominated by the "Big Four." Federal grades were a convenient aid to the bargaining power of the chains as they played the smaller packers against the larger ones. Several chains found increased consumer confidence in their beef when they handled and advertised only U. S. Choice Beef. With the postwar development of self-service retailing of beef, the grade label on beef reassured consumers as to quality.

Beef grades have been oriented primarily toward classifying beef in terms of eating qualities. It has been generally accepted that Prime beef is the most consistently tender, juicy, and flavorful, whereas Choice and Select, in that order, are less consistent and, on the average, possess less of those desirable eating characteristics. Research has shown that there is enough truth in that generalization that it cannot be ignored, although the grades are not nearly as different as popularly assumed. Within fed beef, eating quality of a particular muscle, such as the loin, is not highly variable. Moreover, eating desirability is slightly (rather than highly) related to the visual characteristics on which grades are based.[2] The quality grade assigned to most carcass beef is now mainly a function of marbling (the amount and distribution of flecks of fat in the muscling of the ribeye). The standards have been revised several times since 1927, and they allow considerably leaner carcasses to make Choice now.

Beef is characterized by homogeneous demand and alterable supplies. Prices are positively correlated with grades. Most fed beef currently grades Choice, some Prime, and less still Select, which is the most lean and generally least flavorful grade. The single most important question in beef grading is where the lower boundary of Choice should be. By reducing feeding time, feedlots could reduce the proportions of Prime and Choice and increase the proportion of Select. Market prices of these grades in relation to feeding costs guide the feedlots as to the optimal feeding time. The giant market segment for beef has been composed of retail supermarkets that have traditionally demanded Choice grade, although there is a trend toward many retailers selling leaner Select or ungraded beef. Many restaurants utilize Choice beef. The principal market for Prime is expanding as income increases.

Select-grade beef has a diverse market; it includes more and more retailers, government contracts, and some institutions. Aside from the most tender cuts, such as the loin and rib, the meat that is less marbled than Select usually goes into the manufacturing of ground beef, lunch meat, and sausages. Most imported beef and some of the less tender cuts and trimmings from the higher grades also go to manufacturing, which is a very large market in the United States.

In 1982, the USDA considered and rejected a cattle producer's proposal to change the standards to admit slightly leaner cattle into each of the three upper grades. The proposal encountered resistance from some producer and consumer groups and restaurant organizations. The difficulties led some cattle industry leaders to suggest alternatives to federal grading.

Beef grades now have a dual character. The second dimension is quantitative rather than qualitative. This dimension is a classification as to the retailer's expected percentage yield of retail cuts from a carcass. Customers are not willing to buy a heavy coat (bark) of external fat, as they rarely eat it. Many consumers are put off by the presence of fat. Consequently, very fat cuts must have considerable fat removed before they can be sold. The yield of retail cuts is largely an inverse function of the amount of fat in and on a carcass—the leaner the carcass, the larger the percentage of its weight that the retailer can sell in the meat case.

Yield grades are, of course, of direct interest to the retailer, packer, and farmer but not to the consumer. **Yield grades**—the classifications of beef carcasses (and live cattle) according to their leanness and thus their percentage yield of trimmed retail cuts—are numbered 1 to 5, with 5 being the poorest. Both No. 4 and No. 5 carcasses are usually discounted by buyers several dollars per hundredweight compared to the standard No. 3s. Buyers of live cattle are trained to evaluate cattle in terms of the expected dual grades: quality and yield.

Exhibit 8.3 is an example of a fed cattle grid that a cattle producer might be offered when selling cattle to a processor. The premium or discount changes for each change in quality and yield grade. For better quality and higher-yielding animals, a seller expects to be rewarded. A list of discounts for animals too light or too heavy and for problem animals appears at the bottom of the grid. The key point is that premiums and discounts for animals send signals to producers as to how to manage their animals. Processors benefit from better animals; therefore, they send price signals to producers indicating what qualities are of value. Alternatively, processors could raise animals themselves or contract production.

EXHIBIT

8.3   Example fed cattle grid.

QUALITY GRADE	Yield Grade				
	1	2	3	4	5
	($/CWT. CARCASS)				
Prime	$ 8.00	$ 7.00	$ 6.00	–$ 9.00	–$ 14.00
CAB	$ 3.00	$ 2.00	$ 1.00	N/A	N/A
Choice	$ 2.00	$ 1.00	BASE	–$ 15.00	–$ 20.00
Select	–$ 7.00	–$ 8.00	–$ 9.00	–$ 24.00	–$ 29.00
Standard	–$ 16.00	–$ 17.00	–$ 18.00	–$ 33.00	–$ 38.00

CARCASS WEIGHTS		OTHER	
550–749 lbs.	Base	Dark Cutter, etc.	–$ 25.00
750–950 lbs.	–$ 4.00	Bullock/Stags	–$ 25.00
Less than 550 lbs.	–$ 19.00		
Greater than 950 lbs.	–$ 19.00		

Note: Assumes Choice-Select Spread of $9.00/cwt.

Source: Schroeder and Davis, Texas Agriculture Experiment Station RM1-11.0, December 1998.

Certainly, demand is homogeneous as to yield, because all buyers prefer more yield to less. Similarly, yield is an alterable characteristic. Degree of fatness is partly a genetic characteristic but also is heavily influenced by length of time kept on feed. The problem for the feedlot manager is that quality and yield are negatively correlated. A longer time on feed will generally improve the quality grade and hurt the yield grade. Fortunately, the negative correlation is far from 1.0, so that high-yielding Choice-quality cattle can be produced. Nevertheless, there is a tradeoff, and much of the pressure in recent years to make the quality standards leaner is intended to achieve better-yielding cattle.

Hog and Pork Grades

Hog grades are primarily yield grades. They are used mainly for transactions between producers and packers and for related market news reports. They are not consumer grades.

Because packers rather than retailers cut up the hog carcass and do most of the trimming of fat, the yield of the hog is of utmost concern to them. Yield became of concern to leaders in the hog industry in the 1950s.

A greatly reduced demand for lard meant that hogs yielding a higher percentage of saleable meat (lean cuts) were more valuable than fatter hogs yielding lower percentages. These industry leaders felt it imperative that differences in hog values be reflected accurately to farmers so that they would be motivated to breed and produce the more valuable, leaner hogs. Thus, pork grades are another case of homogeneous demand and alterable supplies. The hogs of today are remarkably leaner than the hogs of the 1950s, although there is still room for improvement.

After researchers had determined the dimensions of the variations in yield and objective methods of identifying them, pork grade standards were made official by the USDA in 1952. These standards apply to young females (gilts) and to young, castrated males (barrows) but not to older breeding stock (sows and boars). These standards involved measurements of hot carcass weight (or length) and average thickness of back fat. The No. 1 grade was generally expected to yield 53% or more of the carcass in the four principal lean cuts (ham, loin, picnic shoulder, and Boston butt). The other three grades had progressively lower yields. To simplify the grading process, which is typically performed visually on a fast-moving line of carcasses in the slaughterhouse, the newest USDA grade standards were adopted in 1984. These new standards reflected the remarkable increase in leanness in the past 30 years; each grade yields 7.4% more lean cuts than the old grades. The new standards depend mainly on estimated back fat thickness over the last rib, with adjustments for thick or thin muscling. Subject to certain restrictions, carcasses with thick muscling are adjusted up one grade from the preliminary grades shown in Exhibit 8.4 for average muscling, whereas carcasses with thin muscling are adjusted down one grade. Today, pricing hogs on a quality system is essentially the norm.

EXHIBIT

8.4   Preliminary pork carcass grades.

Preliminary Grade	Expected Yield of 4 Lean Cuts[a]	Back-Fat Thickness Range
U.S. No. 1	60.4% and more	Less than 1.00 inch
U.S. No. 2	57.4% to 60.3%	1.00 to 1.24 inches
U.S. No. 3	54.4% to 60.3%	1.25 to 1.49 inches
U.S. No. 4	Less than 54.4%	1.50 inches and over

[a]Percentage of chilled carcass weight; reduce 1% for hot carcass weights.

Source: USDA Standards for Grades of Barrow and Gilt Carcasses and Lot Slaughter Barrows and Gilts, *Federal Register,* Vol. 49, No. 242. December 14, 1985. pp. 48669–48676.

Fruit and Vegetable Grades

Grades of fruits and vegetables are used mainly within the trade, although about a dozen consumer standards of fresh fruits and vegetables are used at retail. Apples, potatoes, and onions are the most likely to be grade labeled in the retail produce department, but even they are frequently not labeled. Whether grade labeled or not, they were probably traded on the basis of grades. Generally, the qualities of fruits and vegetables are alterable, although the range is often small. Demands for most fruits and vegetables are presumed to be homogeneous. Thus, grades and prices are ordinarily correlated positively.

The need for grades was recognized around 1900, when production became important in California and other areas far removed from consumer markets. The first federal grade standard was developed for potatoes in 1917. Since then, a comprehensive inspection service has developed that is available on a fee basis to anyone with a financial interest in fruit and vegetables for processing or for the fresh market.

This inspection service has a great deal of flexibility. The USDA inspectors will issue a certificate based on official U. S. grade standards, on a state grade, or on other written specifications furnished by the interested party. Shippers of fresh produce may obtain an inspection at point of origin to verify compliance with a sales agreement. If the sales agreement specifies that the carload of produce will be of a certain condition and quality on arrival, then either the seller or the buyer may obtain an inspection at the destination. Such inspection certificates greatly reduce disputes between buyers and sellers in the fulfillment of contracts. Large institutional buyers, such as large restaurants or schools, routinely may have all produce inspected on arrival to see that it meets U. S. grades or their own written specifications. Grades are frequently used in public market news reports on transactions at wholesale markets for fresh fruits and vegetables. Thus, grades contribute to both operational and pricing efficiency.

Many contracts between growers and processors specify payment rates by grade. Frequently, federal grade standards are used; sometimes federal inspectors are used as impartial inspectors. These same processing grades are often used by processing firms as guides to quality control within their plants. These grades are also used in trade negotiations between processors and retailers for the canned or frozen product.

Thus, grading standards are often used as a basis of trading even when there is no official federal grading. In fact, processors are permitted to use the grade name, without "U. S." in front of it, on their labels without prior government inspection, as long as the grade is used accurately. Hence, the system can function with less inspection without complaints. However, processing grades are not widely used on labels, as most sellers prefer to communicate with consumers in terms of brands. Some consumer groups, however, prefer grade labels.

Milk and Dairy Product Grades

Grades of whole milk for consumption are different from most other food grades. The grade designation on whole milk concerns the wholesomeness of the milk as reflected by sanitation and other health standards in its production and handling. Grade A milk has been certified by state or local authorities, ordinarily on the basis of provisions developed by the federal Public Health Service, not by the USDA.

The quality of milk is clearly alterable. Grade A milk has moved from a small minority to over 90% of all milk. Grade B milk is quite acceptable for most manufacturing purposes. Because the cost differential to produce and market grade A milk is relatively small and because grade A milk is eligible for a considerably higher price when sold as fluid milk, the trend has been for farmers to shift to grade A marketing.

The USDA does have standards for various manufactured dairy products, including butter, cheddar cheese, dry buttermilk, and several other products. These voluntary standards are linked with the mandatory standards of identity of the Food and Drug Administration (FDA). Note, however, that grades are different from standards of identity. As an example, for cheddar cheese to be graded by the USDA, it must conform to the FDA's standards of identity, which, for cheddar cheese, set up the minimum specifications that a product must meet so that it can be labeled and sold as cheddar cheese.

MANAGERIAL IMPLICATIONS

Sometimes quality production is a matter of pride. A farmer may try to produce and feed out Prime cattle because he wants to produce the best. Most of today's farmers are more market oriented. They watch the price relationships among grades and act accordingly. They know the usual market discounts for moisture in their grain and then decide whether it pays them to remove some moisture prior to sale. They know the usual grade-price discounts for foreign matter and broken kernels and then plan their harvesting and drying procedures accordingly. The price differentials between Choice and Good cattle and the discounts for yield grades 4 and 5 serve as guides to whether to feed that pen another 15 days.

The feed miller is conversant with the tradeoffs between the various grades of feed grain, so that he reacts to price differentials among grades. Similarly, the flour miller makes tradeoffs among the grades of wheat.

Agribusinesses are cognizant of the important value differences that vary within grades. Oil content, for example, is important to the soybean industry but is not a grade characteristic. The protein content of milk is of growing economic importance but is not yet a grade factor. Cotton has important characteristics that are not measured by the grading standards. Thus, agribusinesses not only need to know how to utilize the information in grades but also must recognize the additional quality information that is important to their trading.

SUMMARY

1. Grading is sorting for the quality of a commodity by a third party (government) according to standardized criteria.

2. Useful grades aid communication within a market channel about the qualities of a commodity. Grades are sometimes used at only one level, such as packer–wholesaler; other grades may be used at every level, from the farmer to the consumer. Consumer and agribusiness firms may have different uses for grades, so that grade standards of a product such as beef or eggs may differ somewhat at the handler and consumer levels.

3. Grades have numerous benefits. A consumer grade may indicate aspects of product quality that a consumer could not otherwise identify prior to consumption. A trading grade may tell a farmer more about products than she could otherwise identify. But mainly, grades are a quality identification provided among traders to eliminate the necessity of personal inspection. Thus, buyers are enabled to obtain efficiently the particular qualities they seek. Sellers may expect to obtain more total revenue for their products because buyer satisfaction is greater. Disputes about quality are minimized by certification of quality by third-party graders. Likewise, the opportunity for fraud is reduced. Market news is made much more useful by grading.

4. Grades contribute to operational efficiency by saving time and travel costs for traders who are able to buy on the basis of grade descriptions.

5. Grades contribute to pricing efficiency by facilitating recognition of value differences, improving allocation of qualities according to demand, making market news more meaningful, facilitating futures trading, and broadening markets.

6. Grades and grading of different commodities possess some significant differences. Grades of beef and pork carcasses do not change once assigned. The deterioration of quality within the marketing channel of perishables, such as eggs and fresh fruit, presents special problems because the later quality may not match the original grade. Similarly, the percentage of broken kernels of grain can increase sharply as a result of the physical stresses in transport, leading to differences in the grades between origin and destination.

7. It seems likely that the qualities of most farm commodities are alterable within modest limits and that the buyers' demands are ordinarily homogeneous. When both conditions hold, prices, costs, and quality variations within a commodity are correlated positively, and there is opportunity for change in the marketed qualities over time.

8. The design of many farm commodities can be altered considerably over time when changes in market demands make such changes prof-

itable. Hogs arc now much leaner than they were 15 years ago. On
the average, beef is now fatter than a half century ago because more
beef is fed in feedlots. However, fed beef is leaner than it was 15
years ago because many consumers resist fat. Numerous commodities, including eggs, fruits, and vegetables, now reach the consumer
with fewer defects and less deterioration of freshness than was common 40 years ago. Grades have frequently been the communication
device by which changing preferences were transmitted to producers,
who responded by altering the nature of the commodities produced
and sold. Changing demand must be backed by price incentives, of
course, but it is almost impossible to reflect price incentives without
a way to identify qualities, such as grades. Thus, grades in the short
term are a sorting device, but in the long term they serve to modify
the relative proportions produced and even to help in the redesigning
of farm commodities.

9. Although grades have numerous benefits, grading does incur costs.
Because grading is generally voluntary, industry participation is
based on whether benefits are judged to exceed costs. The high
usage of grades in trading many farm commodities indicates a positive judgment. Note, however, that grades are more often useful at
the production level than at the retail level; food processors usually
rely on brands and labels rather than grades to communicate quality
to consumers.

 **STUDY QUESTIONS**

1. Eventually, problems will arise when trading by description. Briefly
describe the problems associated with this type of trading and list
alternatives or complements to this approach.

2. Under what market conditions does quality sorting make sense? How
is grading a special kind of quality sorting?

3. Agricultural economists for the most part accept the definition of
quality as the "sum of the attributes of a product that influence its
acceptability to many buyers and thus the price they are willing to pay
for it." Why would a product's quality be appraised differently by two
different people? Distinguish between homogeneous and heterogeneous demand for quality. How can the quality–price relationship
alter one's view of quality?

4. What are the usual motivations to support grading by agribusinesses?
By farmers? By consumers?

5. How can grading be beneficial to consumers even if grade labels are
not on the commodity?

CLASS EXERCISE

In this exercise, your commodity group should research the U. S. quality grade standards for the agricultural commodity assigned in Chapter 1. Consider the following questions in your research:

1. How are the quality grade standards for the commodity used at the farm, wholesale, and retail level for pricing decisions?
2. How are the grading standards used to instill consumer confidence?

Your group should then prepare to lead a class discussion of your research results. In a follow-up class period, your group should be prepared to discuss how a consumer's purchase might be influenced by the grading standards and how a firm might guarantee quality above the standards.

NOTES

1. Lowell Hill, M. Paulsen and M. Early, *Corn Quality: Changes During Export*, Illinois Agricultural Experiment Station Special Publication 58, 1979.
2. V. James Rhodes, "Acceptance and Yield of Choice and Good Beef: Research Results and Implications," *Journal of Farm Economics* (May 1961): 181–96.

9

PLACE AND TIME ASPECTS OF MARKETING

PREVIEW

- A task of the marketer is to get the right quantity of the right products to the consumer at the right time. If she does poorly, she may lose market share to those competitors who do better.

- Today's shipper faces a fascinating and challenging problem of choosing among transportation alternatives. The deregulation of railroads and trucks has set off large-scale realignments of firms, services, and rates. Consolidation in these sectors has caused logistical issues.

- Huge amounts of grains, oilseeds, cotton, tobacco, and other commodities must be stored between harvests. Farmers and agribusiness must make decisions regarding commodity storing.

- Somewhat similar patterns of prices and costs guide those making decisions regarding both transportation and storage. In each, marketers incur costs of transporting or storing in anticipation of price gains that will cover those costs.

KEY TERMS

assembly

back-haul

carryover

common carrier

contract carrier

demurrage

marketing year

piggyback

private trucking

retail assortment

transport mode

unit train

working inventory (WI)

An American family of four persons will consume almost three tons of food per year. How much simpler the marketing process would be if this typical family would accept annually a three-ton delivery of a single agricultural commodity! Of course this family's unwillingness to base its consumption on an annual delivery of three tons of wheat, potatoes, or apples has a sound basis. Nutrition, desire for variety, product perishability, relative costs of storage in large vs. small amounts, financing costs, and so on all increase the cost and complexity of the agricultural marketing system.

A family of four in a year may buy 450 pounds of beef, 240 pounds of pork, and 800 pounds of vegetables. But those aggregates must be broken down further. These purchases are probably distributed rather evenly over 52 or more food shopping trips in a year. In a given trip, the purchase may be of 2 pounds of ground beef, 3 pounds of chicken, 1 pound of fish, 3 pounds of pork, 2 pounds of yellow onions, 1 head of cauliflower, 2 stalks of celery, and so on. The assortment of items in any particular shopping trip reflects primarily a replenishing of the assortment of this family's food inventory, which reflects the assortment of food products the family chooses to consume.

The consumer has a tremendous food inventory problem. To maintain balance and variety in the family diet and avoid running out of ingredients when they are needed, the consumer must maintain a large number of foods, ingredients, spices, and beverages. The limitations of spoilage (or quality deterioration), space, and money keep the inventory of each item low. Consumers depend on grocery stores to stock the items they need, so that home stocks can be replenished as necessary.

The structure of food retailing attempts to accommodate the consumer's shopping patterns and inventory limitations, providing consumers a convenient source of fresh, varied foods. Similarly, dine-in and dine-out establishments must meet regular demand for fresh products. As people's incomes rise, convenience becomes more and more important.

This chapter discusses the place–time aspects of agricultural marketing: transportation and storage.

PROCESS IN THE FLOW OF COMMODITIES

A typical grocery store stocks a wide variety of foods in relatively small quantities. At the various stages in the flow of commodities, however, the variety and quantity differ. A typical farmer produces fairly large amounts of only a few commodities, or only one, such as milk. The typical processor may handle only a few commodities, at least within a given plant. However, the processor typically handles many times the volume of any farmer, so there is a large discrepancy of quantity between the farmer and the processor. The typical wholesaler handles a much greater variety of food products than the processor but a smaller volume of any given product.

Although the marketing–procurement system is a little different for each agricultural commodity, the process by which the flow of commodities is accomplished can be generalized for most commodities. Wroe Alderson noted the following processes:[1]

1. *Assembly and accumulation.* Farmers from coast to coast produce a wide variety of commodities of varying sizes and qualities, and from January 1 to December 31 these commodities are assembled by a vast array of marketing firms.

2. *Sorting out.* Simultaneously, there is a process of sorting out into fairly homogeneous groups, not only pigs from steers but also, for example, lean, Choice, 600-pound beef carcasses from wasty, Choice, 600-pound carcasses. Quantities are accumulated for shipment in economic lots in cartons by truckloads, carloads, or even trainloads.

3. *Allocation.* Once these "big piles" of homogeneous commodities are accumulated, they are allocated or broken down into shipments to

various markets or intermediate buyers, which may further the processing arm of the original processor.

4. *Assorting (building an assortment).* Finally, the products reach retailers, who generally build up an assortment—a pattern of different products that will appeal to shoppers. In today's supermarket, this assortment is said to number over 20,000 different items. The **retail assortment** reflects the consumer's fundamental demand for a vast array of differing goods to be made conveniently available.

In general, then, we see the big picture as follows:

1. The assembly and sorting of agricultural commodities into giant lots of like commodities
2. The processing and sorting of what are frequently raw materials into still larger amounts of much more varied but still relatively homogeneous food products
3. Shipment, sometimes after long storage, to wholesalers and retailers who build a vast consumer-oriented assortment of food products

Transportation, storage, and processing are generally less expensive per unit when performed in large batches than in small batches. For example, single shipment rail rates for canned goods are much cheaper in million-pound lots than smaller lots. Thus, there are strong economic pressures to accumulate, process, store, and transport agricultural commodities in large lots.

TRANSPORTATION

The processes of assembly, accumulation, sorting out, allocation, and assorting are essential to a specialized and geographically dispersed economy. They are essential complements to the operation of comparative advantage. An equally necessary part of this integrated system is efficient transportation. To the extent that transportation is reliable and economic, a complex and specialized production and marketing system like ours is feasible.

Relationship of Location and Price

A producer's or retailer's mode of transportation is dependent on the location of consumers in relation to production. Price is the visible sign of that relationship. Producers have the ultimate job of getting the commodity to the consumer at the lowest possible price while covering their associated costs.

The Macro Task

Almost all agricultural commodities acquire place and time utility through transportation from producers to intermediate marketing agencies and then to consumers. The price gains that result from those utility increases must cover all transportation costs. Typically, the distances are hundreds of miles, sometimes even thousands. The demand for transportation derives from the demand for the goods at their destinations. The tonnage of freight transported is staggering in an economy as large and geographically expansive as ours. Trucks, railroads, ocean freight, and barges are the important movers of agricultural and agribusiness products. Although air traffic of products such as Hawaiian orchids or fruits makes splashy newspaper stories, the tonnage of agricultural air traffic is small.

Trucks carry most of the shorter hauls because of their accessibility, speed, and convenience, whereas other modes are usually cheaper for long hauls. Thus, trucks handle almost all of the domestic movement of perishables such as milk, meat, poultry, eggs, fruits, and vegetables, as well as the shorter-distance domestic movement of grains and oilseeds. For longer hauls, barges transport grain down the Mississippi River, for example, and ocean liners haul wheat from New Orleans to Iraq.

Generally, the more efficient and economical the transportation, the larger the tonnage hauled. Conversely, an inefficient and expensive transportation system will limit geographic and individual specialization and reduce the tonnages hauled.

The Micro Task

Agricultural and agribusiness users of transportation will find that tremendous knowledge is necessary to choose efficiently among transportation alternatives. We will mention a few important features.

The most significant consideration in transportation is whether the seller or buyer has the responsibility for transportation of a farm commodity or food product. Usually, sellers beyond the farm level will deliver, as an integrated part of their marketing efforts, although there are times when the buyer can arrange transportation less expensively or more to his liking and therefore accepts delivery at the seller's location.

At the farm level, transportation practices reflect various factors, including the regularity and nature of the farm output. Milk is picked up in large, specialized trucks on a regular basis. Packers take possession of cattle at feedlots in the high plains. Generally, a grain or soybean producer delivers his grain to the elevator.

Who operates the transportation equipment? It may be a hired carrier or it may be the shipper (for simplicity, we will assume this to be the seller). The hired carrier may operate trains, trucks, barges, air freighters, or some combination of them. All of these are used in agricultural marketing. At the beginning of the system, virtually all farm-to-market hauling is by trucks. At the end, deliveries from distribution centers to retail stores are also by truck—operated by the retailer or the wholesaler in the case of affiliated stores. In between, the picture is mixed. For reasons to be discussed later, any one **transport mode** (transportation method), such as rail, has net advantages in one situation but not another. **Private trucking** (in which a firm transports its goods by owning and operating trucks rather than hiring that service) has advantages in certain situations.

Grain accounts for a very large amount of traffic. Long-distance moving (interstate or export) is mainly by rail or barge. The variation among transport modes by commodity reflects varying areas of production and varying destinations. Barges on major waterways are generally more accessible to soybeans and corn produced in the Midwest or South than to wheat produced in the Plains. Rates for both barges and ocean shipping are unregulated and vary widely as demand or supply changes. These wide changes are one of the big challenges facing grain traders. For example, Gulf of Mexico to Japan Panamax-size transportation rates ranged from $43 to $73 per metric ton in 2004. In rail transportation, the best rates are obtained by shippers who lease a **unit train,** an entire train and crew to be operated as a unit at the shipper's discretion. In early 2005, unit trains (at least 52 cars) ranged from $22 to $26 per metric ton for wheat shipped from St. Louis to Houston. Shuttle trains (at least 100 cars) were discounted around $4 per metric ton for wheat shipped from St. Louis to Houston. Rail rates decline per ton-mile as the volume shipped and the distance increase. Not surprisingly, rail rates are affected by competition. When two or more railroads serve a grain area, rates are usually lower than when there is only one. Rail rates are even lower in areas close to rivers with good barge service.

Managerial Options of Shippers

Shippers must decide how to ship, whether to handle shipping themselves or use a carrier, and select a carrier, if necessary. The mode of transport is selected first, and then the choice of carrier is made. The typical evaluation process proceeds through two steps:

1. Define a level of desired service.
2. Select the least-cost method of meeting that service level.

Although conceptually simple, this evaluation process can be quite complicated, especially for a large food manufacturer. A number of items tend to interact. For example, excluding barges, the cheapest way to ship is by the trainload. Most grain now arrives at ports by unit trains. But only the larger elevators have the storage and loading capacity to handle trainloads. Food manufacturers and wholesale distribution centers likely cannot accommodate whole trainloads. Although that example may be extreme, it illustrates two of the numerous trade-offs involved in managing transportation. First, inventory costs tend to rise as inventory is accumulated to fill large shipments. The buyer may be much happier with a size and frequency of delivery that does not minimize hauling costs but that creates hauling and storage efficiencies. When defining the desired service, a transportation manager must consider what pleases the buyers as well as how the size, frequency, and mode of shipment fits into the shipper's total operation. Speed and flexibility of service are frequent reasons for choosing trucks, even though their rates are higher than rail. Even such mundane matters as the necessary amount of packaging to prevent product damage may tip the cost scales for a food processor between one mode of transport and another. Let's review the various modes as a shipper might consider them.

Barges

It is logical to begin with the transport mode that generally has the lowest rates: barges. Capability and accessibility of service are their obvious limitations. There are some 25,500 miles of navigable rivers and canals in the United States, but they obviously are not directly accessible to many shippers. Moreover, many miles of the waterways freeze in the winter, so year-round service is not available. Small-volume shipments are not economical—a barge in the Midwest holds about 1,500 tons. Speed is impossible. Barge rates for agricultural commodities are set by supply and demand. Therefore, barges are usually attractive alternatives for nearby shippers of grains and soybeans but rarely for shippers of other agricultural commodities that may spoil or that cannot be handled in large volume.

Rail

Rail service ordinarily has the next-lowest rates, although this is not true for all products. Rail rates are better for carloads than for smaller lots and are best for multi-carload lots. Rail rates are curvilinear with distance (cheaper per mile for longer hauls), so that they are much more competitive for long hauls.

Rail users must also consider demurrage costs of using unit car quantities. **Demurrage** refers to user cost for not utilizing the rail car(s) within a specified period of time. For example, a rail car company might supply a seller with a unit train to load out wheat and by contract specify that the cars must be in transit within 48 hours of delivery of the cars. If the cars are not in transit within 48 hours, then a penalty is assessed to the seller. The seller must decide whether to ship a partial unit train or to pay demurrage and wait for the cars to be loaded.

With about 140,000 miles of track, and much of it east–west, rail is more accessible than barges, but it is much less accessible than trucks, which can travel on 3.9 million miles of roads and highways. Except for special circumstances, train service is slower and often less reliable than trucks. Thus, a shipper must determine whether rail service can achieve her desired level of service.

Trucks

Truck service is more accessible, more flexible, and faster than rail or barges. Door-to-door delivery can be obtained from and to almost anywhere. Truck rates tend to be competitive for smaller shipments because trailers are smaller than railcars and common carriers are better organized to handle less-than-truckload (LTL) shipments.

Four types of truck transportation are obtainable: common carriers, contract carriers, exempt carriers, and shippers' private trucks. **Common carriers** are transporters such as railroads or truck lines that provide regular service to everyone on their routes, much as business and airlines do for passengers. **Contract carriers** agree to provide certain specified transportation services to a few shippers on a regular basis. For example, a contract carrier might contract with several meat packing plants in Iowa to haul all of their fresh meat shipments to the East. They are flexible and often have very competitive rates.

The fourth type of truck transportation is shippers' private trucks. A shipper operates his own trucks to obtain better service or lower costs. It is possible but not easy for a private fleet to be operated as efficiently as a hired carrier, which can better hold down empty miles than a private shipper, who typically faces an empty back-haul. The **back-haul** (the return of a transportation vehicle to its origin after delivering a cargo) allows commercial shippers to generate two income streams: the front-haul and the back-haul. Back-haul rates are often cheaper because the costs of returning loaded are not much higher than the costs of returning empty, although this is not true for livestock carriers. Although a shipper can haul his own goods without regulation, he can rarely haul anything except commodities for anyone else. Private fleets must be managed professionally to attain low costs and require considerable capital commitment (although the trucks may be leased rather than purchased).

Despite these cautions, private trucking is quite important. Private hauling is often best when delivery times are unusual, frequent delivery of small quantities is necessary, special handling is required, or there is a need for a bit of salesmanship by the driver.[2] As a result, most deliveries to retail food stores and restaurants are made by private trucks. Truck service involving new, specialized equipment may be pioneered by private fleets before the hired carriers will make the necessary investments. Private trucking has been profitable where carrier rates were too high. Private hauling also provides better managerial controls and allows better scheduling of loading and inventories.[3] In some instances private trucks may serve multiple purposes; for example, one truck might handle all products for one McDonald's. Each shipper must analyze carefully the advantages and disadvantages of private hauling.

Air

Shipment by air is the fourth transport mode available to the shipper. Rates per ton-mile are ordinarily several times as high as by truck or rail. Thus, airfreight is seldom competitive for food and agricultural products, except in special situations such as the overnight delivery of certain flowers and fruits to premium markets.

Intermodal

The final transport alternative is intermodal shipment. Least-cost shipment of corn from rural Iowa elevators to the Gulf may involve trucking to a nearby barge point or to a nearby elevator that can load a unit train. Long-distance hauling of truck trailers on rail flatcars (**piggyback**) combines the low-cost advantages of rail with the dock-to-dock flexibility of trucks.

Regulation

Twenty years ago, government (state and especially federal) regulations applied to most transportation and, along with competition, helped to determine prices and services. A century ago, railroads were the dominant and nearly the only feasible means of transportation. Although several rail-roads often competed in serving the larger cities, Americans in more rural areas were serviced by a monopoly. Competition was lacking, and in fact, railroads could collude together through Rate Bureaus to decide on rates. In the absence of competition to improve prices and services, society turned to regulation. As common carriers, all railroads were regulated and were obligated to provide a certain quality of service to all prospective shippers, without price discrimination among shippers on any given item. They were obligated to charge reasonable rates. The Interstate Commerce Commission (ICC) was charged with overseeing the fulfillment of these obligations, but regulations have disappeared over the last two decades. The ICC was replaced in 1996 by the Surface Transportation Board.

Railroads rather quickly discovered something about the varying elastic-ities of demand for freight services: Shippers of high-value, low-weight items had far more inelastic demands than shippers of low-value, high-weight items. Estimated elasticities of demand (what railroads called "value of serv-ice") were used to set rates. Specific commodity rates were set at lower levels for each of the major commodities that could not move long distances except at the lower rates. The many items that could pay higher rates were lumped into various classes and class rates assigned. Rates also varied by distance and by carload (CL) vs. less-than-carload (LCL). In addition, "in-transit" rates applied to various types of hauls that were interrupted for sorting, stor-age, and processing. (These rates developed after flour millers located on the way between wheat fields and consumers sought a cheaper through-rate that ignored the fact that the trip was interrupted to grind wheat into flour.) Railroad rates became so complex that traffic specialists were employed by large shippers to calculate the most advantageous ways to ship.

Price discrimination among items in rate setting was facilitated by the fact that many costs were fixed, and variable costs were low and difficult to determine with precision. Railroads, as the only commercial carrier, were expected to haul anything and everything. That they did—but they wielded power to discriminate that amounted to the power to relocate numerous economic activities. Hence, it was the job of the ICC to prevent undue price discrimination.

Then came the competition of trucks traveling on highways of the early 1920s. Truckers rather quickly "skimmed the cream" by hauling many of the higher-class-rate items. The railroads found it increasingly difficult to cover costs on the high-volume, low-rate items. Raising their rates did not help much, as high rates tended to divert more traffic to the trucks or to the barges that grew rapidly in traffic after World War II. The regulated railroad system was in deep financial trouble, especially in the Midwest and the Northeast, and the physical system was rapidly deteriorating into the late 1970s. To meet the competition of the trucks and barges, railroads had to have greater freedom to make loss-reducing decisions. Beginning with the Transportation Act of 1958 and continuing through the important Staggers Rail Act of 1980, much of the elaborate economic regulation of railroads has been remodeled or eliminated.

The common carrier obligation for railroads to provide unprofitable services has been terminated. The Staggers Act allows contract rates between railroads and shippers. In addition, railroads are free to set general rates as low as their variable costs of hauling freight or as high as 180% of variable costs. Rates any higher are assumed to indicate a lack of effective competition (market dominance) and thus a need for more direct regulation. In other words, railroads can now set rates within wide ranges in response to market forces. Moreover, rates can vary by secret contract among shippers of the same commodity, such as grain.

There remain various concerns about the functioning of the rail transportation situation and regulation. Smaller shippers often suspect that their larger competitors are getting much better contract rates, and the secrecy of the rates only increases their frustration. The rapid abandonment of branches and lesser-used lines has left numerous agribusinesses without a railroad. Moreover, because railroads pay high wages and have high labor costs, they hold down labor costs by avoiding business that involves stopping a train to leave a car or two on a spur or siding. Hence, most smaller agribusinesses in small towns use trucks. Bankruptcies and mergers have reduced the number of Class I (larger) railroads since 1960. Tremendous consolidation of railroads in the late 1990s caused bottlenecks as companies sought to merge information tracking systems and cut costs by eliminating unprofitable rail lines. Today, few railroads remain. Regulatory agencies are permitting the railroad companies to become few in number because they believe that larger railroad companies achieve cost economies through more traffic per mile of track and longer hauls and that competition from barges and trucks will prevent the railroads from gaining monopoly power in most markets.

Motor carriers were regulated as of 1935, but are not regulated today. Of the four categories of common, contract, exempt, and private shipping, the last two are most important to agricultural marketing. The general philosophy of regulating common carriers was much the same as for railroads, despite the obvious fact that the degree of monopoly among motor carriers was much less.

STORAGE

S torage adds time utility by making goods available at the desired time—it matches production patterns with consumption patterns. Some storage is unavoidable, in the sense that all agricultural commodities must be stored even as they are being transported, processed, and made available to retail shoppers. However, any movement through a long channel can seldom be a continuously even flow; therefore, there must be reservoirs along the line that allow for uneven flows. Large reservoirs are obviously essential for annual crops. Also, some processors, such as ethanol plants, have to have considerable grain stocks to meet end-user contracts, so they will pay for storage even when macro marketing signals do not favor storing. This is discussed in the section on convenience yield in Chapter 13.

Storage is costly. Those who store anticipate that the gains in price will cover the costs. Just as transport costs rise with the length of the journey, storage costs rise with the length of the storage period. Like other necessary activities in an interdependent system, storage costs cannot be considered in isolation from their total contributions. Sometimes a producer can reduce the total costs of production and marketing by spending more on storage (when it enables a greater decrease in other costs).

The Macro Task

Think again of storage as the reservoir that permits a more even flow of consumption. Exhibit 9.1 presents a stylized picture of the storage pattern for an annual crop such as corn or wheat. Note the large inflow at each harvest, the steady withdrawals through the **marketing year** (the 12 months between harvests of annual crops, or October 1 to September 30 for several crops), and the annual **carryover** (the volume of inventory, or holdings, of a crop at the end of its marketing year). In Exhibit 9.1 the carryover is shown in three possible relations to a **working inventory** (**WI**), which is the minimum amount of a storable commodity in the pipeline that allows normal operations by marketing participants.

Occasionally, as illustrated just prior to harvest 4 (H_4 in Exhibit 9.1), a carryover may fall below the working inventory. It should not be surprising that the degree of perishability is related to the size of the carryover. A highly perishable item that might be stored for only one month may have zero carryover, whereas the grains, cotton, and tobacco that can be stored readily for more than a year occasionally may have large carryovers. Storage plays a far more minor role in a commodity produced year-round, such as meat items, eggs, milk, and even some fresh vegetables. Because there is no once-a-year flow into the reservoir but a fairly even rate of production all year, the reservoir is much smaller (Exhibit 9.2). Even here, storage can be used to make consumption more even than production. For perishable products, storage is often in the form of cold storage stocks of processed goods. For example, hams can be stored for an extended period of time due

EXHIBIT

9.1   A time pattern of storage.

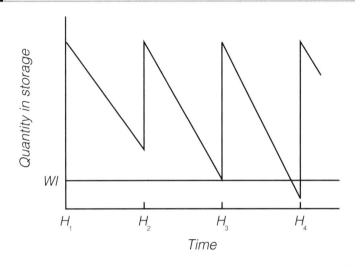

Quantity in storage

WI

H_1 H_2 H_3 H_4

Time

to the curing process whereas rib-eye steaks are typically sold within 16 days of creation. Whether storage is used for a particular commodity depends on the economics of storage.

Product deterioration and its control are major costs of storage. In general, the classification as "perishable" indicates high cost or even impossibility of preventing significant product deterioration in storage. Because of the impressive technological advances of the twentieth century, many perishables can be stored for weeks or even months, but the relative costs may be so high as to keep the volume quite low. Thus, there is much more seasonality in consumption of a perishable product such as apples than wheat because of the higher costs of the refrigerated, controlled atmosphere essential to apple storage.

The technology of minimizing product deterioration varies greatly with the product. Bins and the necessary practices to protect grain from the ravages of weather, pests, fire, pilferage, and other hazards are reasonably cheap and uncomplicated. On the other hand, perishable fruits and vegetables usually must be held in an expensive, temperature-controlled environment.

Storage of agricultural products occurs in two locations: on-farm and off-farm.

On-Farm Storage

The largest amount of on-farm storage is in the country's midsection, where it is used mainly for grains and soybeans. Storage capacity is measured in billions of bushels. On-farm storage is centered mainly in the chief production areas for corn, wheat, soybeans, and milo. Although hundreds of millions of bushels of feed grains (especially corn) are stored on farms and

EXHIBIT

9.2 Another storage pattern.

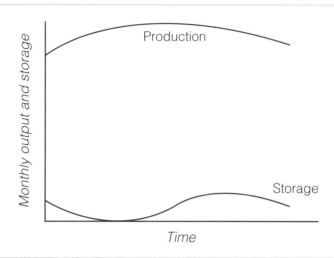

are fed later to livestock, most is not fed on the farm where it was grown because of specialization that separates the grain farmer from the livestock producer. Because most corn is marketed as cash grain, its storage on farms is a marketing function.

Off-Farm Storage

Off-farm storage capacity is also large. As suggested in Exhibit 9.1, much storage capacity used for grains and soybeans will be empty during the latter part of the marketing year as the reservoirs are emptied. The off-farm storage pattern of corn shows a much sharper variation (from seasonal high to low) than the on-farm, as reflected in the "Total" corn stocks line in Exhibit 9.3, which includes both on- and off-farm patterns.

Following are examples of products usually stored off-farm:

- *Cotton stocks* are frequently large. Storage facilities can be very simple, so the protective costs are small. Both U.S. harvests and foreign demand are rather variable, so sizable stocks are usually carried longer than one crop year.
- *Tobacco* (like cheese) improves with some aging. Trade-owned stocks just before the next harvest are usually larger than the harvest.
- More than one-half of *vegetables* (including potatoes) and about 40% of *fruit* are eaten fresh; the rest are eaten after processing by canning or freezing. Considerable portions of fresh fruits and vegetables are stored for usually short periods between harvests.
- *Ham* cold storage stocks are stored to meet seasonality in consumer demand.

EXHIBIT

9.3   Comparison of changes in on-farm and total corn stocks over the marketing year, average for 1999–2004 period.

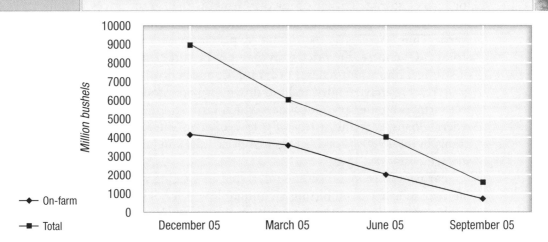

The Micro Task

Those farmers and agribusinesses that store usually have one or two purposes: to accomplish efficiently some associated marketing or production activity and/or to earn income through a price rise over the time during which the product is stored.

The second purpose is feasible only for less perishable commodities and food products. Most retailers, some other agribusinesses, and some farmers store only to achieve the first objective. Most storage is provided as an adjunct to other business activity. For example, much of the grain storage at harvest provided by a country elevator is intended to accumulate enough truckloads of grain from farmers to fill several rail cars for out-shipment. Thus, the elevator's storage facilitates a transition to a more efficient means of transportation than a farmer's truck. When rail abandonment eliminates some country elevators' access to rail service, one of their key economic services is lost.

We want to consider the following managerial questions:

- How much should I store?
- Where should I store it?
- How should I store it?

Although these questions must be faced by each and every market participant, we restrict our attention here to producers and marketers of grain. The decisions of processors and retailers are discussed in later chapters.

Cash grain producers store far more grain on their own farms now than they did 40 or 60 years ago. Their reasons reflect both of the gener-

al reasons cited above. Modern harvesting machinery permits a swift harvest; the resulting grain inundates typical country elevators. Storage in the
grain producer's own bins facilitates an efficient harvest. Another reason
for farmer storage (either on or off farms) is that grain prices usually are
depressed at the height of harvest and bounce back fairly quickly afterward. Thus there is a reasonable expectation of some price gain with
storage. Of course, the price gain may not be sufficient to pay all the costs
of storage. Important federal programs connected with price supports and
grain reserves have tended to hold down farmers' storage costs and to protect farmers against price declines. Much farm storage had been built with
federal loans carrying artificially low interest rates. Grain reserve programs in the 1990s protected against price falls and helped to cover certain
storage costs.

Farmers have also become interested in spacing their grain sales over
the year so as to avoid hitting an annual low price. They hope to outguess
market price fluctuations and sell at the yearly high. Access to storage
either on or off farms is a way to help implement that marketing strategy.
On-farm storage also allows the farmer time to shop around among alternative outlets.

The essentially fixed costs of storage are those associated with the facilities (bins and warehouses). These costs occur whether or not storage is
used. They include interest on the investment, depreciation, repairs, insurance, and taxes. Variable costs directly associated with the volume stored
include shrinkage, quality deterioration, loading and unloading, and quality maintenance (such as aeration and pesticides). Another major variable
cost of storage is interest on the value of the stored commodity. This could
be either an opportunity cost or the charge on borrowed funds to finance
the storage. At 9%, the interest on storing a $6 bushel of soybeans for six
months is 27¢ (not compounded).

Farmers with existing storage bins may hedge in some storage return to
cover the variable costs and contribute something to the fixed costs of the
bins. They may also store until January to postpone the receipt of taxable
income until the following year. A farmer may choose not to store because
his creditors are eager for their money at harvest. Thus, the storage decision
is an individual one; circumstances differ, as do storage decisions.

For most grain merchants, from the country elevator to the giant export
trading companies, storage is an adjunct to trading. One could rarely make
a living by passive storage. Instead, storage space enables a merchant to buy
and sell at separate times in a manner planned to be profitable. Storage
facilitates merchandising; in addition, it may earn some storage fees or profits. For example, a country elevator with a 250,000-bushel capacity may
handle 700,000 bushels of corn during harvest. It moves through 500,000
bushels at harvest and then fills most of its bins with 200,000 bushels. The
elevator might speculate that the price will rise sufficiently during the marketing year to earn good returns. It is, however, more likely to hedge in
whatever storage return that market prices allow. An exporter buys and

sells grain, as opportunities are presented, throughout the year. Sales and purchases are rarely of the same size, nor are they made on the same day. Thus, the exporter facilitates her ability to make profitable sales by accumulating grain and moving it toward the ports. She will likely use hedges to avoid the impact of large price changes.

Clearly, the storage decisions—how much, where, and in what way—are generally parts of more complex strategies of grain traders. Because storage extends into the future, the decision maker cannot be certain what the market price will be when the grain leaves storage.

SUMMARY

1. Great quantities of agricultural commodities are assembled from farms to be stored, processed, and allocated to retailers. Retailers keep large assortments of food products so that consumers can express their specific product demands at any time.

2. Transportation, more than storage, is mainly carried out by specialized firms. Most food transportation is performed by hired carriers: truck, barge, or rail. There is also private motor trucking (PMT) by farmers and by some assemblers, processors, and retailers.

3. Sellers are typically the shippers who arrange and pay for transportation of items sold to their customers. Shippers in isolated areas may have the option of a motor carrier or PMT. In other areas, rail, barge, and additional motor carriers may be options.

4. Commercial carriers have traditionally been heavily regulated because of their monopoly or near-monopoly positions. In recent decades, trucks and barges have provided more competitive alternatives. Consequently, competition has replaced regulation.

5. Shippers choosing among modes of transportation consider both the quality of service needed and the costs. Choices are often rather complex.

6. Most market participants have to do some storing because they must have working inventories to run their plants and serve their customers. A surprising amount of grain storing is done by farmers. Public warehouses provide a significant amount of storage, and grain handlers usually find storage to be an essential adjunct to their business.

7. Farmers store huge quantities of grains and oilseeds after harvest. They store for any of several reasons: for later use, in anticipation of price increases; because on-farm storage facilitates harvest; and because on-farm storage has frequently been subsidized.

8. Storage adjusts continuing consumption to annual harvests for major storage crops such as grains, oilseeds, cotton, and tobacco.

STUDY QUESTIONS

1. What are the basic processes in the flow of commodities from producer to consumer? Illustrate, using an example from the chapter or from your own experience.

2. Discuss transportation as it relates to modern grain marketing. What modes of transportation are used? How much competition exists among railroads in your area?

3. Define storage. Discuss some of the major problems faced by agribusinesses involved in the storage process. Consider processors, wholesalers, and retailers and such problems as product price fluctuations, product deterioration, interest rates, and availability of commercial storage facilities.

CLASS EXERCISE

For your group's agricultural commodity and agribusiness, create a report that includes answers to the following questions:

1. How does the agribusiness procure the commodity?

2. How does the commodity typically get from the producer to the processors?

3. If the commodity is exported, what is the process for moving the commodity internationally?

With your group, prepare to participate in a class discussion comparing and contrasting the alternative procurement and logistical processes used for different commodities.

NOTES

1. Wroe Alderson, *Marketing Behavior and Executive Action* (Homewood, IL: Richard D. Irwin, 1957).

2. Barrie Vreeland, *Private Trucking from A to Z* (New York: Shippers Conference of Greater New York, 1969).

3. Charles House, "Minnesota Co-op Seeks Damages from CP Rail: ICC Successor Gets First Grain-Railer Case." *Feedstuffs*, April 22, 1996, p. 1.

10

BID	OFFER	LAST
7.98	8.00	8.00
24.46	24.50	24.49
24.66	24.68	24.66
10.51	10.54	10.53
44.00	44.03	44.0
5.52	5.53	5.5
70.85	70.86	70.8
3.50	3.51	3.5
33.13	33.20	33.1

UNDERSTANDING AND APPLYING HEDGING USING FUTURES, OPTIONS, AND BASIS

PREVIEW

- Managing for price uncertainty is an important management function in commodity agriculture, as prices tend to be more uncertain than production. Commodity futures/options markets provide a mechanism for farmers and agribusinesses to mitigate price risk.

- Basis tends to be consistent seasonally and between years, so many agribusinesses profit from understanding basis trends.

- Futures and options are used by speculators to profit from anticipated price movements.

- Futures and options are used by hedgers to transfer price uncertainty, for a commodity they own or plan to own, between themselves and other hedgers or speculators.

- Fundamental and technical analyses are used to project current trends, a turnaround, or movement in a futures contract price.

KEY TERMS

arbitrage
at-the-money
broker
call option
commission
commodity basis
commodity futures exchange
forward contract price
forward pricing
fundamental analysis
futures contract
hedging
initial margin
in-the-money
intrinsic value
long (buy) position
maintenance margin
margin call
market carry
open out-call
options contract
option premium
out-of-the-money
physical delivery
put option
short (sell) position
speculating
strike price
technical analysis
time value

WHY IS A COMMODITY FUTURES EXCHANGE NEEDED?

A commodity futures exchange acts as a marketplace for persons interested in buying or selling commodities, based on information today and the perception (or concern) of where prices will be in the future. Buyers and sellers transact this business either to profit or to reduce the risk and uncertainty associated with price movements. Those seeking to profit through the use of futures and those seeking to reduce the risk and uncertainty with price movements are two different classes of individuals discussed later in this chapter. Commodity futures markets grew out of the need for certain parties to guard against undesired price movements over time and the desire by other parties to assume the risk of price movements in return for profit. Futures markets date back to ancient Rome and were established in the United States in the mid-1800s.

Domestic futures markets began in Chicago, as Chicago was then the center for agricultural commodity trade. Producers at the time demanded immediate payment, whereas merchants often had a lag between when payment was made and when they might sell the commodity again. Thus, creditors were quite concerned about merchants carrying on their books a large value of a commodity for which the price could change at any time. Therefore, the initial focus of the domestic exchange was on transferring this price risk away from merchants and to regional business persons who were willing to assume this risk in return for the opportunity to profit in the future by receiving the actual price the merchants received.

From this initial closed trading the Chicago Board of Trade was formed in 1865, allowing for more open trading. Information was made public, commodity quality was standardized, and the sizes of transactions were standardized. Developments of domestic futures exchanges have continued. Today, the commodity exchange serves many of the same purposes as they did in ancient Roman time or in the United States in the 1800s. The Chicago Board of Trade *Commodity Trading Manual* is an excellent source for learning more about the history of commodity futures exchanges.

A futures exchange serves three primary purposes:

1. The futures exchange is a place of price discovery, where persons interact to use assimilated information to determine a market clearing price based on different perceptions of where supply and demand factors will be in the future.
2. The futures exchange serves as a mechanism for persons to transfer cash price risk and uncertainty (for example, seasonality or weather scare) to other persons without the physical exchange of a commodity.
3. A futures exchange allows for public access to information for decision making.

The various participants in an exchange have differing perceptions of how supply and demand will change from now to the future. As these individuals interact, commodity prices are driven to a supply–demand equilibrium. A futures market contract helps facilitate this interaction by making it more efficient and less cumbersome than business transacted physically. As new information enters the futures market, perceptions change and the process of re-evaluating where next the market clearing price will settle begins again. New information is constantly entering the futures market, so prices are constantly changing based on how individuals believe the information will change price. For example, is an 11 billion bushel corn crop big? Some persons may respond yes, while others may respond no—their perception of demand may differ. These differences in perception cause the market price to change continually. For a given change in price, some persons gain and others lose. With every price movement, there is always a winner and a loser.

WHERE DOES FUTURES TRADING OCCUR?

There are many trading locations for agricultural commodity futures markets; however, Chicago remains the location of the main domestic futures exchanges. The Chicago Board of Trade (CBOT) is where agricultural commodities such as corn, soybean, soybean oil, soybean meal, and wheat futures are traded. The Chicago Mercantile Exchange (CME) is where agricultural commodities such as lean hogs, live cattle, stocker cattle, and feeder cattle are traded. In addition to these commodity markets, the New York Board of Trade (NYBOT) facilitates futures and options contract trades for coffee, cotton, orange juice, sugar, ethanol (sugar), and cocoa.

Other domestic and foreign commodity exchanges exist. The Kansas City Board of Trade (KCBOT) facilitates the hard red winter wheat contract, and the Minneapolis Grain Exchange (MGE) facilitates the hard red spring wheat contract and the Pacific Northwest hard white winter wheat contract. These exchanges handle other commodities as well. Outside the United States, the Tokyo Grain Exchange (TGE) in Tokyo, Japan, facilitates exchange of conventional and non-GMO (non–genetically modified) soybeans, conventional corn, and Azuki beans, among others. The China Dalian Exchange facilitates non-GMO soybean trading, among other commodities. The Brazilian Mercantile and Futures Exchange facilitates the exchange of orange juice, soybeans, and ethanol, Arabica coffee, feeder cattle, live cattle, and crystal sugar. As technology allows for better information flow and as countries develop their financial and agricultural sectors, commodity futures exchanges increase globally.

ELECTRONIC TRADING

Electronic trading has evolved into an important conduit for commodities future exchanges. At the time that this book is written, domestically there were only a few examples of electronic commodity exchanges. The Chicago Board of Trade operates an off-hours electronic trading exchange, which is targeted at allowing international traders the opportunity to utilize the CBOT beyond the 9:30 a.m. to 1:30 p.m. CST trading window. The Tokyo Grain Exchange uses a similar electronic trading mechanism for all trading activities. As opposed to open outcry, the TGE electronic exchange provides bid–offer information so that buyers and sellers can make buy or sell decisions without physically interacting. Electronic trading has allowed traders to place trades more efficiently, thus reducing transaction costs (commissions). However, the onus for user error falls totally on the trader, whereas when a third-party broker is used, the broker assumes some responsibility for errors.

BUYERS EQUAL SELLERS

In a marketplace like the TGE or CME, the number of buyers (**long positions**) equals the number of sellers (**short positions**). Exhibit 10.1 describes the positions of buyer and seller. However, no specific buyer and seller are obligated to each other. Therefore, a person is allowed to sell a contract or buy a contract at any time within the trading specifications for the exchange and for the specific contract. However, the number of long positions must always equal the number of short positions.

10.1   Futures market terminology.

Expect price to increase in the future

Price today

A market participant will be long (or a buyer) in the market if he seeks to profit (speculate) through the perception that the market will increase in the future or if he wants to protect (hedge) against an expected price increase. A person who plans to buy a commodity will *long* the market. The options term "call" is synonymous with being a buyer.

A market participant will be short (or a seller) in the market if he seeks to profit (speculate) through the perception that the market will decline in the future or if he wants to protect (hedge) against an expected price decrease. A person who plans to sell a commodity will *short* the market. The options term "put" is synonymous with being a seller.

Expect price to decline in the future

As contract months progress, the market enters a contract expiration month in which participants end up with zero contracts for that trading period. The expiration month is the month in which the listed contract no longer is traded. At the expiration month, the contract goes off the board and a new contract is usually added. That is, if a participant sells or buys one contract, she must buy or sell back one contract prior to contract expiration.

For some commodity futures contracts, physical delivery of the commodity to a predetermined location is allowed in lieu of taking an offsetting futures position (another contract). **Physical delivery** is the process by which a seller (short position) physically delivers a quantity, in proportion to contracts held, to a buyer (long position) at a predetermined location set by the exchange. Mostly grain merchandising firms, exporters, and processors use this option when the price is such that physical exchange at the predetermined location is a good business decision for the seller and buyer. At times, the price is advantageous for short position holders to deliver the commodity in lieu of holding it longer. Likewise, at times the price is advantageous for long position holders to accept delivery of the commodity in lieu of buying it elsewhere.

FUTURES CONTRACTS

n a commodity futures exchange, a **futures contract** is a regulated market mechanism whereby sellers short the market and buyers long the market based on their perceptions of expected prices for a particular month in the future.

Futures Contract Examples

Suppose Bill believes the domestic fall production of corn has been underestimated in midsummer, while Tom believes the domestic fall production of corn has been overestimated in midsummer. Bill therefore believes the price will drop, and Tom believes the price will rise. Using the commodity exchange as a marketplace, Bill sells a December corn futures contract and Tom buys a December corn futures contract. Assume that Bill and Tom sell and buy their contracts for the same price, and that their contracts are held by each other. In three months, Bill must buy back his contract and Tom must sell back his contract. At that time, both individuals will end up with no obligations—this clears the market between the two participants. Furthermore, the contract price is allowed to change in value freely during the three months, depending on changes in supply and demand for the underlying commodity, corn.

Depending on what happens to prices over the three months, either the contract will not change in value or it will appreciate or depreciate. Price changes will have the following impacts:

- No *change in value:* neither person benefits.
- *Value appreciates:* Tom will earn a profit by selling back his contract at the new, higher price, and Bill will lose money by buying back his contract at the new, higher price.
- *Value depreciates:* Tom will lose money by selling back his contract at the new, lower price, and Bill will profit by buying back his contract at the new, lower price.

So, is **arbitrage**—the process whereby a commodity is simultaneously bought and sold in two separate markets to take advantage of a price discrepancy between the two markets—through a commodity exchange really this simple? In some ways, yes. The rules of trading allow for the buying and selling of the contract at any time, and there is no minimum time an individual must hold a contract.

The scenario described above between Bill and Tom is called **speculating.** That is, neither party has actual ownership of a commodity, but both believe they can "outguess" the market. **Hedging,** on the other hand, is the process whereby a person who owns, or plans to own, the commodity uses the commodity futures markets to transfer their price risk or establish a price for the commodity. We will discuss hedging later in the chapter.

Futures Price Quotes

Exhibits 10.2 and 10.3 show typical futures price quote tables for the Chicago Mercantile Exchange feeder cattle futures contract and Chicago Board of Trade corn futures contract. The futures prices represent what the market believes the price will be for the month listed, given all available information at the present time. (Buyers equal sellers, so supply equals demand, resulting in an equilibrium price.) Exhibit 10.2 is read by moving left to right across columns, as follows:

- *Column 1:* "Contract" represents the month and year of the feeder cattle futures contract for which the price quote is given. For instance, Jan 06 refers to the futures contract due to expire in January 2006. The price quote (Column 5) is what buyers and sellers expect the price to be in January 2006, on July 15, 2005.
- *Column 2:* "Open" represents the opening futures price for the trading day.
- *Column 3:* "High" represents the high bid for the trading day.
- *Column 4:* "Low" represents the low bid for the trading day.
- *Column 5:* "Last" represents the most recent bid of the trading day. For example, at 10:30 a.m., the last value would be the most recent bid, and the high and low would be the high and low bids of the day up until 10:30 a.m. "Last" is the price buyers and sellers use to evaluate whether to enter the futures market.
- *Column 6:* "Change" is the price level change between the "Last" value stated and the "Last" for the previous trading day. For example,

EXHIBIT

10.2 Chicago Mercantile Exchange feeder cattle futures price quotes for July 15, 2005.

Contract	OPEN	HIGH	LOW	LAST	Change
Aug 05	109350	109550	107925	108125	−1425
Sept 05	108100	108500	106700	107150	−1300
Oct 05	106750	106950	105450	105775	−1400
Nov 05	104600	104600	103550	104050	−750
Jan 06	101400	101450	100600	100700	−850
Mar 06	98000	98000	97300	97700	−1200
Apr 06	97400	97600	97150	97600	−900

Note: The price quote of cents per lb. can be expressed in dollars per hundredweight (cwt.); e.g., $107.15/cwt. for the September 2005 last price.

EXHIBIT

10.3   Chicago Board of Trade corn futures price quotes for July 15, 2005.

Contract	OPEN	HIGH	LOW	LAST	Volume	Open Interest
Jul 05	2430	2460	2420	2452	4544	1775
Sep 05	2494	2544	2476	2504	41602	301282
Dec 05	2604	2650	2580	2616	98956	298199
Mar 06	2666	2700	2640	2672	4896	42906
May 06	2690	2710	2654	2700	920	7412
Jul 06	2710	2730	2660	2720	1207	15271
Dec 06	2600	2610	2584	2604	2763	18539
Dec 07	2590	2590	2574	2590	32	1235

Note: The price quote is cents per bushel, where the last digit of the number refers to a quarter of a cent (2=1/4, 4=1/2, 6=3/4). The prices may be expressed in dollars per bushel; e.g., $2.505/bushel for the September 2005 last price.

a change of $1 indicates that the most recent feeder cattle price quote is $1 greater than the close from the previous trading day.

In Exhibit 10.3, the first five columns are the same as those in Exhibit 10.2. However, we have added two additional columns that are typically reported:

- *Column 6:* "Volume" represents the number of short or long contracts traded so far that day. For the September 2005 corn futures contract, a volume of 41,602 indicates that 41,602 short positions *and* 41,602 long positions have been taken on that trading day.
- *Column 7:* "Open interest" is the total number of the short and long positions held for the contract since its inception. For the September 2005 corn futures contract, an open interest of 301,282 means that as of July 15, 2005, a total of 301,282 short and 301,282 long positions are being held by sellers and buyers for that contract.

Weekly averages are sometimes reported by news services. These prices reflect the low, high, and close for the week. It is not possible to determine on what day of the week the low or high occurred through weekly quotes.

OPTIONS CONTRACTS

An **options contract** is a derivative of a futures contract that gives a party the right, but not the obligation, to take a position in a specific futures contract at a specific price at any time during the life of the option. Thus, the term "option" refers to an option to get in the futures contract at a predetermined price level.

A **put option** gives the individual the right but not the obligation to *sell* a futures contract at a specified price during a specific time period. A **call option** gives the individual the right but not the obligation to *buy* a futures contract at a later date. Unlike the case of the futures contracts, buyers and sellers of options will not offset each other's positions. In the options market, there are writers of options. These people are like an insurance agency. A writer of an option is willing to take a set premium per unit of commodity in exchange for the risk that the commodity price may move against him. The price at which the futures market can be entered under an option is referred to as the **strike price**. The strike price is a predetermined range of values that is different for each commodity.

Options contracts offer a range of strike prices so that purchasers of options can choose the level at which they may want eventually to take a futures position. At any given time, the range of strike prices quoted will cover values *in-the-money, at-the-money,* and *out-of-the-money.* In, at, and out refer to where the strike price is relative to the underlying futures contract price, as follows:

- **in-the-money:** A put (sell) option is said to be in-the-money if the strike price is *above* the underlying futures price, whereas a call (buy) option is said to be in-the-money if the strike price is *below* the underlying futures price.
- **at-the-money:** Both the put (sell) and call (buy) options are said to be at-the-money if the strike price is *equal* to the underlying futures price.
- **out-of-the-money:** A put (sell) option is said to be out-of-the-money if the strike price is *below* the underlying futures price. A call (buy) option is said to be out-of-the-money if the strike price is *above* the underlying futures price.

A hedger or speculator has the option of purchasing an option at any of these levels. Note that because prices change constantly, the strike price relative to the futures price, and thus the terminology (in-, out-, and at-) also change.

Value of the Option

Two components make up the value of the option: intrinsic and time value. Both of these values are implicit—not observed, but theoretically present.

The **intrinsic value** is the value of the option relative to the underlying futures price. For example, a $76/cwt. put option for feeder cattle has an intrinsic value of $2.50/cwt. if the underlying futures is priced at $73.50/cwt. ($76 − $73.50) This is because the put option could be exercised (one could sell a futures contract at $76/cwt. and buy back at $73.50/cwt.). Typically, a change in intrinsic value of an option is determined by a change in the futures price. However, the change in option price is typically not as large for out-of-the-money and at-the-money options.

The value of an option also has a time component. The **time value** reflects the time between the option premium quote and contract expiration. Typically, the larger the time period, the greater the implicit time value of the option. That is, the greater number of days until contract expiration, the higher the probability that the futures market will change in value enough to improve the intrinsic value of the option.

The **option premium** is the value that a hedger or speculator pays for the right to take a futures position later. The premium is based on the option's intrinsic value (the difference between the strike price and the underlying futures price) and time value (the number of days remaining until expiration of the contract).

Options Contract Examples

Suppose Bill believes that the domestic fall production of corn has been underestimated in midsummer. Using the commodity exchange as a marketplace, Bill purchases the right to sell a futures contract (put) at a predetermined price at a later date, since he believes corn prices are destined to go lower.

If Bill purchases the right to sell (put) a future contract for corn at a later date at a strike price of $2.60/bushel for a premium of $0.15/bushel, and the futures price is at $2.70/bushel that day, then Bill would initially pay the commodity broker $750 (5,000 bushels x $0.15) plus commissions. The $750 would go to the writer of the option. Why would someone write this option? Because if the price does not decline, or if the price rises, the premium will decline over time and the option writer will profit $750 less commissions. However, suppose the futures market price decreases to $2.40/bushel and the premium increases to $0.35/bushel. Then the option would be worth $1,750 for the 5,000-bushel contract. Note that generally there is not a one-to-one relationship between a change in the futures market price and the option premium, due to less risk in the options market. Bill could sell the option for $0.35/bushel, profiting $0.20/bushel ($1,750 received – $750 paid out = $1,000).

Alternatively, suppose Tom purchases the right to buy (call) a futures contract for corn at a later date at a strike price of $2.60/bushel for a premium of $0.25/bushel, and the futures price is at $2.70/bushel that day. Tom pays a higher premium because he is buying an in-the-money call option. Then Tom would initially pay the commodity broker $1,250 (5,000 bushels x $0.25) plus commissions. The $1,250 would go to the writer of the option. Suppose the futures market price decreased to $2.40/bushel and the premium decreased to $0.05/bushel. Then the option would be worth $250 for the 5,000-bushel contract. Thus, Tom would now have to sell the option for $0.05/bushel and incur a loss of $0.20/bushel ($250 received – $1,250 paid out = –$1,000). Note that Tom incurs a loss because the price decreased, whereas Tom would have incurred a gain if the price had increased.

Options Price Quotes

Exhibit 10.4 shows a typical options price quote table for the Chicago Board of Trade corn options contract. Assume that the underlying futures contract price for the December 2005 CBOT corn futures contract is $2.6175/bushel. The table is read by moving left to right across columns, as follows:

- *Column 1:* "Contract" represents the month of interest.
- *Column 2:* "Strike" represents the futures price for which the call (C) or put (P) option contract is currently traded. Notice that many strike prices are listed. This table does not list all the strike prices for this specific contract.
- *Column 3:* "In, At, Out" indicates the relationship between the strike price and the underlying futures price. Note that this information is not specified on a typical options pricing table, but the information is given here for learning purposes.
- *Column 4:* "Open" represents the opening options premium for the day. For instance, a $0.35/bushel open premium for a $2.30/bushel call option was bid at the beginning of the day.

EXHIBIT

10.4   Chicago Board of Trade corn options price quotes for December 2005 futures contract on July 15, 2005 (underlying futures prices is $2.6175/bushel).

Contract	Strike	In, at, out	OPEN	HIGH	LOW	LAST
Dec 05	2300P	Out-of-the-money put	60	70	50	56
Dec 05	2300C	In-the-money call	350	390	350	370
Dec 05	2400P	Out-of-the-money put	80	102	80	92
Dec 05	2400C	In-the-money call	290	330	280	304
Dec 05	2500P	Out-of-the-money put	130	144	120	134
Dec 05	2500C	In-the-money call	260	274	234	250
Dec 05	2600P	At-the-money put	200	210	174	187
Dec 05	2600C	At-the-money call	200	240	190	205
Dec 05	2700P	In-the-money put	250	250	250	250
Dec 05	2700C	Out-of-the-money call	164	190	150	167
Dec 05	2800P	In-the-money put	312	330	312	320
Dec 05	2800C	Out-of-the-money call	140	150	140	137
Dec 05	3000P	In-the-money put	470	480	470	472
Dec 05	3000C	Out-of-the-money call	90	100	80	93

- *Column 5:* "High" represents the high premium for the day.
- *Column 6:* "Low" represents the low premium for the day.
- *Column 7:* "Last" is the most recent premium, or the last price for the trading day.

The value quoted for the option (column 4, 5, 6, or 7) is referred to as the premium. The amount of the premium is related to the strike price. Typically, options in-the-money will have the highest premiums, followed by options at-the-money, and options out-of-the-money will be the lowest. Note that the $2.60/bushel strike put and call options are at-the-money—these strike prices represent the value closest to the underlying futures price of $2.6175/bushel. At lower prices, the put is out-of-the money and the call is in-the-money. At higher prices, the put is in-the-money and the call is out-of-the money.

HEDGING

As stated previously, hedging is the process whereby a person who owns, or plans to own, a commodity uses the commodity futures market to transfer the risk or establish a price for the commodity to be sold at a later date.

When to Hedge

By knowing the enterprise cost of production, a farmer can determine at what prices he might consider **forward pricing** (establishing a future price today for delivery in the future) for portions of his crop. Thus, it is imperative that a producer knows the cost of production when hedging a commodity. For instance, if Calvin the cattle farmer knows that his cost of production on 800-pound feeder calves is $75/cwt., then he might consider forward pricing a portion of his calf crop through the futures market when the futures market price allows Calvin to cover his cost of production plus a profit margin. Because producers have a tendency to want to price at the market high, which is not feasible, it is important that they determine and target an acceptable profit margin. This practice allows them to focus on smoothing out price variability.

Placing a Hedge

Placing a hedge is a simple process. To place a hedge, a person contacts a **broker** and places an order. Most large communities have a broker, who will take an order for a set fee known as a brokerage fee or commission. For the fee, the broker will also provide guidance on how to appropriately place and exit a hedging position. Alternatively, Web-based brokerage firms charge lower fees but offer fewer services. After an individual has placed an order, the broker contacts a brokerage house at the commodity exchange and relays the order. When the order reaches the trading floor of the trading exchange, traders use **open out-call** (verbal sell and buy signals) to match supply and demand. For any hedge that a farmer or agribusiness wishes to place, there will always be either another producer wanting to place a contrary hedge or a speculator willing to take a contrary position for the right price.

Hedging Costs

The costs of hedging are straightforward; however, these expenses can become substantial over time. The primary costs are commissions and margins. **Commissions** are paid to a broker to cover administrative costs, futures exchange operation, and futures exchange regulation. Commissions can range from $9 to $35 or more per order. An order is either a buy or sell order. Therefore, to enter and exit the market, the total costs can range from $18 to $70 or more.

Margin money is paid only on futures positions, not on options positions. The **initial margin** refers to earnest money placed in a brokerage account to cover potential losses. An initial margin is required to start trading. Typically, a futures position requires an initial margin equal to some percentage of the actual cost of the contract being traded, generally between 3% and 10%. For example, a 5,000-bushel corn contract may require an initial margin of $750. The exact percentage is determined by the futures exchange.

The **maintenance margin** is a set level below which the initial margin account cannot drop. It is used to maintain a certain level in the margin account, which can drop because of losses in the market. For instance, suppose the maintenance margin on the corn contract is $500. Whenever the initial margin account drops below $500, the account holder must add to it so that the balance is $750. Whenever necessary, the broker issues a **margin call,** a signal that the contract holder must add funds to the account.

A purchaser of a put or call option must pay the entire amount up front. If you are buying one 5,000-bushel HRW wheat put option and paying a premium of $.20/bushel, then you will pay the brokerage house $1,000 plus commission. This is the most you can lose, and there will be no margin calls.

When a brokerage account balance is higher than the maintenance margin, the account holder may withdraw profits at any time.

INFORMATION AND FUTURES PRICE MOVEMENTS

Information—and how buyers and sellers interpret information—is the cause of futures market movements. **Fundamental analysis** is the use of market and commodity information to predict future price direction. The general availability of information to all market participants is called *symmetric information.* Although market participants all have access to the same data, they assess that data in different ways. In addition, some market participants may have access to private information. This is called *asymmetric information.* Some market participants may use technical signals to trigger buy and sell signals. **Technical analysis** is the charting of trends in current and historical price and trading (volume and open interest) patterns to predict future price direction.

Exhibit 10.5 provides morning, mid-day, and closing comments for the CBOT soybean futures contract. Notice how information impacts the price level. Exhibit 10.6 provides an example of how one might use technical signals to guide buying and selling.

EXHIBIT

10.5   Impact of information on futures market prices, July 14, 2005.

Morning comments

SOYBEANS August soybean futures were up 12 3/4 cents yesterday, closing at $7.14. August soybean meal gained $2.30 per ton to $221.20, while August soybean oil added 39 points to finish at 25.43 cents per pound. Hot and dry forecasts for next week across the Corn Belt boosted prices early in the session yesterday. The lack of meaningful rainfall from Dennis in most areas also suggested that crop ratings are still declining, perhaps across much of the belt this week. The U.S. crush continues at a record fast pace, but reported only monthly, and export movement is very slow at this time of year. Consequently, weather and technical considerations are the dominant inputs to price discovery. It is too early to kill off the soybean crop now, however, so weather forecasts will continue to be the driving force behind this market.

Mid-day comments

SOYBEAN trade is sharply higher on continued weather concerns. Beans are now 16 to 18 cents higher on the day, with meal $6 to $7 higher and bean oil up 45 points. There's good upward momentum in this market; without a major turn in the weather picture next week, the next price target will be the contract highs. Weekly export sales were neutral, coming in at 175 thousand metric tons versus expectations of 60 to 200 thousand metric tons. Meal and bean oil sales also fell within expectations. The NOPA crush number was down 11 million bushels from last month, but up 23 million bushels from a year ago. Traders will be keeping a close eye on use numbers as prices move higher. If demand is sustained at the higher prices it will give added strength to the bullish argument. In the near term, trade direction will be given by weather and rust reports. Fund activity and midday forecasts will be the main market movers during the afternoon session.

Closing comments

Soybeans posted a volatile session with contracts rallying to early 25-26 cent gains followed by a late drop to losses of 6–7 cents. Most of the activity was tied directly to weather forecasts. Morning forecasts called for continued hot and dry conditions throughout the Midwest, while some midday weather models increased chances of rain in the 11–15 day timeframe. Non-commercial traders were active today, buying the market early and propelling contracts to session highs. Once their buying spree was done, reminiscent of three to four weeks ago, the market was left with light, local profit-taking. The lack of buy orders the latter half of the session helped to extend the price break.

Source: DTN AgDayta on-line.

10.6 Example technical analysis chart.

CZ2 D Corn (Day) December, 200X

| | Last | Change | Day's Range | 224'4 – 225'6 |
| | 225'2 | –0'2 (–0.11%) | 52-wk Range | 224'4 – 265'0 |

Source: Adapted from FutureSource.

AGRIBUSINESSES AND THE FUTURES MARKET

How might a livestock agribusiness or grain/oilseed merchandising firm use futures to protect its margin? Obviously, grains and oilseeds can be stored for a considerable time, while livestock is not storable. (Processor procurement is discussed in Chapter 13.)

Livestock Futures

Consider a cattle feeding operation where 700-pound feeder calves are typically purchased and 1,200-pound fed cattle are marketed to processors. Assume the primary input is corn in obtaining a 500-pound gain. Suppose the feeder calves are placed on feed in December with an expected daily gain of 2.5 pounds/day. In this scenario, the calves will be on feed roughly 200 days and sold as fed cattle in July. The feed yard manager knows what was paid for the 700-pound calves, he knows the price at which August live (fed) cattle futures are trading, and he knows where a profit could be made, considering where corn futures are trading. What should he do? He could go short the August live cattle contract, since he will be selling live cattle in July. (The August contract is used because there is no July contract traded.) This will protect him against a decrease in the level of the August live cattle futures contract. Alternatively, he could go long corn futures, since he will be buying corn to feed the animals. This will protect him against an increase in the corn futures price. Either of these options would help to lock in a profit margin.

Grain/Oilseed Futures

Now, suppose a Cargill load-out facility on the Amazon River in Brazil expects to buy 100,000 bushels of soybeans in April. Logistics favor these soybeans being shipped to the United States and crushed in Atlanta. However, the soybeans are not needed in Atlanta until August. On the day of delivery, Cargill might place a short hedge for the September CBOT soybean meal and oil futures contract. This helps Cargill lock in a processing margin (per bushel soybean meal value + per bushel of soybean oil value – cost of a bushel of soybean) when it buys the input six months before the final product is utilized and sold as further processed products. Cargill knows the input costs, but the selling prices are uncertain. So, the company opts to lock in a processing margin.

COMMODITY BASIS

C ommodity basis provides a significant amount of information to producers and agribusinesses for making production, forward pricing, hedging, and storage decisions. Many producers and agribusinesses believe that understanding basis patterns is the most fundamental means of evaluating marketing alternatives. That is, basis tends to follow historical seasonal patterns, and by understanding these patterns a producer or agribusiness manager can make better decisions and reduce risks involved in those decisions.

Commodity basis is the difference between a local cash price and the relevant futures contract price for a specific time period. For a specific commodity, basis is defined as:

Basis = Cash Price – Futures Price

where Cash Price is the cash price for a specific commodity at a given location and Futures Price is the relevant futures price for that commodity. Consider the following example:

Assume Jane Farmer raises corn and feeder cattle in Peoria, Illinois. On November 4, the local elevator is buying corn for $2.23/bushel and the local livestock auction is selling 7–8 cwt. feeder cattle for $84.56/cwt. On this same day, the closing price of the December corn futures price at the Chicago Board of Trade is $2.33/bushel and the closing price of the November feeder cattle futures price at the Chicago Mercantile Exchange is

$82.46/cwt. If Jane Farmer wants to know her basis, she simply takes the cash price and subtracts the futures price for each commodity.

	Corn	Feeder Cattle
Local Cash Price	$2.23	$84.56
Less Futures Market Price	$2.33	$82.46
Basis	−$0.10	$2.10
	(under)	(over)

A negative value represents a cash price "under" the futures price and a positive value represents a cash price "over" the futures price. Exhibit 10.7 describes basis movements. A basis that becomes more positive or less negative over time is said to narrow or strengthen. A basis that becomes less positive or more negative over time is said to widen or weaken.

Hedging and Basis

Basis is a crucial factor in hedging using the futures. Exhibit 10.8 outlines how we describe a gain or loss to either a short (sell to protect against decreasing price) or long (buy to protect against increasing price) hedger when basis strengthens or weakens. A long hedger prefers for the basis to weaken. That is, when buying, the hedger pays less in the cash market relative to the futures market and hopes to gain more from the position in the futures market. A short hedger gains from a strengthening basis. That is, when selling, the hedger realizes a cash price increase relative to the futures price and hopes to gain more from the position in the futures market.

EXHIBIT

10.7   Basis terminology and movement.

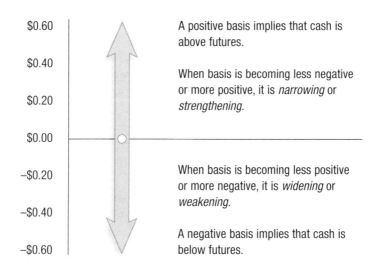

$0.60	A positive basis implies that cash is above futures.
$0.40	
	When basis is becoming less negative or more positive, it is *narrowing* or *strengthening*.
$0.20	
$0.00	
−$0.20	When basis is becoming less positive or more negative, it is *widening* or *weakening*.
−$0.40	
	A negative basis implies that cash is below futures.
−$0.60	

EXHIBIT

10.8 Direction and impact of basis movement for short and long hedger.

	Long Hedge	Short Hedge
If basis weakens (widens)	Basis gain	Basis loss
If basis strengthens (narrows)	Basis loss	Basis gain

Historical and Seasonal Basis Patterns

Basis tends to vary within the marketing year for grains, oilseed crops, and livestock. Understanding seasonal patterns and historical trends can help producers and agribusiness personnel to make proper forward contracting, hedging, and production decisions. As will be shown, basis trends tend to be consistent over time and provide opportunities to those who understand these trends.

Exhibit 10.9 outlines 5- and 10-year average soybean basis trends for Kansas City, Kansas. Clearly, basis is strongest from August to October (old crop) and widens rapidly into the fall (new crop). Historically, soybean basis has strengthened considerably from mid-May until early September. Furthermore, soybean basis patterns have changed little over time, thus the resemblance in 5- and 10-year average basis patterns. This resemblance in basis patterns over time is favorable for persons using basis for marketing decisions.

EXHIBIT

10.9 5- and 10-year average soybean basis for Kansas City, KS.

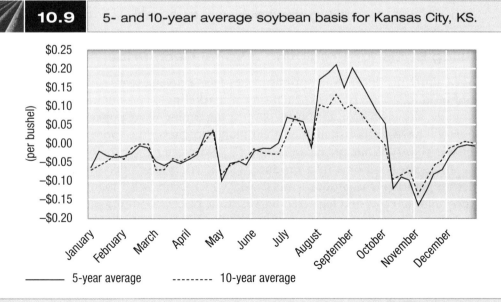

10.10 Sample Dodge City, KS, feeder cattle basis for different weight categories.

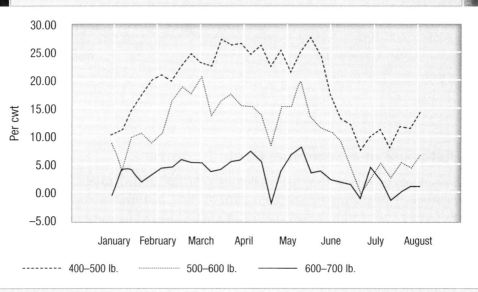

Basis is substantially different for alternative weight classes of feeder cattle, and seasonal patterns differ between weight classes (Exhibit 10.10). Since the feeder cattle futures contract specification is for 700–800 lb feeder cattle, as the cash price quote deviates from this weight price category, the basis typically increases. Also, because feeder cattle are an input into fed cattle production—feeding feeder cattle creates fed cattle—the feeder cattle basis will be affected by feed costs and fed cattle value. Although not demonstrated here, even for livestock basis is fairly stable over time.

Using Basis for Predicting a Local Cash Price

Agriculture producers and agribusinesses face a diverse array of marketing and production alternatives. Each time a marketing or production decision is made, the farmer or agribusiness must determine what impact this decision will have on its risk management plan. No question is more difficult to answer than, "What price can I expect?" No matter the time of year, this question always looms in a producer's or agribusiness's decision process. Before planting, the producer must ask, which crop will I plant given my known input costs and expected harvest time prices? Both prior to planting and throughout the growing season, the producer must ask, should I forward price a portion of my crop? Finally, in the fall the producer must ask, should I store my crop? (Or, for the cow-calf producer, should I retain ownership on a portion of my calf herd beyond weaning?) Similarly, agribusinesses must determine price expectations to know what forward price to offer.

Commodity futures exchange markets provide a mechanism for price discovery on an aggregate level through arbitrage between multiple buyers and sellers. However, price discovery at a given location is not nearly as clearly defined because local supply and demand relationships are not as well known. Historical basis provides a link between these two markets. Therefore, a simple, low-cost, and relatively good predictor of the local cash price is the futures contract (month) price adjusted for a multiple-year average historical basis. An expected price, where E denotes an expectation, is given by:

$$E[\textit{Cash Price}] = [\textit{Futures Price}]_t + E[\textit{Basis}]$$

where t is the futures contract of interest. For example, assume a cow-calf producer would like a forecast for April live cattle prices in the local market in December of the previous year. The producer's best expectation of that cash price might be found by adjusting the April live cattle futures price for an expected basis (say the historical three-year average basis for that area). Similarly, suppose a Brazilian soybean producer wants to decide how the **forward contract price** (the price at which a commodity is sold today for delivery during a specific time period in the future) compares to an expected cash sale. The producer could use the current Brazilian soybean futures price, adjusted using a historical basis, to see how the expected cash price compares to the forward price.

HEDGING: FUTURES CONTRACTS

A cattle producer knows he will be selling a pen of cattle two months from now. Based on the cost of production of these animals, the producer knows that a price of $64/cwt. will allow for a satisfactory profit. What alternatives does the producer have? He cannot sell the cattle now, because they are too light. However, the producer could enter the futures market and offset any loss in value (decrease in cash price) with a gain in the futures market price.

The Short Futures Hedge

Exhibit 10.11 indicates the actions that a hedger might take in placing an output hedge and the outcomes of those actions when the futures price decreases. Because cattle are perishable, the current cattle price is irrelevant. Suppose that you could sell the relevant live cattle futures contract today for $84/cwt. Knowing that you will sell cattle at a later date and wanting to protect against a price decrease, you take a short position in the futures market. Over the next few months, the local cash price decreases to $79/cwt. and the futures price decreases to $79/cwt. At this time you decide the cattle need to go to market. You sell cattle in the cash market for $79/cwt. and buy back your futures position for $79/cwt. Therefore, the revenue from selling your cattle is $79/cwt. plus your $5/cwt. gain from the futures position, less any commission costs. (Commission costs are not

EXHIBIT

10.11 Short hedge example using live cattle futures with cash price decreasing faster than futures (basis weakens).

	Cash	Futures	Basis
Today	N/A	Sell live cattle contract at $84/cwt.	N/A
Later	Sell cattle in local market at $79/cwt.	Buy live cattle contract back at $79/cwt.	0 (even)
		Selling price $79.00/cwt. Plus futures gain $5.00/cwt. Net selling price $84.00/cwt.	

included in Exhibit 10.11 to make the example clearer.) Instead of selling for $79/cwt., you sell for $84/cwt.

Exhibit 10.12 indicates the actions that a hedger might take in placing an output hedge and the outcomes of those actions when the futures price increases. Suppose you could sell live cattle today for the relevant futures contract for $84/cwt. Knowing that you will sell cattle at a later date and wanting to protect against a price decrease, you take a short position in the futures market. Over the next few months, the local cash price increases to $87/cwt. and the futures price increases to $89/cwt. At this time you decide the cattle need to go to market. You sell cattle in the cash market for $87/cwt. and buy back your futures position for $88/cwt. Therefore, the revenue from selling your cattle is $87/cwt. less $5/cwt. lost from the futures position, less any commission (not shown in the exhibit). Instead of selling for $87/cwt., you sell for $82/cwt.

EXHIBIT

10.12 Short hedge example using live cattle futures with cash price increasing faster than futures (basis strengthens).

	Cash	Futures	Basis
Today	N/A	Sell live cattle contract at $84/cwt.	N/A
Later	Sell cattle in local market at $87/cwt.	Buy live cattle contract back at $89/cwt.	−$2.00/cwt. (under)
		Selling price $87.00/cwt. Less futures gain $5.00/cwt. Net selling price $82.00/cwt.	

The Long Futures Hedge

Exhibit 10.13 indicates the actions that a hedger might take in placing an input hedge and the outcomes of those actions when the future price increases during the hedging period. Suppose you could purchase corn today for $2.35/bushel and the relevant futures contract is trading for $2.50/bushel (basis is $0.15 under). Since corn is storable, you are interested in what happens to basis. Knowing that you will need the corn at a later date and wanting to protect against a price increase, you take a long position in the futures market. Over the next few months, the local cash price increases to $2.60/bushel and the futures price increases to $2.80/bushel. At this time you decide you need to purchase corn for the production of feed. You purchase the corn in the cash market for $2.60/bushel and sell back your futures position for $2.80/bushel. Therefore, the cost of the grain to you is $2.60/bushel less $0.30/bushel gained from the futures position, plus any commission costs (not shown in the exhibit). Instead of paying $2.60/bushel, you pay $2.30/bushel.

Cash and Futures Prices Both Decrease

Exhibit 10.14 indicates the actions a hedger might take in placing an input hedge and the outcomes of those actions when the cash price decreases by more than the futures price during the hedging period. Suppose you could purchase corn today for $2.35/bushel and the relevant futures contract is trading for $2.50/bushel (basis is $0.15 under). Knowing that you will need the corn at a later date and wanting to protect against a price increase, you take a long position in the futures market. Over the next few months, the local cash price decreases to $2.20/bushel and the futures contract price decreases to $2.40/bushel. At this time you decide you need to purchase corn for the production of feed. You purchase the corn in the cash market for $2.20/bushel and sell back your futures position for $2.40/bushel. Therefore, the cost of the grain to you is $2.20/bushel plus $0.10/bushel lost

EXHIBIT

10.13 Long hedge example using corn futures with cash price increasing faster than futures (basis strengthens).

	Cash	Futures	Basis
Today	$2.35/bu.	Buy corn contract at $2.50/bu.	−$0.15/bu. (under)
Later	Buy corn in local market at $2.60/bu.	Sell corn contract back at $2.80/bu.	−$0.20/bu. (under)

Cash paid price	$2.60/bu.
Less futures gain	$0.30/bu.
Net buying price	$2.30/bu.

10.14   Long hedge example using corn futures with cash price decreasing faster than futures (basis weakens).

	Cash	Futures		Basis
Today	$2.35/bu.	Buy corn contract at $2.50/bu.		−$0.15/bu. (under)
Later	Buy corn in local market at $2.20/bu.	Sell corn contract back at $2.40/bu.		−$0.20/bu. (under)
		Cash paid price	$2.20/bu.	
		Plus futures loss	$0.10/bu.	
		Net buying price	$2.30/bu.	

from the futures position, plus commission costs (not shown in the exhibit). Instead of paying $2.20/bushel, you pay $2.30/bushel.

HEDGING: OPTIONS CONTRACTS

Suppose you are a grain merchandiser working for a large grain company. Your job is to buy corn for today's use and forward contract corn deliveries for future use. Let's say you forward purchase 5,000 bushels of corn to be delivered 12 months from today at a fixed price of $2.50/bushel. More than likely, the corn to be delivered will be from next year's crop. What price risk does the company face by agreeing to buy corn 12 months from now at a price established today? The company faces the uncertainty that it would be able to purchase corn cheaper, say at $2.00/bushel, 12 months from now. How would a grain handling firm "protect" against this? The firm may use the futures options market to hedge against a potential price movement.

Put: Cash Price Decreases and Option Value Increases

Exhibit 10.15 outlines the example of a short hedge in corn, using a put option, where the cash price and futures price both decrease. A change in the futures price is assumed to be inversely related to a change in the put option value. Thus, when the futures price decreases, the option value increases. Suppose that Calvin Corngrower knows today that he will be selling corn a few months from now. Additionally, Calvin knows that given the current cash price of $2.35/bu., he has the potential to profit. However, he is concerned that the price may decrease before he sells. Calvin purchases a $2.50/bu. in-the-money put option for $0.20/bu. When Calvin is ready to sell the corn, the cash and futures prices have decreased to $2.15/bu. and $2.20/bu., respectively (no change in basis). The futures price has decreased so that the put option is now further in-the-money. Therefore, Calvin sells the corn for $2.15/bu. and sells his put option for $0.35/bu., for a $0.15/bu.

EXHIBIT

10.15 Short hedge example using corn options—cash and futures prices decrease.

	Cash	Futures	Options Price	
Today	$2.35/bu.	$2.40/bu.	Purchase $2.50/bu. put at $0.20/bu. (pay $1,000)	
Later	Sell corn in local market at $2.15/bu.	$2.20/bu.	Sell $2.50/bu. p\ut at $0.35/bu. (receive $1,750)	
			Cash price received	$2.15/bu.
			Plus option premium gain	$0.15/bu.
			Net selling price	$2.30/bu.

gain in value. In this case, Calvin has improved his selling price of the grain from $2.15/bu. to $2.30/bu. ($2.15/bu. plus $0.15/bu. gain in option value). (Commission costs are not considered.)

Put: Cash Price Increases and Option Value Decreases

Exhibit 10.16 outlines the example of a short hedge in corn, using a put option, where the cash price and futures price both increase. When the futures price increases, the option value decreases. Suppose that Calvin Corngrower knows today that he will be selling corn a few months from now. Additionally, Calvin knows that given the current cash price of $2.35/bu., he has the potential to profit. However, he is concerned that the price may

EXHIBIT

10.16 Short hedge example using corn options—cash and futures prices increase.

	Cash	Futures	Options Price	
Today	$2.35/bu.	$2.40/bu.	Purchase $2.50/bu. put at $0.20/bu. (pay $1,000)	
Later	Sell corn in local market at $2.60/bu.	$2.65/bu.	Sell $2.50/bu. put at $0.05/bu. (receive $250)	
			Cash price received	$2.60/bu.
			Less option premium loss	$0.15/bu.
			Net selling price	$2.45/bu.

decrease before he sells. Calvin purchases a $2.50/bu. in-the-money put option for $0.20/bu. When Calvin is ready to sell the corn, the cash and futures prices have increased to $2.60/bu. and $2.65/bu., respectively (no change in basis). The futures price has increased so that the put option is now out-of-the-money. Therefore, Calvin sells the corn for $2.60/bu. and sells his put option for $0.05/bu., for a $0.15/bu. loss in value. Note that the option value only has time value remaining. In this case, Calvin has decreased his selling price of the grain from $2.60/bu. to $2.45/bu. ($2.60/bu. less a $0.15/bu. loss in option value). (Commission costs are not considered.) However, Calvin had the potential for unlimited gains with limited losses.

Call: Cash Price and Option Value Both Increase

Exhibit 10.17 outlines the example of a long hedge in corn, using a call option, where the cash price and futures price increase. An increase in futures price is assumed to be positively related to a change in the call option value. Thus, when the futures price increases, the option value increases. Suppose that Heidi Hogfarmer knows today that she will be purchasing a pen of segregate early weaned pigs a few months from now. Additionally, Heidi knows that given the current corn cash price of $2.35/bu., she has the potential to feed-out these pigs for a profit. However, she is concerned that the corn price may increase before she purchases the hogs. Heidi purchases a $2.50/bu. out-of-the-money call option for $0.20/bu. When Heidi is ready to purchase the hogs and corn to make feed, the cash and futures prices have increased to $2.60/bu. and $2.65/bu., respectively (no change in basis). The futures price has increased so that the call option is now in-the-money. Therefore, Heidi purchases the corn for $2.60/bu. and sells her call option for $0.35/bu., for a $0.15/bu. gain in value. By purchasing a call option, Heidi decreased her cost of purchasing the grain from $2.60/bu. to $2.45/bu. ($2.60/bu. less $0.15/bu. gain in option value). (Commission costs are not considered.)

EXHIBIT

10.17   Long hedge example using corn options—cash and futures prices increase.

	Cash	Futures	Options Price	
Today	$2.35/bu.	$2.40/bu.	Purchase $2.50/bu. call at $0.20/bu. (pay $1,000)	
Later	Buy corn in local market at $2.60/bu.	$2.65/bu.	Sell $2.50/bu. call at $0.35/bu. (receive $1,750)	
			Cash price paid	$2.60/bu.
			Less option premium gain	$0.15/bu.
			Net buying price	$2.45/bu.

EXHIBIT

10.18 Long hedge example using corn options—cash and futures prices decrease.

	Cash	Futures	Options Price
Today	$2.35/bu.	$2.40/bu.	Purchase $2.50/bu. call at $0.20/bu. (pay $1,000)
Later	Buy corn in local market at $2.15/bu.	$2.20/bu.	Sell $2.50/bu. call at $0.02/bu. (receive $100)
			Cash price paid $2.15/bu.
			Plus option premium loss $0.18/bu.
			Net buying price $2.33/bu.

Call: Cash Price and Option Value Both Decrease

Exhibit 10.18 outlines the example of a long hedge in corn, using a call option, where the cash price and futures price decrease. As the futures price decreases, the option value also decreases. Suppose that Heidi Hogfarmer knows today that she will be purchasing a pen of segregate early weaned pigs a few months from now. Additionally, Heidi knows that given the current cash price of $2.35/bu., she has the potential to feed-out these pigs for a profit. However, she is concerned that the price may increase before she purchases the hogs. Heidi purchases a $2.50/bu. out-of-the-money call option for $0.20/bu. When Heidi is ready to purchase the hogs and corn to make feed, the cash and futures prices have decreased to $2.15/bu. and $2.20/bu., respectively (no change in basis). The futures price has decreased so that the call option is now even more out-of-the-money. Therefore, Heidi purchases the corn for $2.15/bu. and sells her call option for $0.02/bu., for a $0.18/bu. loss in value. In this case, Heidi increased the cost of purchasing the grain from $2.15/bu. to $2.33/bu. ($2.15/bu. plus $0.18/bu. loss in option value). Heidi was not as well off as she would have been had she bought in the cash market, but she exceeded her initial goal of locking in a $2.35/bu. corn price. (Commission costs are not considered.)

SUMMARY

1. Commodity futures markets allow market participants to transfer risk and provide a means for price discovery as buyers and sellers assess information to determine where they expect prices to be in the future. Commodity options markets are derived from commodity futures contracts. Options are a form of insurance against price movements.

2. Hedgers enter the market to transfer price risk for a commodity that they own or plan to own. Speculators enter the market to profit from price movements. Speculators are important to the market because they increase liquidity, which allows for easy entry and exit from the markets.

3. Whereas taking a futures market position permits unlimited gains and losses, purchasing an option permits limited losses and unlimited gains.

4. Hedging and options trading occur at futures market exchanges. The primary domestic exchanges are the CBOT, CME, and NYMEX. Additional futures market exchanges exist or are developing around the globe. The increase in futures market exchanges has resulted from technology, which facilitates information flow and the globalization of agriculture.

5. Basis is the difference between a cash price and futures price. Basis is a critical marketing tool because it indicates whether the local market is saturated or deficit relative to other current markets and relative to other points in time for the same market.

6. Combining a local historical basis and a futures price allows one to develop a simple cash price projection.

STUDY QUESTIONS

1. Discuss how a hedger would evaluate the performance of a hedging strategy over the past five years.

2. Describe the process of writing a put or a call option.

3. Describe and provide an example of a minimum price contract.

4. Discuss the opportunity costs of hedging. What are the economic costs of hedging?

5. How would ADM use futures to lock in a margin for buying wheat in July and selling the wheat to a buyer in December?

6. Graphically show, using futures and spot market figures, the impact on basis of the start-up of an ethanol processing plant in a major corn producing region.

7. Discuss what a pork producer might do to lock in a comfortable profit level.

8. Choose one international futures exchange and discuss the history and organization of the exchange.

9. **Market carry,** defined as the between-futures contract spread for storable commodities, indicates a return to storage. For the data presented in Exhibit 10.3, what is the expected return to storage for holding corn from December 2005 to March 2006? Should a producer store?

10. Find out the current Japanese yen to United States dollar exchange rate and describe whether a Japanese importer or U. S. importer would be more likely to prefer the current exchange rate. Describe how an importer would hedge the exchange rate.

 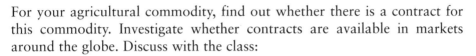

CLASS EXERCISE

For your agricultural commodity, find out whether there is a contract for this commodity. Investigate whether contracts are available in markets around the globe. Discuss with the class:

1. Why contracts do or do not exist
2. Contract specifications and delivery points

CHAPTER

11

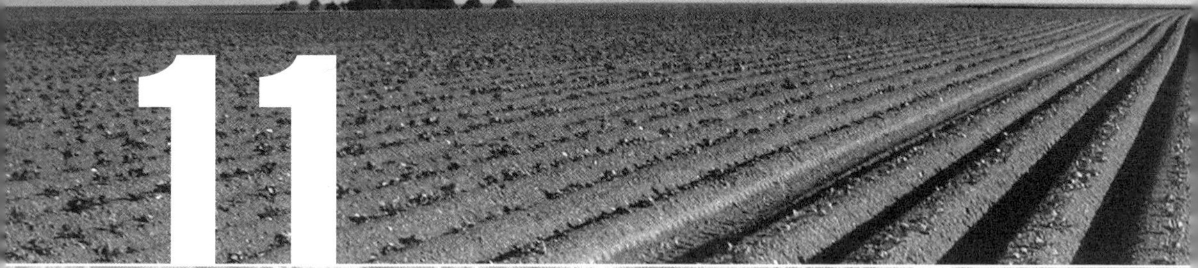

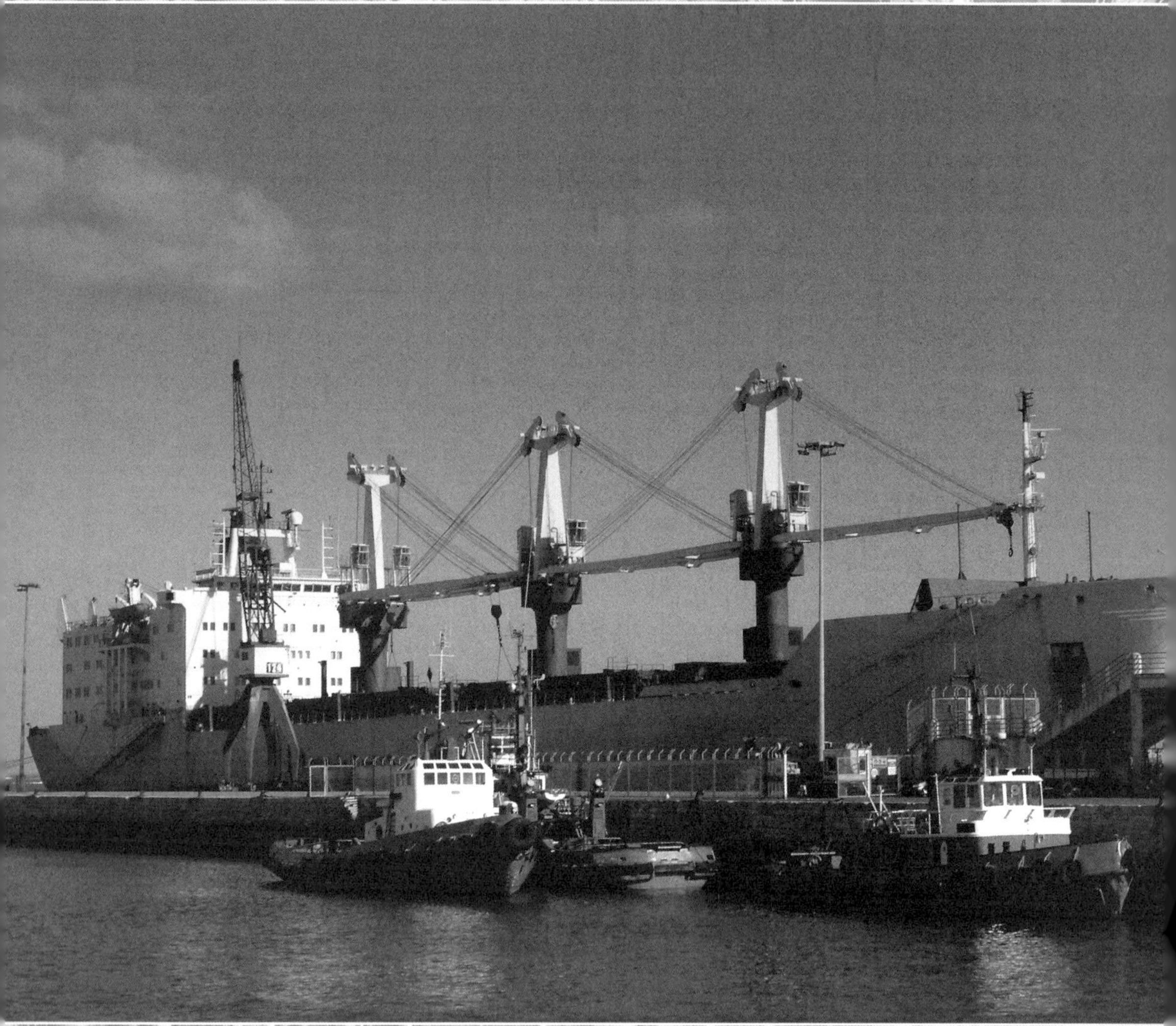

PARTICIPATION AND LEADERSHIP IN THE MARKETING–PROCUREMENT CHANNELS

PREVIEW

- Marketing–procurement (M–P) channels vary considerably in length and complexity. The more typical ones involve various intermediaries such as assemblers, processors, further processors, wholesalers, and retailers.

- The ownership and control of intermediaries varies in two dimensions: (1) vertically integrated vs. independent intermediaries, (2) among independent intermediaries, merchants vs. agents and brokers.

- Firms such as processors and retailers generally consider it advantageous to influence the behavior of customers and suppliers.

- Many channels have a channel leader. Channel leadership follows from ownership of popular brands, large market share, economic power, and innovative ideas, among other factors.

KEY TERMS

assembler

boxed beef

brand name

channel leader

manufacturers' brand

merchant

private label

sales branch

trademark

W e have described many of the massive tasks involved in matching the amounts of commodities supplied and demanded and in physically handling food supplies through the marketing system. In this chapter we describe various types of market channels, the roles played by different kinds of agencies, and the varying forms of channel leadership. The concept of the struggle for channel leadership between processors and wholesale retailers is introduced.

VARIATIONS IN CHANNELS

R ecall that we have treated a channel as a sequence of firms through which a product moves from producer to consumer. We have avoided the customary practice of referring to such channels as marketing channels because the process is frequently procurement rather than marketing. We will generally refer to them as marketing–procurement (M–P) channels. Conventionally, the firms in a channel are pictured as being in a vertical alignment (Exhibit 11.1).

EXHIBIT
11.1   Selected variations in M–P channels.

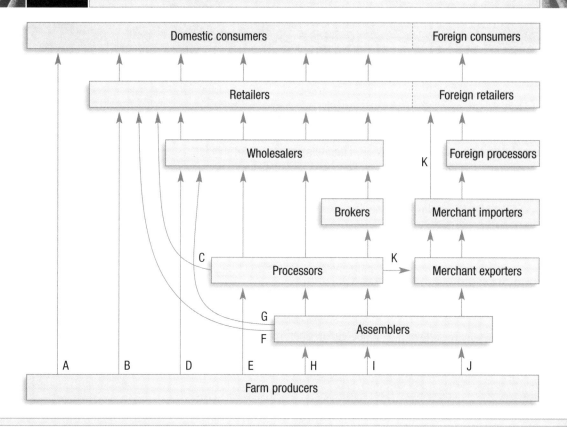

Marketing–procurement channels vary considerably in complexity and length. The 11 M–P channels illustrated in Exhibit 11.1 do not exhaust the possible variations. Moreover, those firms that specialize in storing and transporting the product at various stages are omitted.

Direct sales by a farmer to consumers form a simple, short channel (A) that may be properly called a *marketing channel*. That is, the farmer organizes a method (home delivery or roadside market) by which he markets a commodity. He generally is the leader in making this channel operate. Such channels handle relatively small volumes but are of growing importance in agriculture. Direct channels have the most opportunities in commodities such as eggs, poultry, milk, floral and nursery items, fresh fruit, and vegetables that may be sold in their raw form. The opportunities are best where farmers and consumers have easy geographical access to one another.

At the other extreme, the tenth and eleventh (J and K) channels are perhaps the longest geographically and the least understood by the farmer–producer. The channel for reaching foreign consumers of U. S.

wheat, rice, oilseeds, cotton, tobacco, and other products likely involves more firms than shown. The farmer rarely is the leader who organizes and directs the flow of products through this channel. A large, international grain company is more likely the moving force of such a channel that makes many of the key decisions as to what happens when and where.

Channel K, that of processor to export merchant to foreign retailer, is growing due to increased disposable income in foreign economies. Increasing income has two effects. First is a wealth effect, in that individuals and businesses can afford convenience foods as opposed to staple foods. Second, as their income grows, individuals learn of comparative advantage—that a foreign producer can produce a commodity and ship it to the country more cheaply than it can be made inside the country. For example, the United States imports coffee and bananas rather than growing them domestically.

Channels C, D, and E are the typical channels for major commodities sold in domestic markets. Processors and retailers are almost universally present in M–P channels of agricultural products; one or the other often plays a key leadership role. Between the processors and retailers is usually located one or more types of wholesalers, and between farmers and processors are one or more types of commodities assembler. Processors, retailers, and farmers are usually independent, single-stage firms, although there are important exceptions where units at two or even all three stages are owned by one firm. The firms in between, such as wholesalers and assemblers, may either be controlled by a firm at the stage above or below or be independent.

Channel C is becoming a preferred model for most processors, as processors convert existing facilities and acquire or build further processing business units. Tyson's poultry business unit was a leader in this model. Consumers may observe this leadership at the grocery store, where Tyson packaged poultry products are prominent. Many other large meat processors have followed Tyson's lead.

Are costs of marketing too high because there are too many intermediaries? Are channels too long? President Lincoln was once asked about the proper length for a man's legs. "Long enough to reach the ground" was his reply. Likewise, marketing channels need to be long enough to do the job most efficiently. Although very direct channels like A and B have an appealing simplicity, it is obvious that most of the production of U. S. farms cannot be sold directly to U. S. consumers or directly to retailers.

Competitive market theory suggests that a particular stage will be bypassed if the marketing function can be performed more effectively without it. For example, manufacturers may do their own wholesaling rather than selling to independent wholesalers, if they can do the job more cheaply or more to the manufacturer's liking. Note that bypassing an independent wholesaler does not eliminate the wholesale function. Instead, the manufacturer simply adds on the wholesale function to its responsibilities. However, one should not assume that the status quo is necessarily the most efficient possible M–P channel. Change takes time. It may take years for a new, more efficient channel organization to replace an obsolete one.

There probably are too many firms at certain stages. For example, assemblers were recently too numerous, and their numbers have been decreasing. As farms get bigger, their operators typically search over a larger area for competitive bids for their output. In the process, the small, local assembly establishments tend to be bypassed and eventually close down.

Nineteenth-century America, with millions of small farms tied to thousands of cities by railroads, depended on a very extensive system of assembler firms to get farm commodities to processors. It also relied on another very extensive system of distributors to get the food products to the millions of small food retailers. Major growth in size and a reduction in the numbers of farmers and processors has permitted the development of more direct marketing between farmers and processors. Intermediaries are still present in most cases, but their relative importance has often declined. Larger farmers are frequently doing their own selling rather than relying on commission agents.

OWNERSHIP AND CONTROL OF INTERMEDIARIES

The ownership, contractual relations, and functions of intermediaries (middlemen) are quite varied. Very often the firm that performs an assembly or wholesale function is owned by farmers, processors, or retailers. Other firms are independent. Thus, a first distinction among intermediaries is whether a firm is independent or is vertically integrated with a firm at another channel stage. Independent firms may be distinguished according to whether a firm is a merchant or an agent or broker. For the most part **merchants** are intermediaries who buy and sell, ship, hold inventories of commodities and products, and even finance sales. They typically take ownership title of goods handled, whereas agents and brokers do not.

At any intermediary stage, one or all of four different types of operations may be found:

1. Merchants
2. Brokers (agents)
3. Vertically integrated operations of sellers (such as farmer coop elevators at the assembly stage)
4. Vertically integrated operations of buyers (such as flour miller–owned elevators at the assembly stage)

There is apparently no overwhelming advantage of one type of operation over another. All four types are found at both the assembly and the wholesale distribution stages.

When merchants take title to goods, they take risks—both the physical risks of theft and accidental destruction and the financial risks of price changes. Merchants of nonperishables, such as grain and cotton, often store them for weeks and months. This risk exposure encourages most merchants to resort to futures or options contracts to reduce price risks (see Chapter

10). Merchants typically need considerable capital to finance their holding of commodities.

Brokers operate differently from merchants. They are intermediaries who arrange transactions for a commission but do not take ownership or finance customers. Because brokers do not take title, they avoid price risks and most physical risks, so they need far less operating capital than merchants need. However, life is not all roses for brokers. They must satisfy those for whom they work (who are sellers, except in the case of those few buyers using order buyers). Their volume of business and income are partially dependent on the business decisions of others over whom they have no control. Although they do not bear the losses of a sudden price decline, they also never receive the gains of a sudden price increase in a commodity they handle.

Assemblers

The thousands of **assemblers** have much in common with other intermediaries. They collect many small shipments from producers into larger-volume units for sale and shipment to processors or to wholesalers. Assemblers may be independent or may be owned from above or below. Those assemblers owned by farmers are called *marketing cooperatives*. Assemblers owned by farmers may be viewed as the farmers' marketing representatives and as a first step toward a channel that is a marketing channel for farmers rather than a procurement channel for processors.

Processors do much of their own assembly through salaried buyers. The salaried livestock buyers for meat packers are a familiar sight as they canvass the feedlots, farms, auctions, and central market agencies to buy livestock. Similarly, the salaried tobacco buyers make their rounds of the tobacco auctions each season to purchase tobacco for the major tobacco companies.

Independent assemblers may be brokers buying on commission for processors or selling on commission for farmers, or they may be merchants taking ownership. Rural auctions are typically held by independent brokers who assemble and sell on commission—especially cull breeding stock and feeder animals. In livestock procurement both merchants and brokers are found. Order buyers at auctions and terminal markets buy on commission. Other individuals and firms serve as livestock dealers (merchants) and take ownership of the livestock they assemble and sell to packers. These merchants have much smaller market shares than agents and brokers in livestock assembly.

Rural grain elevators cover all three forms of assembler ownership. Many are farmer cooperatives, many others are independent firms, and some are "line elevators" owned by large grain merchants. The elevators ordinarily take ownership, although it is not unusual for them to pass that ownership hastily to larger grain companies—usually before the grain is shipped.

Milk assembly is performed mainly by farmer cooperatives. Dairy farmers are one of the leading commodity groups in terms of developing a marketing channel for themselves.

As farm producers grow larger, the need for farm product assemblers has declined. Today, many farm producers are able to ship a truckload of hogs or cattle to processors, and this ability encourages sales direct to processors.

Some commodities, such as eggs, fresh fruits, and vegetables, move directly from assemblers to wholesalers or retailers (channels F and G of Exhibit 11.1). A large part of the food supply moves through one or more stages of processors (channels C, E, H, I, or K). Exhibit 11.1 shows sectors called *Brokers* and *Wholesalers* between processors and retailers but the picture is more complex than that; there are many kinds of arrangements.

Wholesale Distribution

Processors must make sure that their products flow smoothly and efficiently through the market channel. Historically, processors sold to wholesalers. Today they sell to various outlets, typically preferring to sell not to consumers or to individual retailers but to larger-volume retailers. Processors may sell to independent wholesalers, or they may organize their own warehousing and wholesaling activities in a vertically integrated operation. Thus, processors may maintain distribution centers that warehouse products within, say, two days' shipping time of any retail customer. They may operate their own sales branches and offices in many urban markets.

Food processors in dairy and meat sell sizable volumes through branches or offices. A *sales office* does not stock merchandise for delivery, whereas a **sales branch,** a processor-owned facility that inventories and sells processed foods, does. Manufacturers are inclined to rely on independent wholesalers in less important markets and on sales branches in their most important metropolitan markets.

As an alternative to their own sales branches, processors may sell through agents or brokers, paying a commission on sales. Food brokers sell many of the dry groceries (the nonperishables) to food wholesalers and retailers. Each broker knows the food market in a particular geographical area. The typical food broker is an independent sales agent for a number of different and usually noncompeting food processors. She calls on wholesalers, makes sales, coordinates shipments, handles complaints, and provides information to both the supplier and the wholesalers. In short, she does just about everything that an employed sales force would do. A canner or other food processor can obtain sales representation in a trade area for the usual commission of 3% to 6%, depending on the services provided by the broker. The processor's alternative is to maintain his own sales force, which is often more expensive and less effective than a broker, especially for smaller processors.

Another alternative to sales branches is for the processor to sell to independent merchant wholesalers who take ownership and possession of the product. They may perform various services for their customers, who are typically retailers, food service institutions, or other wholesalers.

A third alternative is for the processor to sell to an integrated whole-saler–retailer. Chain stores such as Wal-Mart tend to have their own distribution centers that perform the wholesale function of breaking down bulk. As described later, many independent retailers own cooperatively a distribution center performing the same wholesale function for them.

The distribution channel for any given commodity group, such as canned fruits and vegetables, may contain all of the previous elements. The larger canners may have distribution centers and sales offices. They may sell direct-ly to some merchant wholesalers and to many integrated wholesaler–retailers, and they may also sell through brokers. The smaller canners are more likely to rely entirely on brokers for reaching those same customers.

CHANNEL COORDINATION AND LEADERSHIP

One can imagine a totally dispersed, nonintegrated market channel (resembling perfect competition) in which there is no leadership. Ownership is exchanged within open, competitive markets between each pair of adjoining stages. If a problem arises of concern to some partic-ipants, such as grading or market information, they will likely turn to government for its resolution. As long as the channel has the described attributes, coordination by any participant is unnecessary. Free and open competition requires reasonably efficient functioning of the participants and of the system.

Such dispersed, nonintegrated market channels have existed; some still may exist. However, most channels involve elements of monopolistic com-petition and oligopoly. These channels usually include some participants who both perceive the advantages of providing channel leadership and find the means to do so.

Therefore, most food market channels contain elements of channel lead-ership. This leadership may vary from the extreme of vertical control and dominance, to ownership and contracts at several stages, to some much small-er degree of market influence exercised by the larger or more innovative firms.

The type, forcefulness, and degree of acceptance of leadership vary among channels and also over time within a given channel. Sometimes mar-ket channels resemble an orchestra led by a strong, dynamic conductor. Sometimes, several would-be conductors are striving to lead; occasionally, no leader is apparent.

The integrated channel provides the most obvious examples of how chan-nel leaders operate. For example, auto manufacturers make decisions from design, promotion, and pricing all the way to retail, where they influence most decisions. The auto manufacturers deal with only one stage of independ-ent firms—the dealers—in their marketing channel. Moreover, through their long-time establishment of consumer-brand loyalties, reinforced continually by advertising, auto manufacturers have been able to set up a franchised sys-tem of retailing that gives them great retail influence. There can be no debate as to who are the leaders in the marketing channel for autos.

In the food service industry, the fast-food franchise chains have been the leading innovators. McDonald's, because it has influenced other stages, is probably the single firm that could best claim to be the channel leader in the past few decades.

What about channel coordination and leadership in a non–vertically integrated channel? Perceptions of common interests within the market guide coordination. Retailers' perceptions and observations about which pork products sell best will influence their purchases from packers, who in turn will reflect those perceptions in their demand for hogs. The continuation of the old marketing–procurement routines requires little leadership. Significant leadership is more evident with new products, new procedures, or changes in a product flow.

Independent firms within a channel perceive dissimilar interests along with common interests. Farmers and packers are likely to feel that retailers charge too much for too little service. Hog farmers would like to see more retail promotion of pork—more ads, better displays, lower retail margins. Packers agree, but in particular they want more retail push of their own packer brands of bacon, hams, and so on. Retailers have their own interests, of course. Although retailers are happy to carry popular packer brands, they may want to build up the sales of their own store brands. After all, if a retailer does a good job with pork, she wants it to reflect favorably on her store. These observations apply in general to other commodity channels. What is optimal for one firm in a channel is not necessarily optimal for others.

Within a channel, firms have purposes that are both similar and conflicting, so their behavior is both competitive and cooperative. Much is accomplished in concert: products are marketed, frequently with dispatch and efficiency. However, conflicting objectives result in some activities at cross-purposes. Sometimes it may be exceedingly difficult for firms at any level—producers, processors, or retailers—to mobilize and redirect channel activities. University and government researchers have played important roles in such industry efforts as developing a "meat-type hog" or a new set of beef-grading standards.

Usually the firms at some particular market stage within a nonintegrated channel exercise most of the leadership in that channel. These **channel leaders**—whether farmers, processors, wholesalers, or retailers—take the initiative in getting things done. When prices are set, these firms frequently lead in their setting. They are the ones who develop the popular brands and sustain the necessary promotion. If new products, new packages, or new market development efforts are underway, these channel leaders probably made most of the decisions and motivated the rest of the channel to go along. If former independents are being vertically integrated into an adjacent level, the leaders are likely the integrators.

Channel leadership is often essential to improving productivity. For example, manufacturers have pushed to obtain industry use of a uniform-sized shipping pallet at all stages, and manufacturers and larger retailers worked together to develop the Universal Product Code (UPC). Today, Wal-

Mart uses the UPC to collect data that is available to suppliers, who then assume inventory management, freeing Wal-Mart of that burden.

Channel leadership may seem abstract. To whom does it belong? Leadership is earned and grasped—it may reside at any level of the channel, although a processor or a retailer is the most likely leader in food channels.

In nonfood channels, manufacturers typically have been the leaders. The manufacturer develops a product with consumer appeal, makes consumers aware of it through advertising, and develops a method of getting it to consumers. Often the manufacturer places his product into an existing wholesale network. He negotiates how extensively it is handled, educates wholesalers and retailers about the product, and likely provides various incentives to wholesalers and retailers to promote his product.

At times, the manufacturers' leadership has been more forceful. Failing to receive the type of wholesaling effort she desires, a manufacturer develops her own sales offices and branches, thus building her own wholesale outlets.

In some cases, manufacturer integration is carried forward into retailing. The manufacturer, as channel leader, then directs employees rather than seeking to motivate and persuade independent wholesalers and retailers. The distinction may be a bit exaggerated; employees also must be motivated and persuaded. Moreover, the size and width of the product line place a limitation on vertical integration into retailing. General Motors may supply an adequate product line for an auto dealer, but a fruit and vegetable canner cannot supply the 20,000-plus grocery, meat, and produce items of a modern supermarket.

In the past half century, processors (the historic leaders in food channels) have faced a growing leadership challenge from retailers. In a few cases, they have encountered challenges from organized farmers. Both retailers and farmers sometimes seek to reorganize the market channel in such a way as to serve their interests better. Although such attempted reorganizations sometimes involve attempts to take market functions away from another level, they also include efforts to change market behavior. For example, retailers or farmers may seek more active competition among processors. (In fact, every business firm is interested in more active competition among its suppliers and its customers, although it usually considers competition at its own level to be too active!) The major challenge to the leadership of processors has come from retailers who have used their large size and their own brands to force processors to compete for retail shelf space.

The Demanded Brands

A key factor in channel leadership is the successfully branded product. To the extent that consumers demand a brand, the brand's owner has a greater share of channel control. The reasons are so apparent they require little elaboration.

Because of the strategic importance of brands and trademarks, it is important to understand some of their more significant features. *Branding* is the identification by brand names, trademarks, and so on of products or services by a seller (or sales group). A **brand name** is a word or group of letters that can be spoken. **Trademarks** include brand names, symbols, and other marks that have received legal recognition as branding devices.

Brands are a communication device. Imagine talking about automobiles without using such names! Imagine the difficulties of advertising a product without brand names. As a communication device, their usage has long been protected by common law. Legal rights in interstate commerce were defined further by the federal Lanham Act of 1946. In general, if ownership of a brand is contested, rights ordinarily go to the firm that can show first and continuous usage of it for a product or class of products. Ownership rights can be protected only by a civil suit; the government does not prosecute an infringer of a brand.

Although every seller seeks to popularize her brands so that potential customers readily recognize them, there is a paradoxical danger of too much success. Aspirin was once a brand name, but the brand name was lost when it became the common descriptive name for any pill containing its ingredient. How often do you say "Kleenex" when you mean "facial tissue"?

A brand is often associated with its manufacturer—Heinz "57" food products, Gerber baby foods, and Busch beer. But retailers may also sell products to which they attach their own brand; for example, Hy-Vee chocolate chips. Thus, we find the large retailers such as Sears, Target, and Wal-Mart selling many products under their own brand names.

Therein lies a story. Marketing people often use the phrase "battle of the brands" to describe the competition between **manufacturers' brands** (the branded products of the larger food manufacturers; the better-known ones are often called *national brands*) and retailer or distributor brands (often called **private labels**). The battle of the brands is a strategic aspect of the struggle for channel leadership. If consumers prefer and even insist on Kellogg's Corn Flakes, Kellogg's has brand identity it can leverage in marketing campaigns. Almost any processor can supply store-brand corn flakes, but only Kellogg's can supply its brand.

Branding is of varying importance in the battles for channel leadership in the food business. Although it is not always obvious why some foods have much more successful brands than others, three conditions for brand success can be stated:

1. A meaningful brand must offer homogeneous quality over time so that buyers can identify and rely on it.

2. A successful brand should be easily identified.

3. A successful brand usually must be backed by an aggressive and likely expensive promotional campaign that convinces many potential buyers of its merits.

Generally, these conditions for successful branding are met more easily for the more processed food products such as cake mixes, baby foods, or processed cheese than for raw commodities such as fresh fruits or even minimally processed items such as fresh meat. There are exceptions. The

Sunkist cooperative has successfully branded oranges, and there is hardly a food item that some firm has not tried to brand.

The point is that successful branding of some foods is at least a partial explanation of the location of channel leadership. Branding is an important means of access to channel leadership, but it is not the only means.

Other Means of Access to Channel Leadership

The level in the channel with the financially strongest and largest firms is a likely candidate for channel leadership. This argument admittedly has some circularity because channel leadership itself may help firms to become larger and stronger. Nevertheless, it is fairly obvious that a multimillion-dollar corporation has the assets, the talent, and the motivation to try to organize a market channel. On the other hand, a small proprietor is usually busy doing today's business, with little time to consider how he might get the channel reorganized. In fact, he may have little understanding of any part of the channel other than his own.

Events, both economic and technical, that are totally outside the control of channel participants may shift advantage from one level to another. Many retailers have channel strength today because they are large, powerful firms. Much of food retailers' present financial strength may be attributed to their good management. It is clear that their success is due also to the development of a large, prosperous class of consumers who think themselves too busy for anything but one-stop shopping.

Milk provides a specific technical example. As long as milk was sold in cumbersome, returnable glass bottles, families usually appreciated home delivery. The development of disposable plastic milk containers greatly increased the attractiveness of buying milk at the supermarket. This technical development is one of the reasons why the retailer became more important in the milk distribution channel.

THE DYNAMICS OF CHANNEL ORGANIZATION: THE LIVESTOCK–MEAT INDUSTRY

Numerous industries have undergone substantial reorganization during the past two centuries. New technologies and new systems of communication and transportation have often been the precursors of change. This section reviews one major channel as a case example of how channel organization can change.

In the livestock–meat channel, the first giant firms were at the meat-packing stage. A key technical development was the practical refrigerator car—developed mainly through the efforts of such early packers as Gustavus Swift. The refrigerator car allowed a packer to ship fresh meat long distances and thereby reach many markets, rather than only a small market in the environs of the slaughterhouse. Another key technical development was the disassembly line (for breaking the carcass into parts), by which important labor economies were achieved. The early adopters of these new technologies swiftly became the giants of meat packing as they displaced small, local butchers.

These giant firms rather quickly organized national systems of livestock procurement and meat distribution. Beginning in the late 1800s, they relied on the chief national transport system of the day, the railroads. Huge multistory packing plants were located at key railroad centers in the livestock areas, in cities like Chicago, Indianapolis, St. Louis, St. Paul, and Omaha. The locations of these plants became terminal markets to which livestock was readily assembled by railroad and from which meat could be readily distributed nationwide.

Farmers were too small, too weak, and too disunited to organize a livestock marketing system. It was packer and railroad management and capital that located the plants and built and operated the terminal markets for almost all livestock in the period from 1890 to 1920. We do not mean to imply that farmers would necessarily have organized a different system if they had been the channel leaders, although they might have. Our point is that the packers, along with the railroads, exercised strong channel leadership.

Prior to this time, meat retailing was generally in the hands of one-man butcher shops. They had neither the capital, the information, nor the expertise to organize a meat procurement system. Consequently, packers had no competition from retailers in organizing national meat distribution. Each one of the "Big Five'" packers (they later became the "Big Four") developed national systems of branch houses and sales offices to provide wholesaling as well as processing functions.

When truck transportation became competitive with railroads in the 1920s and 1930s, packers reorganized the livestock-procurement system. Buying points and plants were dispersed widely across the production area, and the terminal markets with their associated commission firms soon lost their dominance. Independent agencies and farmer cooperatives could compete in organizing livestock assembly points in this new truck economy. More and more livestock were purchased at the feedlot or at the packers' docks or buying stations.

Retail Grasp for Leadership

The integration of meat markets into grocery stores and the growth of large supermarket chains and wholesale–retail groups led to a retail challenge to the packers' systems of distribution. Meat is now typically purchased in very large orders on the basis of a chain store division's or a wholesale group's entire needs. Although some packer branch houses and sales people still call on individual retailers, these are no longer typical. The shift from individual retailers buying beef by the carcass to chains buying by the car lot marked the end of the packer-organized distribution system. Furthermore, today we see processors playing the role of the old supermarket butcher by delivering branded case-ready products directly to the retailer.

The decline of the dominance of big packers over the packing industry during the mid-twentieth century seems to have both aided and resulted from the retailers' grasp for channel leadership. The entry of new, smaller packers was facilitated by the ready market of new, integrated wholesale retailers, which eliminated the costs of building a branch house distribution system. In short, integrated retail–wholesale organizations have now taken most but not all of the wholesale function away from packers.

Today, packers and retailers share leadership and control of the livestock–meat channel. Packers still exercise leadership at the livestock end of the channel, and they still exercise more leadership in product development and innovation than do the retailers.

Boxed Beef and Packer Leadership

Perhaps the most vivid and interesting example of change in the packaging of meat concerns **boxed beef.** The story is complex, and the final chapter cannot be written yet. However, a short summary is instructive in understanding the workings of the marketplace.

Most retail cuts were traditionally fabricated, weighed, packaged, and priced in the backroom of the local supermarket. It was difficult to achieve much labor efficiency considering the relatively small volume of each supermarket. The problem was much greater with beef than with pork. Pork arrives at retail in primal cuts (loins, butts, hams, and ribs) or in retail-ready packages (bacon, sausage, picnics, and ham portions). Pork processing at retail is minimal, and cutting involves little more than transforming loins into chops, roasts, and country backbone; butts into pork steak or roasts. In contrast, until the 1970s beef traditionally arrived in sides or quarters. The 175-pound quarter or 350-pound side was not easily handled. Moreover, extensive labor was required to cut the steaks and roasts, dice the stewing beef, and grind the ground beef.

Why the difference in pork and beef processing? Hogs were always disassembled into primals at the packing house because it was obviously the efficient site for curing hams, bacon, and picnic hams and for making sausage. In contrast, virtually none of the beef carcass is cured except for a few briskets. Quality, shrink, and handling problems were reduced when the side or quarter was left intact as long as possible.

Researchers and progressive retailers began to tackle this efficiency problem in beef in the late 1950s. That the industry is still in transition decades later verifies that major changes in an industry do not take place overnight.

Some attempts were made to emulate the bacon example: beef was cut and packaged in retail-ready packages at the packing level or at a retail distribution center. The industry soon concluded that the pork loin was the better model. Beef would be cut into primals and subprimals prior to reaching the retail store, and then the final cutting into steaks and roasts would still take place in the backroom. The difficulties of keeping an attractive appearance on beef cuts for more than three days after cutting have been a primary hindrance to emulating the bacon approach. New technology in packaging films solved this problem, and meanwhile the industry has moved mainly toward primals.

The general term of *fabricated* or boxed beef is used to characterize this new distribution method because the fabricated primals and subprimals are shipped in boxes, whereas quarters and sides were shipped hanging on rails. The handling life of the primal unit is prolonged by a heavy, protective film that is vacuum-shrunk to fit.

Boxed beef has several advantages in addition to labor efficiency. Shipping costs are reduced by removing very sizable amounts of fat and bone at the fabrication plant rather than transporting them to market centers. Moreover, the fat and bone have more salvage value in large lots than in supermarket-sized lots. Increases in efficiency also result from better matching of supply and demand for the various beef cuts. Some supermarkets have customer demand for more roasts or ground beef rather than steaks. If customers generally prefer round steaks in one market area and T-bone steaks in another, boxed-beef facilities meet those wants. Finally, wages are usually lower at packing houses than for retail meat cutters.

What does boxed beef have to do with the organization of the meat channel? Just this. Where shall the primals be prepared: at the retail distribution centers or at the packing house? If and when some retail-ready cuts are substituted for primals, will the retailer or the packer prepare them? Currently, three packers control over 80% of meat packing as a result of the boxed beef phenomenon. Each packer has retail-ready beef in its brand-name packages. Some retailers have a different vision, one that includes the retailer name on the package.

SUMMARY

1. No two market channels are organized exactly alike. Very few channels are now organized as they were a half century ago. Firms are motivated by their interdependence within a channel to work together, but awareness of their interdependence also invites efforts to dominate or to obtain channel leadership. Technological developments within or outside the industry present opportunities to reduce costs through new methods of marketing. Given a certain environment, these tensions and profit opportunities lead to channel reorganization. Reorganization of a channel is no simple matter, usually requiring more than a decade.

2. Although each market participant may be motivated to organize the market channel in a particular fashion, only a few have what it takes to do so. Generally, it takes a strong consumer allegiance to one's products or services and/or strong economic power relative to other participants. The two frequently go together. This is not to downplay

the small participant with innovative ideas. He may have an impact by convincing those who control the necessary capital. Moreover, any reorganization is shaped by the technology and the economic relationships of the day. In the late 1800s, the livestock–meat system had to be organized to utilize the rail network, whereas today it must be organized to utilize the interstate highway system.

3. It is doubtful that any complete reorganization of an industry is carefully planned in total by the leaders. There is always a fog of uncertainty. Most firms and leaders have quite short-range views. Reorganization is the cumulative result of decisions made by industry leaders as each pursues advantageous changes.

4. Meat packers gained channel influence, and even dominance, by developing giant firms controlling not only packing but also wholesaling and delivery to the retailer's door. Other food processors used national advertising to build strong demand for their brands as a means to achieve channel leadership. Retail chains have used their large buying power and their own brands to offset the market power of processors.

5. Channel leadership is neither a necessary nor a sufficient condition for survival as a channel participant. Many independent agencies with little market power survive in the marketplace. The demise of the independent wholesaler, which has been predicted by various seers since 1900, continues to be avoided by managements alert and flexible enough to adjust. Amid all the talk about trends toward vertical integration in the food industry, the independent food brokers have quietly increased their volume by performing services more cheaply for retailers and processors than they could perform for themselves.

6. Operating at the leadership level can contribute to a firm's continued success but does not ensure it. Suppose that you are a vegetable canner who is negotiating a sale to a major chain. Would you expect an easier time of it if you are selling Green Giant vegetables or if you have no well-known brand and are negotiating to pack under the chain's brand?

7. Generally, farmers have not occupied leadership roles except insofar as they have done so through their cooperatives. Group collective action is generally the only access that farmers have to channel leadership (see Chapter 12).

 STUDY QUESTIONS

1. John Jones buys feeder cattle on the Oklahoma terminal market. Is he a wholesaler, processor, assembler, or retailer? Is he a merchant or an agent–broker? Are most retailers also merchants? What about processors?

2. Does the term *integrated channel* imply a certain type of firm behavior and coordination?

3. What is meant by leadership? How can one gain leadership in marketing–procurement channels? What type of resources are needed? Give an example of a firm that has gained channel leadership or is in the process of attaining a leadership role in today's agribusiness world?

4. Using the Internet, find out what has been the trend in Japanese consumption of U. S. beef, both processed and unprocessed. Why do you think this trend has occurred?

5. From your own observations, are retailers or processors the leaders in the marketing channel for cheese? Soft drinks? Bread?

6. What is meant by the "battle of the brands"? Who seems to be winning in breakfast cereals? Soft drinks? Potato chips? Fluid milk? Beer?

 **CLASS EXERCISE**

For your group's agricultural commodity and agribusiness, research the agribusiness's efforts to develop branded products. Find out the following information:

1. Why the business has or has not pursued branding

2. The level of concentration for the industry segment of your commodity (use USDA and Census Bureau data)

Your group should prepare to lead a discussion on how opportunities for your agribusiness might arise through branding. For example, branding played a role in the development of microbreweries when concentration in the brewing industry was rapidly increasing.

12

MARKETING BY FARMER GROUPS: COLLECTIVE ACTION

PREVIEW

- Theory and experience indicate that producers can often benefit economically by working together in groups. Theory and experience also indicate that it is surprisingly difficult to obtain such group action.

- Commodity (industry) associations, marketing cooperatives, farmer bargaining associations, and new generation cooperatives are similar in the important sense that each represents a group effort by farmers to market their output.

- Marketing cooperatives differ from investor-owned firms and have a unique set of managerial problems to solve.

- The Capper-Volstead Act played a critical role in society's license of marketing cooperatives.

- Bargaining associations play a role in contractual markets.

- New generation cooperatives are closed cooperatives that attach delivery rights in proportion to ownership and pay back to owners on an annual basis.

KEY TERMS

bargaining association

Capper-Volstead Act

centralized cooperative

cooperative (coop)

federated cooperative

generic promotion

investor-owned firm (IOF)

new generation cooperative

patronage refund

B y acting jointly, farmers can achieve marketing objectives that they cannot achieve by acting separately. We have discussed the limited marketing options faced by the individual farmer. If farmers are to reach forward in the marketing–procurement channels with a marketing program of their own, they must work together. It is only together that farmers can bargain on equal terms with a processor. It is only together that farmers can process their own products and market them to retailers or consumers, and it is only together that farmers can expect to benefit from commodity promotion. The few instances where an individual farmer does those things are limited exceptions.

There are several institutional mechanisms (organizational forms) by which farmers may group together to perform certain marketing functions. The most important is the marketing cooperative; the bargaining cooperative or association is similar. Less commonly used organizational forms, which will not be examined here, include regular corporations and limited partnerships. Also quite important to group efforts are marketing orders and commodity promotion programs. The latter two activities require some coercion to motivate group participation. They take place under government supervision and include possible sanctions after a favorable vote by producers of a commodity.

What are the opportunities for farmers to achieve an improved marketing system by grouping together? Generally, groups of producers seek one or more of the following objectives:

1. To improve industry demand
2. To regulate supplies and qualities more in line with demand
3. To improve competitiveness and efficiency in the marketing channel
4. To gain more channel control and leadership for farmers

Commodity (generic) promotion contributes to the first objective and somewhat to the fourth. *Marketing cooperatives* often contribute to all four objectives but especially to the third and fourth. *Bargaining associations* mainly contribute to the fourth. *Marketing orders* are also used in conjunction with all four objectives but especially with the first, second, and fourth. Marketing orders are not discussed extensively in this text because the market order is a very unique program targeted at very few commodities.

During the past 10 years, U. S. agriculture has undergone many changes related to collective action by farmers. Farmer interest in vertically integrating up the value chain has led farmers to act collectively to pool resources. Of course, there are other reasons for collective action beyond financial resources, such as access to adequate supplies to achieve economies of size in processing. Another factor is geographically spreading production risks over large areas so that high-valued crops can be supplied in sufficient quantities. Collective action also motivates the sharing of information across a broad group of farmers. Finally, the public favors farmer collective action because it stimulates economic development in rural areas.

Producer collective action has faced many challenges. Farmer–owners often know little about technologies available or managing processing or marketing products. Sometimes a collective action project is undercapitalized because only the minimum number of members invest. There are logistical challenges related to placement of the business—whether it should be located "in the backyard" or at the optimal location. Often, local economic development interests clash with selecting the most economically feasible location. It can be challenging to hire good management into rural locations. Furthermore, a farmer–member board often suffers internal conflict because the business buys from the farmer–members. For example, what corn price should a farmer–member board set for buying corn from farmer–members?

Recently, producer collective action business ventures have taken a new path by changing organizational structure to address some of these challenges. Some agricultural cooperatives have reorganized themselves as limited partnerships or corporations to allow for partnering or joint ventures with non–farmer owned companies or, in the case of corporations, to allow for a public stock offering to raise capital. No doubt the future will bring many changes in organizational structures of producer-owned ventures as their needs change.

GROUP PROMOTION OF AGRICULTURAL COMMODITIES

Generic promotion is the promotion of a particular commodity (rather than a brand-name product) financed collectively by producers of that commodity. Promotion includes advertising and numerous other activities designed to increase the demand for the commodity. No single producer can afford to go it alone in commodity promotion because the individual benefits will certainly be less than costs. For a group, the benefits may exceed the costs.

The purpose of generic promotion is to change demand to raise the price of the commodity or to increase the volume that will clear the market at a given price. Thus, the task is to move the intersection of the commodity demand and long-run supply curves to the right. Assume that D_1 is the present demand curve (Exhibit 12.1). Obtaining D_2 through promotion will benefit producers by raising prices to the intersection of SRS_1 and D_2 from the intersection of SRS_1 and D_1. However, in the long run, if the position of D_2 is maintained through more promotion, then producers will increase supplies and reduce price to the intersection of LRS, SRS_2, and D_2. Thus, some of the short-run price gains from promotion tend to be reduced over time.

Generic promotion of agricultural commodities is tiny in relation to the many billions spent on product advertising in the total economy, but it appears large when one considers that most of it is financed by quasi-voluntary means. The many types of commodity programs include cotton, wool, wheat, soybeans, citrus fruit, dairy, eggs, beef, pork, potatoes, California dates, almonds, and about 75 others.

In addition to domestic programs, the Foreign Agricultural Service of the USDA cooperates with industry groups and foreign firms and governments in sponsoring market

EXHIBIT
12.1

Possible impacts (short run and long run) of advertising on commodity demand.

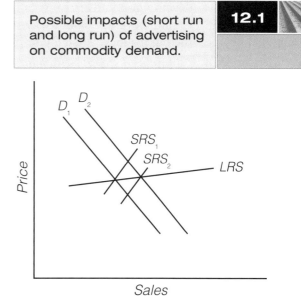

development programs. Such foreign market programs for a variety of agri-cultural commodities cost more than $100 million per year.

Program for Generic Promotion

An effective program for generic promotion should do the following:

1. *Adopt clear, measurable objectives.* For example, the turkey industry set out to promote year-round consumption as an alternative to sales being made almost solely at Thanksgiving and Christmas.

2. *Develop a strategy that fits the commodity, the marketing system, and buyers' attitudes.* For example, the turkey industry developed sales of parts and boneless portions for the nonholiday season and promoted these "new products." The grain sorghum industry did not advertise on TV. Instead, they contacted feed grain purchasers abroad and con-vinced them to try U. S. grain sorghum. The pork industry has felt that a big problem is the negative image of pork developed by nutri-tionists and physicians, plus threats of possible government prohibition of nitrites in curing. Thus, their efforts have included edu-cation, research, and even legal actions aimed at those key groups. The "other white meat" promotional campaign helped to change pork's image. The Florida citrus industry developed an aggressive pro-gram of industry promotion including the distribution of nearly 2 billion consumer coupons for frozen concentrated orange juice. Coupons have both an advertising and a price-discounting effect on consumers; they also stimulate the interest of retailers.

3. *When advertising is part of the adopted strategy, use a good profes-sional advertising agency.* Producer committees cannot be expected to develop good advertising campaigns. When the milk industry is trying to take beverage sales away from Coke and Pepsi, they are playing in the big leagues. Their "Got milk?" campaign is an effective one.

4. *Obtain and spend sufficient money to achieve a high probability of obtaining the objectives.* Small expenditures are often a total waste because they are too little to capture the attention of potential buyers.

5. *Set up a program to evaluate results.* It is best to obtain outside, objective help in evaluation. If the objectives are being met, pass the good word to those who are providing the funds. If the objectives are not being met, seek out the difficulties and correct them. If more trials still do not attain the objectives, take a hard look at whether they are attainable. After all, there is no economic law that generic promotion will pay for every commodity.

The costs of a promotional campaign are usually quite concrete and measurable. As a result, industry groups spend many dollars on them, and paid staff and unpaid volunteers devoted many hours to these efforts. Unfortunately, the benefits are not so readily measurable. Did the demand curve move to the right or become less elastic during or after the promotional effort? It requires a sophisticated price analysis to answer that question. Was there a linkage between the movement of the demand curve and the promotional effort, or did other factors cause the movement? That requires an even more sophisticated analysis. A few such analyses have been done in areas such as dairy, eggs, beef, cotton, and citrus.[1] Some industry groups have received expert guidance as to how to allocate their efforts by market and by type of activities. Generally, most industry groups have spent so little on economic evaluation of their promotional campaigns that they have lacked good evidence as to what benefits, if any, were achieved. Perhaps some industry leaders spend so little on evaluation because they fear the outcome.

MARKETING COOPERATIVES

A cooperative (coop) is a special type of business firm: "a user-owned and -controlled business from which benefits are derived and distributed equitably on the basis of use."[2] Cooperatives are not unique to agriculture (Exhibit 12.2). This definition tries to capture several distinctive aspects of the cooperative firm. As a firm, a cooperative is ordinarily incorporated and differs significantly from an investor-owned firm (IOF) because the coop's users (customers or suppliers) are also its owners, whereas an IOF is owned by investors who have ownership rights and dividends proportional to ownership. As owners, the coop's users have the additional

EXHIBIT

12.2 Top 10 cooperatives, by revenue, in 2003.

Cooperative	Revenues ($, million)	Assets ($, million)	Industry Sector
CHS, Inc.*	9.399	3,808	Agriculture
Dairy Farmers of America	6,933	2,153	Agriculture
Wakefern Food Corp.	6,578	1,074	Grocery
Land O'Lakes, Inc.	6,320	3,398	Agriculture
TOPCO Associates, LLC	4,600	—	Grocery
Associated Wholesale Grocers	3,721	721	Grocery
ACE Hardware Corp.	3,159	1,149	Hardware & lumber
Unified Western Grocers	2,819	720	Grocery
Do-it-Best Corp.	2,334	602	Hardware & lumber
Ag Processing, Inc.	2,127	733	Agriculture

*CHS Inc. is a publicly traded business, but corporate governance qualifies CHS Inc. as a cooperative.

Source: National Cooperative Bank.

perspective of users; as users, they also have the owners' perspective on how they can affect services and activities. They believe that the coop is operated for their benefit. An IOF's customers have no such perspectives.

Several guiding principles have developed during the rather long history of cooperatives. These principles have varied slightly from country to country and over time, and consumer coops often have a slightly different perspective than agricultural coops. The following three principles are currently the most important for agricultural coops:

1. User ownership (ownership by coop member–patrons)
2. User control (democratic member control rather than investor control)
3. User benefits (the coop provides and distributes benefits to its users on the basis of their use)[3]

The first principle is central to the basic distinction between a coop and an IOF. The other two principles are supportive of the first. For example, democracy has been a goal in itself, but it also contributes to the successful operation of a firm that depends on all its members for both capital and day-to-day business. Because the member–patrons are the owners, they have claim to the savings (profits) generated by the coop. They also have control over the various services provided.

Virtually all agricultural coops were organized as small local businesses. Coops have been organized to erect and operate a local grain elevator, a local farm supplies store, a packing shed for shipping fresh fruit, an electric distribution network for the farmers of a county, and, recently, to add value through processing of commodities. Over time many coops have failed, but others have grown, and some have associated with one another to manufacture farm supplies and mine fertilizer materials, to generate power, to export grain, and to manufacture and market butter and cheese. Two alternative organizational structures developed to handle these larger-than-local cooperative activities. Currently, the large coops are known as federated, centralized, or a hybrid mixture of the first two types.

The **federated cooperative** was built from the ground up. Local coops formed a second-level coop to perform various marketing functions such as processing, distribution, advertising, and merchandising. Thus, a federated coop is a cooperative of cooperatives. Its membership is local coops, whose membership in turn consists of farmers. Farmers exercise their control of the regional federation through a board of directors elected through the local coops. Control is exercised by the local member–owners and not by upper levels. The local coops own the superstructure, not vice versa.

Farmers are members directly of a **centralized cooperative**. The coop's total operations are owned and controlled as a unit. The merger of numerous local coops into one regional coop was often the beginning point of a centralized coop. Farmer members vote directly for directors. Farmer control seems to be more direct and democratic, yet at the local level the reverse may seem to be true, because the local elevator, farmer's exchange, or processing plant is not owned and controlled by local members but rather by the entire membership, located in many communities and even in many states. Centralized marketing coops appear to have been more successful than the federated type.

A number of large coops are some combination of the two organizational types. For example, a federated organization may rescue some local units that are in financial trouble by purchasing their assets. Thus, it moves from a federation toward a centralized organization. Farmers' perceptions of their degree of democratic control may depend more on how committed the top management is to farmer objectives than on which organizational form is used. Certainly, the issues of how well the coop responds to its members' wishes and how that response is generated are crucial issues in both types of coops.

One of the largest centralized cooperatives is Dairy Farmers of America (DFA). Founded in 1998 as a federation of four regional milk marketing and processing cooperatives, today DFA's 4,000 employees represent nearly 22,000 dairy farm families. In 2005, DFA's sales were $8.5 billion. DFA is a global marketer of dairy commodity and value-added products. One of its most well-known brands is Borden cheese. DFA provides producer–members with services ranging from milk pickup to financial recordkeeping to lobbying policy makers on behalf of the U. S. dairy industry.

A very successful federated cooperative is Florida's Natural Growers (part of Citrus World, Inc.), a producer-owned orange processing cooperative. Initially the cooperative was formed as a marketing cooperative, but the members' desire to add value required coordination of quality and quantity to develop a branded product through processing.

Many agricultural coops either market farm commodities for their members, furnish them farm supplies, or add value to producer-owned commodities. As the example of DFA indicates, some do more than one. Our discussion will focus on marketing rather than supply coops. Later, we will discuss bargaining groups, which include a third kind of coop called a *bargaining association*. While our discussion focuses on cooperatives, it should be noted that today producer–owners use many alternatives to the cooperative business structure. However, the operating and management principles that drive these new business structures derive from the cooperative structure.

Goals of Marketing Cooperatives

Early in this chapter, four objectives of group action were listed. The following is a more specific statement of goals that a marketing coop may have in serving its members:

1. *To provide the most efficient marketing outlets.* Coop members typically want the highest possible returns for their marketed commodities. Thus, their coops must be efficient in the marketing tasks they perform. An efficient coop also provides a competitive yardstick that pressures IOFs in the same market to be equally efficient. If the IOFs are not as efficient as their coop competitor, they may be run out of the market.

2. *To expand demand for their members' commodities.* Expansion of demand can increase returns over time; thus, some coops have suc-

cessfully sought demand expansion. The increase in demand may arise from one or more of the following causes. First, producers may be better able to manage quality and thus provide consumers with a higher quality product. Second, the coop as an integrated processor may develop better products and promote them so effectively as to increase retail demand. Ocean Spray is an example of such successful product development combined with effective promotion.

3. *To provide better coordination between production and consumption.* Production and consumption often do not match well in time and space. Although it is the task of most marketing firms to coordinate production and consumption, coops have often been innovators in improved coordination.

4. *To provide more dependable market outlets, including sometimes the only remaining outlets.* Assurance of market access is becoming a more important objective of coops. Producers of many specialized commodities and even producers of other commodities in isolated areas often depend on market outlets operated by one or two buyers. In a good crop year, canneries may be unable to process the total crop, so some tonnage cannot be sold. The lack of market power in such situations and the insecurity of possibly losing all market access are often powerful incentives toward cooperative vertical integration. Specialized producers of nuts from long-lived, expensive orchards are perhaps among those farmers most concerned about continued market access. Generally, producers with large, highly specific investments in a particular crop have been the producers most willing to commit large investments in coops to ensure continued market access.

5. *To achieve channel leadership, including vertical integration and even market power for the members.* Farmers look to coops to help them achieve more control over their destiny. They perceive themselves as weak price takers in a market environment in which others are more knowledgeable and powerful. In varying degrees, some coops have set out to obtain market power. Marketing coops handling certain fruits and vegetables and other specialized commodities have been quite successful.

Coops Compared to IOFs

The coop goals reveal some of the subtle ways in which marketing coops differ from marketing IOFs. The IOF is not concerned with stimulating competition—there is always too much from its perspective, because competition usually reduces profits. It is responsible only to its investors. The IOF often wants to expand demand for its products and services, which may or may not expand demand for the farm commodities that it currently handles. The IOF generally feels little obligation to maintain a market outlet for a particular group of farmers. An IOF fruit and vegetable processor generally is less motivated than a coop to find a home for the entire output of growers. The IOF achieves channel leadership to benefit its owners and management rather than farmers.

These differences reflect the fact that the coop is tied to its members and to their commodities. True, a typical coop has open membership, so that its members can change over time. True, some coops have quit marketing certain commodities for members after suffering financial losses in marketing them. Nevertheless, in the short term (measured in years or decades), a coop is tied to the farmers of a particular community, state, or region. Its management is committed to serve the best interests of those producers. It will suffer low profits and even losses before closing a market outlet. It will often provide new services demanded by its members, even though they do not appear profitable. In contrast, the management of the IOF provides services equal to those of the coop as long as it has close ties to an area or any group of farmers. The coop's willingness to sacrifice profits in some areas and activities is dependent, of course, on profits in others. The coop, like any other capitalistic firm, must make ends meet—it cannot endure net losses very long. In fact, coops sometimes fail because they try to do too much for their members.

Reasons for Farmer Membership

Many farmers of prior generations helped organize coops because of their interest in the coop goals enumerated above. Often organization was a reaction to oligopsony. For example, grain marketing coops were organized in reaction against the chains of line elevators that often repressed competition in the bidding for farmers' grain. Many dairy farmers recognized that there could be little competition in the localized buying of their milk for manufacturing use. They reasoned that it is better to be their own buyer and cheese maker (through a coop) because cheese can be shipped into a more competitive market. Of course, producer–members do not have to sell their entire production to the cooperative.

Why do farmers continue to belong to marketing coops? A general answer is because they believe that they will receive net benefits as compared to any other alternative. Prices received are always important but are not necessarily the only objective. Coop members may benefit from a nearby assured market outlet; others may stay for reasons of loyalty. These loyal members perceive no net gain for themselves but believe in the purposes of the coop and are willing to support it in a modest way.

Society's Institutional License to Marketing Coops

American farmer coops have been around in one form or another for almost 200 years. Marketing coops became important in the early twentieth century. Similarly, the present legal character of society's license to farmers as a marketing group has been determined in the twentieth century. Although that societal license continues to evolve through occasional legislation, regulation, and adjudication, its main features were cast by the Capper-Volstead Act of 1922.

Extent of Antitrust Exemption

It may be surprising that the degree of antitrust exemption for coops is one of the basic and sometimes controversial parts of society's license to them. But what if a coop markets most of a commodity for a region or even for the nation?

The **Capper-Volstead Act** of 1922 established the right of farmers to act together within cooperative marketing associations. Since the Capper-Volstead Act, such joint action in itself is not an antitrust violation. Coops often are able to join together in pricing or marketing arrangements or even in mergers in ways that are not permitted for IOFs. However, coops may not include IOFs in the above arrangements without being subject to the same restraints that affect IOFs.[4] One would not expect a complete blanket exemption. In the 1970s, both the Justice Department and the Federal Trade Commission discussed ways of limiting the antitrust exemptions of coops. Moreover, the Secretary of Agriculture is empowered by Section 2 of the Capper-Volstead Act to intervene with any coop that he finds to be raising unduly the prices of any agricultural product through restraining trade. Although many of the specific details are controversial, the general license is clear. Society gave farmers, as weak individuals, a power to group together. If farmers transform their individual weakness into a group that unduly enhances prices by the exercise of monopoly powers or that engages in predatory acts, they can expect societal restraints.

Federal Taxation

Income tax laws and regulations recognize the distinctively different nonprofit nature of coops. Generally, a coop can qualify so that it has no taxable income on member business as long as it provides its net savings to its members as **patronage refunds**—the distribution of a cooperative's earnings to its patrons in proportion to their business volume. To the extent that the coop does not return or allocate savings to members, those savings are taxed as income under the usual corporate income tax rules. The refunds to members are taxed as personal income.

Cooperatives are taxed on income from nonmember business. They sometimes choose to pay taxes on some member business as well. An IOF corporation pays income taxes on its profits. To the extent that those profits are paid out as dividends (often half or more are not), the dividends to the owners are taxed again as personal income. Thus, there is double taxation on the part of the IOF corporate profits paid out as dividends, whereas there is only single taxation of the coop savings.

Special Problems of Managing a Coop

Managing any agribusiness presents many challenges and opportunities. Although the management of a coop and that of an IOF share similar problems, the distinctive characteristics of a coop present some special ones. Discussed here are problems associated with raising capital, being responsible to customer–owners, helping directors direct but not manage, and competing with other coops.

Raising Capital

Obtaining capital has been and remains a most important problem for coops. Of course, lenders will loan much capital against plant and equipment and other marketable assets. However, there must be a hard core of risk capital (equity) first that provides a cushion of protection to the lenders. This equity capital is obtained for any corporation by the sale of shares and by retained earnings. Obviously, the initial capital is from sale of stock shares. But shares of coop stock tend to have little or no market value because earnings mainly accrue to patronage, not to stock. Owners rarely receive more than 6.5% interest on their shares and typically receive nothing. Thus, the coop faces the extremely difficult problem of selling something of very limited market value.

Consequently, most coops have started out undercapitalized. If business went well, capital was gradually built up by retentions from the earnings (patronage refunds) or from sales (capital retains). Without delving into all the variations and complications, the main point is that current income is withheld from the members, is used as capital in the business, and is eventually rotated back to the members (or their estates) some years later. Member acceptance of the method of raising capital depends on many factors including the overall success to date of the coop, member understanding, and future business prospects of the coop. Nevertheless, the members, through their boards of directors, often underestimate the amount of capital required, relative to what management considers to be needed.

The capital problem became particularly acute for many marketing coops during the 1970s and 1980s. Those firms often expanded debt rapidly in the inflationary, booming 1970s. Then the abrupt rise in real interest rates in the 1980s, accompanied by a declining farm economy, caused many coops severe financial stress. As income improved during the 1990s, so did the fortune of many coops. However, the current competition of the agricultural economy has resulted in many cooperative mergers and caused one federal cooperative, Farmland Industries, to dissolve through bankruptcy.

Responsibility to Patron–Owners

The author talked to a top executive of a coop who had recently been in IOF management. When asked what was different about coop management, he replied, "Having farmers call me up and tell me how to manage this business!" The statement illustrates that dealing with user–owners is different from dealing with ordinary patrons. It obviously requires diplomacy and skill. An individual user–owner cannot be allowed to take advantage of the coop and fellow members. Nevertheless, for reasons cited earlier, the patron–owners as a group will be treated somewhat differently. They may resent a sales manipulation or a pricing policy that might seem completely ethical when applied strictly to customers. Patron–members may insist on services that impinge on coop earnings. On the positive side, they may provide valuable feedback, in terms of evaluation of services provided or of conduct of employees, that is superior to that obtained by an IOF.

Helping Directors Direct but Not Manage

There is a fairly clear conceptual difference between the sphere of the directors and that of management. It is the job of directors to set policy and to obtain a management that will carry it out. It is the job of managers to operate the coop within those policy guidelines. Coops vary as to how their directors and managers interact. At one extreme of board direction, the board selects all the management and enacts policies so detailed as to tie the hands of management. At the other extreme, the management keeps the board in the dark, gets them to rubber-stamp policies devised by management, and generally avoids any independent effective direction or supervision by the board.

If a coop is to serve the group interests of farmers, it must have a dedicated board of directors. The directors must represent the members, keep informed about the critical problems and major opportunities facing the coop, evaluate carefully the performance of the coop, and provide proper incentives to management, including that ultimate incentive of dismissal if it is ineffective. Generally, a good board results from active efforts of management to obtain and educate it. A shortsighted management may be tempted to seek a docile, uninformed board. To do so is to undermine the purpose of the coop as a method of group action by farmers. Moreover, a weak board may endanger the viability of the firm. Some less involved members and many nonmembers dismiss any coop as "a firm run for the benefit of the managers." If the management and board allow that charge to become true, the coop loses its base of support and its reason for being.

Competition with Other Coops

At both the local and the regional level, two or more marketing coops may compete for the patronage of the same farmers. Numerous coop managers say that they compete with all competitors regardless of whether they are IOFs or coops. In a society that depends on competition to motivate good economic performance, it is easy to applaud that managerial stance. Yet many thoughtful farmers ask why they should use their capital against each other within organizations that employ farmers' capital for a common effort. They recognize that they, as farmers, bear the costs of duplication of coop facilities, staff, and services. In Sweden, the dairy marketing coops for many decades had nonoverlapping territories so that there was no direct competition. Nevertheless, economic performance was impressive. One reason may have been the persistence of indirect competition. If one Swedish dairy coop paid slightly more for milk than another one did, the underpaid members were quick to demand an explanation from their coop.

Organizational Variations and Innovations

A few examples will illustrate some of the broad diversity among coops. Some of this diversity reflects different philosophical approaches or different historical developments, and much of it reflects the varying marketing objectives of different commodity groups and the varying amounts of capital required to achieve those objectives.

Midwestern/Great Plains Grain and Livestock

The typical grain or livestock coop in the Midwest or Great Plains performs a simple assembly-and-sales function and does little or no processing. Consequently, capital needs are low relative to sales. Membership is open and may be obtained automatically by selling grain or livestock to the coop. Returns from coop savings provide the equity capital. A farmer often regards coop membership a bit casually and may sell to two coops and a competing IOF during a single season.

American Crystal Sugar

American Crystal Sugar is a notable exception to the usual practice of a coop beginning as an undercapitalized, small business. The cooperative began in 1973 with nearly 1,400 members, an investment of $86 million in six sugar beet factories, $20 million of equity capital, and a market share of almost 13% of the U. S. sugar beet market. There were obviously some unusual circumstances behind the birth of such a large cooperative.

One of the most concentrated sugar beet–producing areas of the world is the Red River Valley shared by Minnesota and North Dakota. Many of the area's beet growers belonged to the Red River Valley Sugar Beet Growers Association, formed in 1943 to represent their interests in relation to processors. By the early 1970s growers were concerned about a principal processor, American Crystal Sugar Company, which had been gradually closing its factories throughout the nation, including the Red River Valley area. Growers wanted expansion of processing, not retrenchment.

Gradually growers became convinced that they should acquire their own processing facilities to maintain and expand market outlets for their beets. They found that American Crystal management and stockholders were willing to sell the entire company. Long and complex negotiations were required to organize a marketing coop, raise the necessary investment capital from growers, borrow many millions from bankers, and meet all legal and tax requirements.

The growers' strongest motivation was to preserve a good market for a traditionally profitable crop. Grower–members provided initial capital equal to $100 per acre of beets grown and signed a five-year contract with the cooperative to market all of their beets through it. In this situation, the interdependence between the member and the coop is easy to see: the coop is not just an additional outlet to be used if it happens to be paying higher prices than its competitors, but it is the growers' marketing arm, in which they have a great deal invested.[5]

West Coast Fruit and Vegetable Processing

The fruit and vegetable processing coops on the West Coast typically have high capital needs relative to sales. The growers often have high fixed costs in orchards and in harvesting machinery. Thus, they are anxious to find a home for their full output. Even though they have strong demands for their capital in farming, many growers belong to processing coops as a way to assure a market outlet. A typical method of raising coop capital is through sales retains. For eight years, the coop retains a certain percentage of the market value of a member's deliveries. After those equity capital contributions are completed, there are no further retains on the member's sales. When she leaves the coop, her capital is then paid back over the same eight-year schedule.[6] The financial commitment to the coop is obviously much greater for this producer than for the Midwestern grain producer or even for the Red River beet grower.

To achieve a group effort while avoiding certain features of coops (democratic voting, undercapitalization, open membership, or specific tax provisions), some growers have utilized the regular corporate form of organization.[7] To analyze these efforts would lead us too far afield. It is important to note that various innovations are being tried to deal with certain perceived deficiencies in the way that marketing coops work.

Other innovations include joint ventures between a coop and an IOF. One of the longer lasting of these has been an arrangement by which a Florida coop supplies oranges to the Minute Maid division of Coca-Cola Company. The processor is assured of a steady supply that it handles for an assured processing fee. The coop is guaranteed a market that has been traditionally high priced, but it bears all risks of fluctuations in the orange juice market. However, coop capital needs are much lower than if it attempted its own processing. A far less successful joint venture was the now-terminated one between a California grape growers coop and Heublein for the joint ownership of a winery.[8]

Criteria for a Successful Marketing Coop

To be successful, a marketing coop must run a viable business, and it must keep producers in control of the board and the board in control of the coop. Achieving those goals is not easy.

Inadequate management and inadequate capital have been the ruin of many coops and particularly of the smaller locals. Farmer–members have often contributed to the management problem by being loath to pay competitive salaries and interfering with managerial decision making. Every farmer is in favor of good management, but he may also prefer policies and procedures, such as low salaries, expensive services, nepotism, and overly conservative investment, that are the antithesis of a good, sound business.

We accept the view of most farmers that a coop should operate to serve the purposes of its farmer–owners. On the other hand, it is easy for the management and employees of any large corporation—IOF or cooperative—to fall into the assumption that the firm is to be operated for their own benefit. Sometimes, a large stockholder or new conglomerate purchaser of stock shakes the management of an IOF out of such self-centeredness. But who is there to shake the management of the large coop?

Seldom does any cooperative member have an economic self-interest in trying to discipline management. The potential costs exceed the potential benefits. Although all members together may have an economic incentive, the rational choice is for each individual to hope that the others will make the effort while she reaps the benefits. This is a form of the free rider problem that often hinders any sort of group action.

The problem of farmers maintaining control of their group effort is serious and complex but not hopeless. It often increases as the organization grows, yet the remedy is hardly to cease growth. It is very difficult to maintain the vitality of an organization that is no longer growing. Moreover, economies of scale have been rising in many areas so that growth is often essential to continue efficient operation.

The remedy, rather, lies in dedicated efforts by farmers and coop management to ensure continued farmer control. Trite as it may sound, the participation of citizens is necessary to the survival of democracy—in the nation and in the coop. Management must continually inform and educate members as to the operation of the coop, and it must respect and strengthen the role of the farmers' board of directors. Neither farmers nor management can afford over the long run to do anything less. If giant coops become little more than the private empires of their top management, society will eventually remove the license that it gave to struggling groups of individual farmers through the Capper-Volstead Act.

What accomplishments can be expected of a coop that is a viable business dedicated to serving the interests of its members? We can summarize the previous discussion in terms of two expected accomplishments:

1. Increased demand at the farm level for the marketed commodity

2. Increased assurance in the minds of the members that they have dependable, efficient market access with some power and influence in the market channel and that they can protect their position in the foreseeable future

New Generation Cooperatives

The **new generation cooperative** is a distinct business entity from the traditional cooperative. The traditional coop principles include the following:

1. Open membership
2. No supply controls
3. Member profit retained as growth capital
4. No secondary market for equity

For new generation cooperatives, the coop principles are:

1. Closed membership
2. Upfront equity position by members
3. Delivery rights in proportion to equity position
4. Transferability of delivery rights and the existence of a secondary market for delivery rights
5. The possibility of immediate return of profits to members

There are several variations of the new generation cooperative model. Many of the ethanol plants constructed in the late 1990s and early twenty-first century were capitalized by producers under the new generation cooperative structure. This business structure has been popular because returns are proportional to ownership and member profits are returned quickly.

We shall use an example of an ethanol plant to describe how a new generation cooperative operates. This discussion will help readers appreciate the differences between a new generation cooperative and a traditional cooperative.

In the new generation cooperative model, membership and investment are closed. The new generation cooperative offers a set number of ownership shares, only entities owning shares are members. In contrast, the membership of a traditional cooperative is open; any entity can join the cooperative at any time. For the ethanol plant, financial capitalization is the first step, and this is when the number of shares is determined.

The number of shares to be sold is based on a target capitalization level. Suppose the ethanol plant is designed to use 15 million bushels of corn annually and produce 45 million gallons of ethanol annually, and that such a plant will cost $60 million to build and start up. The desired level of equity is determined to be $30 million. This $30 million represents the amount to be sourced from potential member–owners. The board of directors determines that one share will cost $30,000 and that each share will carry delivery rights of 7,500 bushels of corn. To raise $30 million, 1,000 shares must be sold. The 1,000 shares represent 7.5 million bushels of corn to be delivered. Suppose 500 producers buy two shares each. These 500 producers are now the member–owners of the ethanol plant, and each of the 500 members will have two votes each in policy decisions. In contrast, for a traditional cooperative the shares do not determine membership, and each member receives one vote. For example, a traditional ethanol cooperative might have 500 members that each deliver between 100 and 100,000 bushels of corn, and each member receives one vote.

The new generation cooperative producer–owners will elect a producer board of directors to oversee strategic planning and evaluate management. Since the producer–members will supply only one-half of the necessary corn, the other 7.5 million bushels can be supplied from members or nonmembers. For a traditional cooperative, the bushels could be sourced from both members and nonmembers, and members have no set minimum requirement of bushels to be delivered.

Now, assume that in the third year of operation the ethanol plant turns a $15 million profit. Profits are distributed in proportion to member ownership; hence, each member will receive $15,000 per share for that year. If the next year there is a $1,000 profit, then each member will receive $1 per share for that year. In case of a loss, the management of the new generation cooperative builds financial reserves (members typically do not pay in to cover a loss). The primary goal of the new generation cooperative is to maximize the dividends paid to member–owners.

The traditional cooperative, on the other hand, will retain (keep) all of the profits and only allocate dividends back, based on business in the cooperative, at a much later time. For example, a traditional cooperative that allocates dividends when the producer–member turns age 65 will set profits aside for the member and on the member's sixty-fifth birthday pay the member a lump sum. This is the traditional cooperative model for building reserves for new opportunities or in case of financial troubles. The members do not see the fruits of their membership until late in their involvement with the cooperative, unlike the members of a new generation cooperative, who receive distributions every year. For members of a new generation cooperative, if a new business opportunity is present, then a new business is formed and new shares are offered with right of first purchase to existing members of the original cooperative.

FARMERS' BARGAINING GROUPS

A farmers' **bargaining association** is a coop that represents its members by collectively negotiating terms of trade but does not engage in the physical aspect of marketing, such as assembly, processing, and distribution. Thus, the marketing activities of a bargaining group are much more limited than those of the typical marketing coop.

Let us be clear as to what a bargaining association is not. A bargaining association is not a cartel that controls the supply of a commodity and raises farm price to a revenue-maximizing level. Farmers have often hoped for such results, but a voluntary association of large numbers of sellers has never succeeded for long as a cartel. The incentives to free ride are too large. Whereas association members support the price by holding back much of their output, the free riders sell *all* their output. The obvious gains from free riding cause other association members to break ranks, and soon the game is up. Exceptions arise when government prevents free riding or when the number of sellers is so few that they police one another (review the discussion of oligopoly in Chapter 2).

The importance of group bargaining is directly related to the decline of open markets in agriculture. Generally, bargaining associations have operated in contractual markets, engaging in both marketing and production contracts. Individual producers lack the marketing information and power to bargain effectively in markets that are mostly or entirely contractual.

The bargaining association generally has more clout when it clearly has control of the commodity. On the other hand, when a processor lacks persuasive evidence that the bargaining association really can commit delivery of commodity, then he lacks assurance that group negotiation is useful and that avoidance of group negotiation would be harmful.

The function of the bargaining association—to bargain price and non-price terms of trade—can be performed only when a buyer is willing to negotiate with it. Sometimes buyers are not willing. In a number of cases, large cannery firms have strongly resisted any group "coming between us and our growers." Why, then, would any buyer consent?

Initially, buyers usually consent to bargain when they are faced by a united group representing a large segment of their usual supplies. Therefore, they bargain because they expect it to be less costly than not bargaining. Processors usually discover that there are advantages as well as costs and that they can adjust profitably to this method of doing business.

Bargaining associations have been most active in dairy, fruits, vegetables, sugar beets, and other specialty crops. Capital requirements and operating expenses are small. Bargaining associations are generally financed by deductions from crop receipts, although some groups receive dues from growers.

Membership in bargaining associations, like other coops, is voluntary, but once undertaken it involves definite rights and duties. The association is generally the agent for the farmer in selling the commodity (most associations handle only a single commodity), and the member must sell only through the association for some definite period of time.

Randall Torgerson explains the bargaining process as follows:

> The basic notion of bargaining is that it is a way of discovering price and other terms of trade. This implies an orderly process of meeting with handlers or other buyers in an atmosphere of coming to terms over items placed on the table. It is assumed that substantial economic analysis is conducted concerning crop size, yield, quality, and product demand as well as the operating "health" of the bargaining opponent. Producer power at the bargaining table is then determined by the relative size and internal strength of the farm segment compared with that of buyers; access to sound marketing intelligence; effectiveness of strategy and tactics used in the negotiating process; an institutional mechanism that facilitates bargaining; and the rules by which the bargaining game is played.[9]

Bargaining Accomplishments

Group bargaining involves the strategic use of maneuvers, offers and counteroffers, and threats and counterthreats. The outcome of any individual session is not predictable, but the long-run outcome is fairly predictable. Net prices are a little higher on the average than they would have been without bargaining. Prices are likely to be more stable from year to year. Moreover, prices may be more equitable among producers within the group. Although bargaining associations are prone to claim big gains in price, and such gains do occur in individual seasons, economic analysis has generally found the longer-term gains to be small or sometimes nonexistent.

Often, the bargaining association negotiates important nonprice terms. For a contract with a cannery, these terms may concern such items as the provision of shipping containers, hauling allowances, harvest scheduling, determination of grades, delivery quotas, harvesting techniques, and costs. Significant gains in efficiency may be obtained through group negotiations. Moreover, individual growers gain security and confidence that they will be treated like all other growers, whereas they can be capriciously discriminated against when they are not in a group.

An inexperienced bargaining association may be tempted to attempt too much—to operate like a cartel. Gaining a high price this year invites a larger production as soon as possible from members and nonmembers. Thus, this year's success can become the source of next year's crisis. Ralph Bunje, the long-time manager of the California Canning Peach Association, expressed the aim of bargaining this way: "to establish the highest price and best terms of sale that can be economically justified in the marketplace."[10] He leaves no doubt that he gives full force to all supply-and-demand factors in considering what is "economically justified."

In contractual markets, producers in the experienced associations typically feel that they are better off negotiating as a group than as individuals. Those who have experienced chaotic market conditions in the absence of group bargaining appreciate greatly the improved conditions for price making that group bargaining brings.

Fruits and Vegetables Bargaining

The California Canning Peach Association (1922) is one of the oldest bargaining associations. Canning peaches are a highly perishable commodity with only one market: canneries. The association has been bargaining for more than half a century. It takes ownership of the commodity and then pools returns to members. (Most bargaining associations pool their marketings so that each member receives the average price of that grade of the crop. Some associations act as agents and do not take ownership.) The entire peach canning industry is in California, and the association handles a slight majority of the state's production. The association seeks to negotiate all contract terms before harvest, but negotiations are sometimes prolonged to a much later date.

Bargaining associations tend to seek out price negotiations before annual crops are planted. Processors usually prefer an open-price contract with producers that specifies that the product will be traded but leaves the price determination to the discretion of the processor at harvest time.

Society's Institutional License to Farmer Bargaining

The basic legal status of farmer bargaining associations is the same as for marketing cooperatives. The Capper-Volstead Act has thus far been interpreted as permitting farmers to associate together in a bargaining coop, but it does not grant antitrust exemption for monopolizing or other such activities.

However, bargaining associations have sought additional license because of some special problems not shared by marketing coops. The organizing of bargaining associations has often been met by strong resistance. Although new marketing coops were not always welcomed by their private competitors, there were generally plenty of firms in the marketplace that were willing to do business with them. Bargaining associations usually do not face an open market; they face a very few firms, and in a particular area they may face only one firm. If the firm or firms are strongly opposed to a group effort by what they might paternalistically refer to as "our growers," they may be able to stop the bargaining association before it even bargains.

Ralph Bunje, as manager of the California Canning Peach Association, was a leader of the legislative fight to obtain protection for farmers of their right to organize. His 1966 testimony before Congress indicated why he sought more legislation:

> Our experience is that processors will, as a matter of good business, resist and undertake to destroy the opportunities for growers to create organizations that will come between them and their grower suppliers with respect to their purchase of fruits and vegetables. The same arguments and same objections would prevail here and, in fact, do prevail here that prevailed in opposition to the development of organized labor unions. Nevertheless, if farmers are to take their rightful place in today's society, they must be given protection with respect to the opportunity to organize in order to bargain for the sale of their production under the circumstances that exist today.[11]

Fair Practices

Out of the lobbying efforts of Bunje, the American Farm Bureau, and others came the Agricultural Fair Practices Act of 1967, often known by its Senate bill designation of S.109. Its proponents had intended to win solid protection for farmers from discriminatory practices of buyers. Instead, because of the strong lobbying of processors, they were unable to obtain more than a weak bill that specified some "fair practices" for both sides but that did recognize the right of producers to bargain. Farmers have some protection against being dumped or boycotted by a processor just because they joined an association.

Several attempts have been made since 1967 to obtain further license for bargaining associations. Some proposals would merely strengthen the language favorable to producers, whereas others emulate the approach of the Wagner Act for labor.

Volunteer Bargaining

The federal license for farmer bargaining is not the same as for labor bargaining. There is no procedure by which a farmer bargaining unit may win election and be recognized as the bargaining agent with which a handler–buyer must deal. Farmer bargaining is purely voluntary on both sides.

Some states in which group bargaining is common have given farmers a broader license than has the federal government. California has a law aimed at requiring processors to bargain with qualified bargaining associations. Michigan has experimented with a more far-reaching approach. The Michigan Agricultural Marketing and Bargaining Act of 1973 provided that processors must bargain with accredited associations while also meeting the free-rider problem. It provided that the accredited association bargains for all producers—members and nonmembers alike—in the market involved, and that all must pay marketing service fees. Thus, the bargaining association was made somewhat similar to a union with an agency shop, where workers pay for union services and work under union-established conditions, even though they are not required to join the union. However, the Michigan Act was invalidated in 1984 by the Supreme Court.

SUMMARY

1. Marketing coops and bargaining coops were the major vehicles in which farmers historically grouped together to accomplish various marketing goals. Each of these vehicles demonstrated accomplishments as well as limitations. Today many alternative organizational structures exist, but their business principles are very similar to those of the original coops. The new generation cooperative is now one of the most popular alternatives.

2. Marketing coops are the farmer-owned vehicle for integrating forward into the first-handler level (or beyond) in the market channel. On the other hand, bargaining associations give farmers group power in dealing with the first handler level. Although marketing and bargaining coops perform different functions, there is sometimes a merging of activities. Dairy coops are typically involved in both bargaining and marketing operations.

3. Although there are obvious economic incentives for individuals to group together to do those things that they are unable to do individually, every group must deal with the opposite incentive—that each

member would like to "let Joe do it." If benefits are available free to those outside the group, the free riders will likely destroy the group.

4. Farmers face three types of possible failure in group action. First, the group action may be a business failure for various reasons common to any business operation as well as a few reasons unique to producer groups. Second, the successful group action may encounter severe limitations by society if it seems to be accomplishing too much for farmers. Third, a large group action may be a business success, but farmers may totally lose control of it and therefore accomplish little of their goals as farmers. This last danger is more likely for marketing coops than for the other types of group action.

5. Farmers have accomplished some significant gains through group action, although it is important to realize that group action is not the answer to each and every problem in agriculture. The group actions that bring the most long-term benefits to producers are those that increase demand at farm level rather than those that try to manipulate supplies. Group actions usually have the merit of leading many farmer participants to become more market oriented.

 ## STUDY QUESTIONS

1. Who are the owners of a farmers' marketing coop? Who controls it? Is it more like a partnership or a corporation?

2. How important are coops in the marketing of farm products? Can you think of any reasons why they are more important in dairy products than in livestock?

3. What is the problem of the free rider? How might the problem be handled by the coop?

4. Distinguish between a bargaining coop and a marketing coop.

5. Are coops growing bigger to serve the objectives of management or of their members?

6. Why are the market shares of coops so much larger at the first-handler stage than at later stages?

7. Describe the economics of a complete cartel with open entry concerning what it can accomplish in the short term and in the longer term for its members.

 ## CLASS EXERCISE

For your group's agricultural commodity, provide an example of how producers are working collectively to market or add value to the commodity.

Be prepared to participate in a discussion with the class about why differences exist between commodities in regard to the level of cooperative actions by producers. For example, why is it that Blue Diamond of California markets branded almonds, but the Big River Resources LLC ethanol plant in southeast Iowa only processes corn for marking commodity ethanol and distillers dried grains?

NOTES

1. Stanley Thompson and Doyle Eiler, "Determinants of Milk Advertising Effectiveness," *American Journal of Agricultural Economics* (1977): 505–508. R. W. Ward and J. E. Davis, "A Pooled Cross-Section Time Series Model of Coupon Promotions," *American Journal of Agricultural Economics* (1978): 393–401.

2. *Positioning Farmer Cooperatives for the Future,* USDA Agricultural Cooperative Service, 1987.

3. Ibid.

4. Alden Manchester, *The Status of Marketing Cooperatives Under Antitrust Law,* USDA-ERS 673, February 1982.

5. USDA, *American Crystal Sugar: Its Rebirth as a Cooperative,* Washington, D.C., FCS Information Bulletin 98, June 1975.

6. Harvard Business School, "Suzy Bel, Inc." Case 4-580-570, Rev. 1/80.

7. Ibid.

8. L. H. Myers, M. J. Phillips, and Roy Goldberg, "Joint Ventures Between Agricultural Cooperatives and Agribusiness-Marketing Firms," Marketing Alternatives series, Cornell University.

9. Randall Torgerson, "A Critique of Bargaining Efforts in Agriculture," *Proceedings of 20th National Conference of Bargaining and Marketing Cooperatives* (Washington, D.C.: U.S. Department of Agriculture, 1976), p. 13.

10. Ralph Bunje, "Reflection from Twenty-five Years of Bargaining," *Proceedings of the 18th National Conference of Bargaining Cooperatives* (Washington, D.C.: U.S. Department of Agriculture, 1974), p. 65.

11. Statement by Ralph Bunje, U.S. Congress, Subcommittee of the Senate Committee on Agriculture and Forestry, *Hearings on S. 109,* 89th Congress 2nd session, 1966, p. 160.

PROCESSOR PROCUREMENT SYSTEMS

PREVIEW

- A processor strives to maintain an adequate margin and volume.

- To produce the commodity rather than to procure it is sometimes an alternative for a processor.

- Procurement contracts have replaced current market procurement for some commodities.

- The procurement strategies and activities of a soybean processor are far different from those of a green bean processor.

- Overcapacity, commodity trading, and price risk management create some special problems.

- Market news (market intelligence) is used in different ways in different commodity areas.

KEY TERMS

adequate volume

back-to-back trading

basis pricing

basis trading

convenience yield

grade-and-yield buying

on-track buying

processor's margin

spot spread

Processors frequently organize and coordinate the procurement systems through which farm products move into consumption, as we have already seen. This chapter examines the nature and operation of various types of processor procurement systems. We will examine logical classification of such systems and look further at some actual commodity procurement systems. Just as Chapter 12 emphasized the farmer's point of view, this chapter emphasizes the processor's point of view.

Think of the processor as a problem solver. Her short-term problem is to keep her organization running with a flow-through that is profitable. A profitable operation requires careful management of volume and margin.

Adequate volume is always of prime importance to a processor. Any modern processor has considerable capital invested as well as many fixed costs associated with staff, leases, and other matters. It is almost invariably true that average costs are minimized when a firm (and its plants) are operated at nearly full capacity rather than at some lesser or greater rate. Therefore, the volume of the product processed affects average costs substantially.

Adequate margins are also a prime concern to a processor. You will recall that a **processor's margin** is what he obtains for his services; it is the difference between his selling price for a unit of output and his buying price for the farm inputs necessary to produce that output. Assume that selling price is a function of industry output and therefore almost entirely outside the control of the processor. Then, margin setting becomes a "price minus" operation—a subtraction of one's margin from the given selling price to obtain the offer price. Market conditions may or may not permit the setting of a full margin. Nevertheless, the processor continually seeks the goal of an attractive margin. That is an oversimplified view of what actually happens, but it is a good approximation.

Obviously, a processor generally cannot control, over time, the farm price of any commodity. That price depends mainly on basic demand and supply conditions. We noted in Chapter 3 that, in many situations, the processor is much more interested in the level of farm price than in the size of her margin. Now, we need to recognize that there are also situations in which the processor is definitely affected by the level of farm price and the size of farm output because of her particular procurement system.

CLASSIFICATION OF PROCUREMENT SYSTEMS

Exhibit 13.1 indicates five alternative procurement systems for a private processor. The sixth option, cooperative processing, excludes by definition the private processor. Because we discussed the cooperative processing option in Chapter 12, we simply note its place in the classification here.

A Basic Management Decision

The make-or-buy decision is basic to any business firm as it analyzes input purchases. For example, the giant auto companies decide to make many of the components of the cars that they assemble, but they decide to buy other components as well. Presumably, they decide for each item whether it is more profitable to "make or buy."

Conceptually, processors of agricultural commodities are faced with the same question: Buy or produce themselves? For many products, the only practical answer may be to buy. The huge amounts of capital used in farm production are a serious obstacle to processors doing their own production of some commodities. But for a number of farm products, a real choice between making and buying does present itself. Moreover, the number of such commodities has risen in recent years, and there are reasons to expect further increases.

Exhibit 13.1 suggests that there are further options within the make-or-buy decisions. A processor may acquire a commodity in the current market, by procurement contract, or through a cooperative sales agency. A processor may produce through two alternatives: production contracts with farmers or his own production facilities using his own employees.

EXHIBIT
13.1 Production marketing–procurement alternatives.

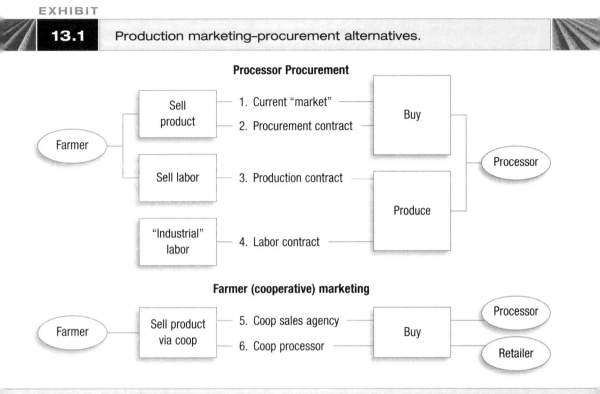

The first four alternatives in Exhibit 13.1 may be seen as progressive steps from conventional agricultural markets toward industrialized agriculture—a total agribusiness system. Thus, alternative 4 utilizes not farmers but industrial labor. Generally, processors' ability to organize and control various aspects of their procurement increases as they move down the list of alternatives. Also, the complexity of processor management increases in the same direction.

Few commodities are actually procured entirely by means of a single one of these options; rather, the use of two, or even three, is more common. A number of major commodities are still predominantly current market but not solely so; the list would include the major grains and oilseeds. Tobacco is almost solely current market. As we noted in Chapter 7, marketing–procurement or procurement contracts are very common in fluid-grade milk, sugar beets, and fruits for processing. Production contracts are highly dominant in broilers, pork, and vegetables for processing.

Processors are increasingly handling production on their own farms or in their own facilities. Agri-pharmaceutical companies have begun to invest in some crop production. This is because the size of production required for pharmaceutical processing is not large, but it is of high value, and it is necessary to minimize the risk of commingling genetically modified plants with community crops. Alternative 5, the cooperative sales agency, typically involves marketing contracts negotiated collectively rather than individually.

This option is used mainly in processing fruits, vegetables, and nuts and is seldom the sole option for processor procurement.

To emphasize the differences between these procurement alternatives, we will discuss each system as if it were the only system used by processors. Later, we discuss some actual commodities that utilize a mix of these options.

Procurement in the Spot (Current Cash) Market

By definition, many decisions in an open market are made by entities other than processors. However, processors do develop their own procedures of procurement or buying within such a market. Farmer–sellers are typically numerous, competing in a fashion similar to perfect competition. Competition among processor–buyers is usually fairly intense, although it frequently is more like monopsonistic than perfect competition.

We have mentioned that farmers are paying more and more attention to the timing of sale of nonperishables. Processors have long emphasized its counterpart—the timing of their purchases. Larger processors carefully study the volume and timing of purchases. Generally, through inventory accumulation they manage to keep their plants operating evenly despite the uneven pace of purchases. There are times, however, when prospective processing margins are so unattractive that purchases are insufficient to maintain full output. The processor who buys at a lower average annual price than her immediate competitors usually achieves that advantage by better timing of purchases rather than by consistent lower-price bids. She learns how to anticipate when farmers are anxious to sell and develops an understanding of market psychology.

Of course, some processors manage inventories for quality reasons first and price second. For example, Anheuser-Busch has storage capacity for 18 months of barley use because the appropriate quality of barley is an important aspect of the flavor, and thus the marketing, of its products.

Importance of Information

Procurement in the current market requires a heavy flow of information. The processor monitors both private and public sources of market intelligence as to forthcoming volume of production, recent price transactions, recent volumes offered for sale and actually traded, qualities and weights, and other facts. In addition, a processor with numerous buyers must coordinate carefully their purchases. A large packer will coordinate her buyers by telephone or computer on an hourly basis. To facilitate coordination, the staff of a large grain buyer will be housed together in the same office. Although the processor is not very interested in the absolute level of farm prices, he is most interested in purchasing at levels no higher than his competitors. Almost constant communication is necessary in this pursuit.

Volume variability creates inefficiencies in the use of resources. It need not necessarily be a source of financial loss to the processor, however, insofar as he and his competitors are able to adjust margins to cover their costs. All quantities produced in agriculture tend eventually to become available for process or procurement. Farmers may hold storable items for a better price, but perishables, by definition, must move quickly. Although these observations may seem so obvious as to be trivial, they do not necessarily hold in other procurement options. An individual farmer can seldom afford to withhold part of his perishable harvest from market. Some grain and oilseed production contracts stipulate a buyer's call clause, where the processor (contractor) notifies the farmer (contractee) a short time before delivery is required. Thus, the farmer has the storage risks.

Processors compete by nonprice as well as by price competition. Employing more buyers may sometimes be as effective as more aggressive buying prices in enlarging one's share of market procurement. Typically, however, not many other nonprice devices are effective in current markets; more are available in the contractual markets.

Procurement Contracts

The processor reduces both her flexibility and some of her uncertainties with procurement contracts. The size and nature of that reduction depends, among other things, on the nature and extent of her procurement contracts. Through procurement contracts, a processor may be able to schedule for several days or weeks ahead the volume and price of her procurement. Most processors would be unwilling to guarantee price that far ahead unless either their competitors are doing the same[1] or the price risk can be largely transferred through the futures market. When volume is planned in advance, deliveries will seldom perfectly match the plan, because nature tends to affect crop yields and animal production to some degree even within the last month of production. In fact, procurement contracts sometimes recognize the unpredictability of yields by specifying the output of X acres rather than X bushels or tons.

The appendix to this chapter provides an example in the marketing of soybeans. The contract specifies all details related to buyer procurement and seller expectations. This contractual agreement is entered into before the crop is planted. Why? From the producer's side (contractee), he must be assured of a market premium because the cost of producing specialty crops is higher than that of commodity crops. The processor (contractor) has a specific end-use or end-user for the processed specialty crop, so she must know how much is contracted in order to make management decisions.

Flexibility for Management

Although processors like the assurance of scheduled supply availability, they find the other side of the coin inconvenient—a commitment of scheduled receipts. Numerous contracts give the processor an out in case of strikes, civil disturbances, and "acts of God" that make difficult or impossible the receipt of scheduled deliveries. Similarly, many contracts allow for price discounts or even refusal of delivery if commodity quality does not meet the contract specifications. Some contracts may allow the processor to cut off deliveries when processing a greater volume appears unprofitable.

Procurement contracts may or may not fix price. Procurement contracts for sugarcane and beets have a formula relating farm price to raw sugar price or to the processor's net proceeds from the sale of the product. Thus, the processor has less risk than with a fixed price. Procurement contracts with dairy farmers generally leave price to be set within the context of a marketing order or other formula. Procurement contracts in hogs and cattle typically tie a base price to a cash price or further processing margin and offer quality premiums (see Chapter 8 for an example grid).

Holding Down Risk and Price Competition

The likely variation in, say, a month's period in prices of many farm commodities is frequently very large compared to the usual processing profits. A processor who sets price a month in advance of delivery is quite concerned about changing price levels. Thus, she tends to hedge such contracts in livestock and grain.

A processor may reduce the competition she faces by using a procurement contract. Overt price competition may be supplemented by nonprice measures. Each processor has her own contract version, and comparing contracts is sometimes difficult. It is often observed that farmers shop around less actively for the best bid with contracting than in cash markets.

Market intelligence is important in procurement contracting, but the emphasis is on estimated production, current crop conditions, estimated marketings during the given month, and so on rather than on price. The exception is livestock and grain, in which price information is still very important because contract prices are set in relation to the nearby futures market price. Information about procurement contract prices is gathered and disseminated to some extent by private organizations and by federal and state market news services. Market news can be difficult to interpret owing to the lack of comparability among some contracts.

Procurement by Production Contract

A production contract is an agreement between two business entities to produce a good. The contractor, for example a pork processor, pays the contractee, for example a farmer, to produce a predetermined quantity and quality of hogs for a set price. Production contracts put processors into the business of production. They do not buy a farm commodity; they produce and process it. There is no farm price for market news services to gather and report.

The processor assumes much of the production and all the price risks with production contracts—if chilled broiler prices plunge 5¢ per pound, the poultry processor takes the loss, not the farmer. The processor's margin, which is now a much broader one embracing production costs, is less easily controlled. Cost control necessarily becomes a prime management objective.

Whereas any farmer has ready access to market outlets in a cash market and, usually, in a procurement market, access to production contracts is more limited. A vegetable processor selects his producers to minimize transportation costs to his plants and to maximize the seasonal length of the pack. A broiler processor selects her producers to match their capacity to that of her feed mills and processing plants. She likewise builds a production area close to her facilities to minimize transport costs. More distant would-be producers are out of luck. The pork sector has followed the poultry sector in production contracts. However, for pork production, it is often advantageous to locate different stages of production in different regions for climate, health, economic, and environmental reasons.

Procurement by Labor Contract

A labor contract is an agreement between an employer and employee to carry out specific tasks. Production in one's own facilities by one's own employees represents complete vertical integration. It goes one step beyond the production contract, but production and labor contracts have many similarities. In both, the processor is the producer. There is no separate farm price, and the production risks are the processor's, as are the accompanying profits or losses.

Unlike a production contract, a labor contract offers the hired labor various benefits such as a minimum wage, unemployment compensation, and retirement benefits, all of which are not available to farmers under contract. More capital is required of the processor because land and buildings are not furnished by farmers.

It has been argued that vertical integration by either of these last two options—production contracts and labor contracts—would guarantee industry stability, because the variability of the aggregate production of many small farmers would be replaced by the stable aggregate production of a smaller number of sophisticated businesspeople. Thus far, the evidence from the broiler industry has not supported the product stability argument. Nor is there anything in competitive economic theory to lead us to expect more stability, unless the processors were to form an illegal cartel or become a tiny oligopoly in which all recognize their mutual dependence. Whether there are 50 or 5,000 price takers operating in perfect competition with biological lags and uncertainties of one another's actions, the same unstable outputs result.

Procurement from a Bargaining Cooperative

Procurement from a cooperative has some similarities to procurement by contracts with individual farmers. The processor bargains with the cooperative over price and, probably, over quantity. Prices paid by all processors are very likely to be the same, a result that processors favor. Processors also like the assurance of supplies. Processors negotiate procurement prices with the aim of obtaining a reasonable processing margin. They are fearful that if they pay higher prices, their margin will be squeezed or the volume demanded at the retail and consumer level will be reduced significantly. Although the bargaining group may facilitate arriving at uniform production practices, processors may prefer to contract directly with producers because necessary communications with individual growers concerning the application of insecticides, fertilizer, and irrigation may be unnecessarily complicated by the bargaining group.

Producers favor bargaining cooperatives because of quantity sales, higher prices, and a more efficient market timing program. Also, producers that are too small to market directly to a processor can do so through a bargaining cooperative.

Procurement Alternatives Compared

Procurement alternatives differ as to the role of market reports; the entrepreneurial independence of the farmers; the extent of decision making, capital investment, and risks assumed by the processor; and the role of intermediate market agencies. When the processor is also the producer, she is vitally concerned about the total crop and its unit value, whereas these matters are of less concern when she is a buyer setting her processing margin.

Two production alternatives maximize the processor's control over the size and nature of production. Fruit and especially vegetable processors have frequently felt that these two options (production vs. labor contracts) were essential to obtaining immediate and full utilization of a plant in a new area. After the initial startup was accomplished, processors have sometimes felt it possible to relax production control and depend more on procurement contracts.

Most procurement systems are an amalgam of two or more procurement options. Perhaps such amalgams reflect a diverse industry in which an option that is best for one processor is not best for another.

The broiler industry evolved in less than 20 years from an open market system to the use of procurement contracts to almost totally production contracts. That example led some observers to believe that once an industry began contracting, it would evolve rapidly and totally into production contracts and processor production. Other observers, including these authors, believe that there are important differences among commodities, that an industry may simultaneously employ two or more alternatives for a long time, and that there is not an inevitable evolution toward processor production.

We turn now to examining a few procurement systems in operation.

LIVESTOCK PROCUREMENT SYSTEMS

Most beef cattle and hogs are procured through non-cash methods: recent reports and surveys indicate that over 85% of hogs and over 70% of cattle are procured using non-cash methods. This change in percentage of hogs marketed through non-cash methods has occurred over the past 20 years, while for cattle the change has occurred over the previous 10 years.

Much debate has surrounded the change in procurement methods for pork and beef. While the advantages of contract production include known quantity available for processing and known price range to be paid, some participants express concern. Negative perceptions of a high percentage of animals procured through contractual arrangements include a loss of market price information, processors having asymmetric information about quantities available, and processor control over who sells when.

Packers use procurement contracts and other devices to facilitate the daily and weekly scheduling of processing. The custom in the High Plains cattle feeding areas of allowing packers to receive delivery at their discretion within 7 to 10 days after purchase greatly facilitates scheduling daily slaughter. Packers use a combination of procurement contracts and purchases with delivery at their discretion to schedule their slaughter.

Packers determine specific price offers on contracts through a process that can be explained fairly readily. Price is set in relation to the price of the futures contract in the market month in which the livestock will go to slaughter or based on the previous period price. Packers consider the costs of hedging, including interest on the margin account and provision for a normal basis considering grade and location, when computing the offer price.

Considerations of Management

The decisions of a packer in organizing his total procurement system for hogs or cattle must be based on several considerations. How large is his operation relative to his nearby competitors? Are his purchases large enough to affect market price in his area? To what extent are supplies available through nearby organized markets—auctions and public terminal markets? In the case of hogs, to what extent are supplies available through cooperative or independent assembly points in his general procurement area? What size are the producers, how many are in the area, and what are the trends? Is grade and yield an accepted pricing method in his area, or is live price the only method?

Although there is hog production and slaughter in almost every state, about four out of five hogs are produced in the north-central region, and the Corn Belt accounts for most of this region's production. There are a few eastern and California slaughterers who routinely import live hogs hundreds of miles, but most hogs are slaughtered close to production. Most livestock in major production areas are slaughtered within 75 miles of the feedlot.

Beef packing and procurement have adjusted to two major shifts since 1960: the growth in proportion of cattle fed in large, commercial lots and the westward shift in production. Cattle feeding was once concentrated in the Corn Belt. The development of large feed grain production—particularly of milo—in the irrigated High Plains after 1950 was followed by the development of several concentrated areas of cattle feeding in Colorado, Texas, Kansas, Nebraska, and Oklahoma. These areas now feed most of the nation's cattle, and most cattle are fed in large feedlots. California has had considerable feeding in commercial (large-sized) lots for several decades. Packing plants have generally followed feedlots, after a lag of a few years.

Large packing plants are almost exclusively single species, meaning that they are either cattle or hogs, whereas plants built before 1940 were usually multi-species. There are, of course, many small, local firms that have multi-species slaughter plants. Most of the slaughter capacity built since 1975 in both beef and pork has been in plants much larger than the earlier plants.

Hog and Cattle Procurement Systems

The livestock procurement system has changed tremendously over the past quarter century. The procurement contracts that began in the broiler industry 50 years ago, as well as the production contracts that followed them, are still prevalent in the turkey and pork industries today. The cattle industry has rapidly adopted procurement contracts (Exhibit 13.2) but rarely uses processor production contracts. In this section we explore livestock processors' motives for procuring animals through contracting.

Pork Procurement System

Pork procurement methods have evolved rapidly over the past decade (Exhibit 13.3). Processors began in the early 1990s to offer an expanded

EXHIBIT

13.2 Percentage of domestic cattle sales through non-cash negotiated to total cash market cattle sales.

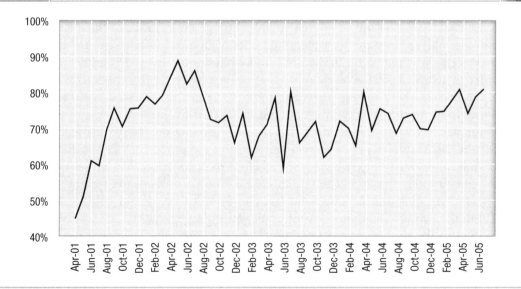

Source: USDA.

EXHIBIT

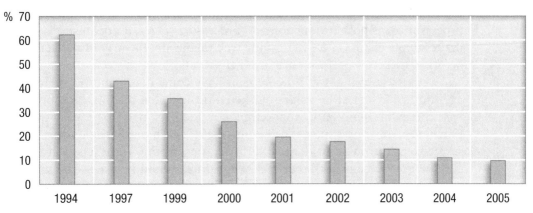

13.3 Percentage of hogs sold on the cash market.

Note: No data available for 1995–1996 and 1998.

Source: 1994 and 1997 studies by University of Missouri, *Pork* magazine, PIC, DeKalb Choice Genetics, National Pork Producers Council, Land O'Lakes. 1999–2005 studies by University of Missouri, NPPC data. National Pork Board. 2002–05 USDA/NASS. Used with permission.

menu of marketing contracts, including ledger, window, basis, and cost-plus contracts partly as a result of changes in industry structure. The focus on economies of size in the late 1980s and 1990s motivated hog producers to expand rapidly, which they accomplished through tactics to improve production management efficiencies, including production contracts. With expansion to 10,000-animal herds—some mega producers even had 500,000-head herds—came the need for producers to limit their market price risk. Negotiating long-term marketing contracts with processors provided some degree of confidence to growers and their financers that a profit could be obtained on such large quantities of animals. At the same time, processors faced shrinking processing margins, which caused management to increase efficiency by focusing on pushing processing utilization to capacity. What better way to ensure full capacity than by contracting for deliveries so that management knows ahead of time how close to capacity the firm will be? On the coattails of these changes were improvements in genetics allowing producers and processors to better gauge the quality of animals being procured.

Another change occurred as processors vertically integrated either up, down, or both up and down the pork value chain. A processor who integrated to the production-level gained more control over both quality and the timing of hogs going to market. Again, this change resulted in more pork production contracts for independent growers. In addition to gaining quality and market timing advantages, vertically integrated processors can smooth their profits over two sectors, reducing the tendency for the processor's margins to be inversely related to live-animal price. Of course, the processor considering vertical integration must evaluate the make-or-buy decision. When pork processors have failed in vertically integrating toward the production level, the true cause of their financial problems was likely more complex than just the decision whether to produce. In general, when a processor owns both production and processing stages, if one business stage in the supply chain is not performing well financially the negative effect may be offset by better performance in other stages.

With these changes in procurement have come many questions. Today, as little as 14% of all hogs are marketed through the cash market, but the base price in many hog marketing contracts is tied to a cash price. Obviously, this raises questions about whether cash market sales are representative of the value of hogs sold through marketing contracts. But if the cash market price is not used, then what price should be used—the futures price, the wholesale price, the retail price? Lastly, the rise of ownership and marketing contracts has raised issues about market power. How much power do such procurement methods place in the hands of the processor, and are marketing contracts tilted toward the processor in the long run?

Cattle Procurement Systems

A procurement system for a cattle packer involves a staff of cattle buyers. In the High Plains and the West, fed cattle are bought almost entirely at the feedlots. In the Corn Belt, most purchases of fed cattle are made in the farm feedlots, although considerable but declining numbers are purchased in the pens of the public terminal markets or at the many livestock auction centers that dot the area.

Quite obviously, a packer does not send out his staff of buyers each week with instructions no more specific than "Buy cattle!" Most packers maintain an excellent communication system. Buyers receive changing instructions during the day as to the quantities desired and the top offer price for a particular pen vs. average weight and quality. The instructions to buyers change, of course, as the day's buys of all the packer's buyers accumulate and as the packer changes his appraisal of the wholesale beef market and the live market prices expected the following day.

Market news of a general nature is central to the latter two appraisals as well as to the success of buyer negotiations in the field. The packer has an internal electronic information network that may be available as an Internet site providing a continuing stream of information on transactions in both the wholesale beef market and the cattle market. Most of the beef market information is gathered by two private organizations known familiarly as the Yellow Sheet and the Meat Sheet, as well as by the Agricultural Marketing Service (AMS) division of the USDA. The AMS Market News is the chief source of information on the live cattle market for most of the country.

Other publicly gathered market intelligence also plays a role in the day-to-day decisions of packers and cattle feeders. Data are gathered and reported monthly by the National Agricultural Statistical Service on the numbers on feed by weight classes, the new placements on feed, and marketings for the seven largest feeding states: Arizona, California, Colorado, Iowa, Kansas, Nebraska, and Texas. Packers and feeders make judgments about future market trends on the basis of this information. These judgments affect the interest of packers in making procurement contracts or in feeding their own cattle.

Grade-and-Yield Buying

Packers prefer to buy on carcass **grade and yield** rather than buying on a live weight. The basic idea is simple: Instead of bidding a certain live price based on estimated carcass weight and grade, the buyer bids a carcass weight price for each grade. Final returns to the farmer then depend on the realized weight and grade of the carcasses. There are as many different programs for figuring grade and yield price as there are packers (and maybe more).

Agricultural economists usually support the grade-and-yield pricing method because it is a more accurate method, paying a producer for the final product that she actually produces. Although grade-and-yield evaluation in the carcass is not a perfectly accurate representation of wholesale product value, it is more accurate than buyer evaluation of live cattle and hogs.

Whereas some producers are willing to accept this pricing method, most are not. A farmer with animals yielding below average would rather play the averages than face the carcass cutout results.

A more general problem for a packer is the credibility of the system. How is the farmer to be sure that her returns do not suffer from errors—accidental or deliberate—by the packer's employees in keeping track of her load of animals and in weighing and evaluating the carcasses?

Instead of bidding a firm price, the packer agrees to pay on the basis of wholesale carcass prices on the day of slaughter. Thus, the packer eliminates the risk of price change between time of purchase and slaughter. The producer feels rather powerless, of course, when he ships without a firm price. In contrast, the method of grade-and-yield procurement of cattle in Iowa is the same as for hogs.

PROCUREMENT SYSTEM FOR PROCESSING MIDWESTERN VEGETABLES

The vegetable processor's procurement problems and procedures vary in important ways from a meat packer's, even though both firms process perishable products.[2] The value to be attributed to the raw product in vegetable procurement depends on numerous market factors that are often difficult to anticipate, including the carryover from last year's pack (amount processed) and the size of pack of closely competing vegetables. Whereas the meat packer determines buying prices daily, the vegetable processor makes an annual determination. Moreover, the vegetable processor generally obtains more control over the amount of product he processes, the daily timing of its delivery, and the quality of that product. Whereas it is almost unthinkable for a meat packer to refuse—at any price—to slaughter healthy hogs because of their particular quality or because he has too many this season, a vegetable processor may refuse delivery for either of those reasons.

Restricted Competition

The typical vegetable processor does not face much direct competition in negotiation of contracts. She procures mainly within a 50-mile radius of her plants. There often are no more than two or three other processors within that area, and sometimes not even two. Most growers, nevertheless, are not easily exploited in this oligopsonistic situation because they also raise alternative crops. The net returns that a farmer anticipates from alternative crops forms the lower limit of what he will accept to produce a canning crop. For example, dry, edible bean prices increased in 2005 from low production in 2004 and also from $10/bushel soybean prices, since soybeans are a substitute for producers making production decisions.

The canner's field representatives contract the desired acreage before spring planting. The actual pack is likely to deviate from early season plans. One reason is that the acreage contracted may be less than desired. More important, yields may be above or below average because of weather and other impacts of nature. If the potential crop harvest is too big, the canner may resort to passed acreage, that is, unharvested acreage.

Each canner has her own contract form designed to meet her needs. Careful analysis suggests that on net balance the returns to growers are fairly comparable among canners, although the contracts may appear on the surface to be quite different. When one considers that there is no organized market and no public reporting of a going price on contracts, the processor has procured effectively when he buys as cheaply as his competitors.

Production Contracts

The contracts for Wisconsin's two main processing vegetables—sweet corn and green peas—are usually production contracts. Under such contracts, the growing crop is the legal property of the canner. Thus, the canner has absolute assurance that the crop will not be diverted to another outlet. The grower provides the land and the production labor. The canner may provide the seed, fertilizer, herbicides, and pesticides. The processor specifies the required production procedures: rate of seeding and timing and rate of pesticide application, along with other activities. In addition, the processor may provide the harvesting equipment.

Compensation is based on tonnage and quality of the harvested crop. Thus, the grower is hurt badly by low or zero crop yields but is helped by high crop yields. The processor, like any farmer, may be hurt both by her own low crop yields (low output) and by industry-wide high crop yields (low selling prices).

Guiding Production

Processors use a number of incentives to guide production. The canner, unlike the typical meat packer, buys entirely on grade and yield. For example, yields of peas are less when quality (tenderness) is highest and rise as quality deteriorates. The typical canner has a quality–price schedule that encourages the grower to harvest at the quantity–quality tradeoff preferred by the canner. Bonuses also encourage some growers to take the added risk of planting later in the season. Plant utilization is improved, of course, by having some late acreage.

Even though a prime motivation for contracting is to coordinate production and harvests to processing capacity, the system is not perfect by any means. The canner sometimes either cannot handle some acreage because of unusual weather or yields or does not wish to handle it because the cumulative pack is considered too large. The canner may choose to "pass" some contracted acreage. Some contracts provide for partial compensation to growers for passed acreage. The practice of passing acreage can be a source of difficulty between a canner and growers.

Canners rely less heavily on market intelligence than do livestock buyers. The canner is interested in all that he can learn about the total size of the pack, the speed with which last year's pack is moving through retail, and the contract offers of other processors. The National Agricultural Statistical Service does provide data on planting intentions, acreage planted, acreage harvested, and total production for each of the major processed vegetables. During the harvest period, the canner is interested in the probable total pack and possible changes in general demand. But this news is much less than the continuous flow of information during every working day of the year that guides the meat packer. There are no futures market contracts for processed vegetables in which a grower or canner can transfer price risks to speculators.

PROCUREMENT SYSTEMS FOR
WHEAT, CORN, AND SOYBEANS

Differences in the ultimate markets for wheat, corn, and soybeans and in their processing are important, but these crops have sufficient commonalities to warrant their combination in this discussion. The production areas of the three overlap, especially those of corn and soybeans. The same elevators may handle all three in the first link of the procurement system, and the futures markets are heavily used by market agencies for all three. All three share a heavy dependence on a comprehensive market intelligence system that has worldwide inputs and significance. Often, the same merchant or processor will handle all three commodities. Perhaps most important, the market participants of all three share the problems and opportunities of a commodity harvested once a year but utilized every day.

Grain and oilseed processors affect local prices through the level of demand that they present relative to local supply. Thus, we find grain and oilseed prices varying across the country. Exhibit 13.4 is the spot corn bid map for September 12, 2005. As discussed in Chapter 5, exports contribute significantly to domestic use of agricultural commodities. As the Mississippi River is the primary transportation method to the Gulf and on to export markets, we typically observe strong cash prices along the river. On August 29, 2005, Hurricane Katrina hit New Orleans and effectively shut down the port of New Orleans to Mississippi river barge traffic. On Exhibit 13.4, you can easily identify southeast Missouri and southwest Illinois locations where spot bids along the river were some of the lowest in the Midwest relative to historical levels. Although harvest was full swing during September, demand was minimal because barge traffic was at a dead stop.

Exhibit 13.4 also shows the line between the 2005 drought area and the good production area (the line runs from northeast Iowa to southwest Iowa). Some of the highest grain prices for this date were in southwest Kansas, the location of many cattle feedlots. Because the demand for feed milling corn is larger than local production, the local price was bid up to motivate arbitragers to transport grain from surplus areas to the deficit southwest Kansas area.

Grains and oilseeds are major commodities in both domestic and foreign markets. Several important developments have affected the

EXHIBIT

13.4 Spot corn bid map for September 12, 2005.

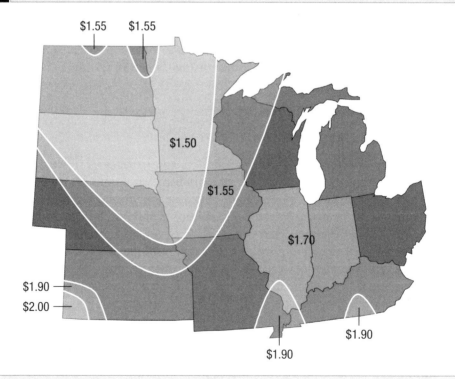

Source: DTN AgDayta.

marketing–procurement system for grains and soybeans during the past few decades. They include sharp growth, subsequent decline, and growth again in exports; greater price fluctuations; changed influence of government price supports; larger total marketings; growth in the use of multiple-car trains; increased demand for new uses of commodities; and reduced regulation of transportation. Any industry that experiences large shifts in its demand curve must make various adjustments in how it operates.

Grain and soybean channels have considerable vertical integration. Flour millers own a sizable share of terminal and subterminal elevators, commission merchants, and some country elevators. Exporters, likewise, have similar backward (procurement) integration. Cooperatives have important market shares at the country elevator and commission merchant levels, a smaller share (about one-fifth) at the terminal elevators, an even smaller toehold in export, and only a trifle at the flour milling level. Much the same pattern of vertical integration is found in soybeans, and some of the same firms are involved, particularly the exporters. For soybeans, crushers and exporters are of the most interest. After crushing, a portion of the meal goes to export and a larger portion goes to feed manufacturers. Similarly, the oil is provided to refiners and then to manufacturers of such products as margarine, shortening, salad oil, cooking oil, and various industrial products.

Limited Organization of Channel by Processors

The grain and soybean procurement systems are more like livestock than the canned vegetables. However, in some ways, the grain and soybean procurement systems are even less organized by processors than is the case for livestock. First, there are more intermediary firms—some of which are independent traders—in the grain and soybean systems. Second, the geography of procurement is not as important as in livestock or vegetables.

Most soybean processors are too large to rely principally on direct receipts from farmers. For example, a modern soybean crusher may process 50,000 bushels per day. Thus, processors rely on the elevator network in the production areas. It has been estimated that soybeans move an average of about 400 miles by rail from country elevator to crusher.[3]

Procurement Methods of Country Elevators

Country elevators procure grain and soybeans from farmers through a variety of methods. Brief descriptions of farmers' contracts with elevators were given in Chapter 7. Procurement methods used are:

1. Forward pricing
2. Cash purchase at harvest
3. Store farmers' grain in elevator and buy later
4. Purchase after harvest from on-farm storage
5. Take delivery at harvest on procurement-contracted grain
6. Purchase at harvest on a delayed pricing contract

The country elevator faces increasing competition from subterminals, a cross between locals and large terminals, with train-loading facilities. Whereas the typical country elevator buys mostly within a radius of 10 miles, a subterminal offering better bids may pull a third of its grain from more than 20 miles and sometimes as far as 100 miles. The subterminals, by combining functions of both terminals and country elevators, are taking business away from both.

Inventory Management

Grain and soybean processors generally obtain their supplies through the open market, buying either on the spot (cash) market or by some form of short-term procurement contract.

Independent country elevators are the first off-farm purchase point and reservoir in-pipeline to market. These elevators operate on such a small margin that grain price movements present considerable risk to them. Each one must consider how much price protection she wants and how to obtain it. Many of them maintain ownership of the grain for only the few hours it takes to ship it to terminals and processors. Buyers make immediate purchases from country elevators through various trade practices.

One practice, called **on-track buying,** or track country station, is the trade practice of a grain purchaser paying today's market price of grain at the country elevator that is, or shortly will be, loaded on railroad cars at the seller's elevator. The merchant or processor–buyer, as owner, takes the price risk and pays the transportation. The "to arrive" contract amounts to the same thing except that the seller delivers to the buyer within a normal delivery period. Actual prices in both such contracts are usually computed from the market price at the buyer's location with allowance for who pays the transportation. Although the country elevator might achieve nearly the same result by hedging, he often prefers to leave hedging to the more experienced, large-volume buyers. A country elevator or other merchant who ties together buying and selling so that they match her ownership risks is said to practice **back-to-back trading.**

Country elevators do hedge in certain situations. For example, the bids from usual buyers may fall temporarily because of a strike, a transport interruption, or a temporary oversupply to the buyers. The country elevator operator may decide to hedge for a while and wait for a more favorable market. As another example, the operator may purchase some grain under a deferred pricing plan. One alternative is to pay the farmer the same basis under a specific futures (say, in March) as existed on the day that the farmer delivered the grain. The farmer can then select the date of sale anytime up until March. By selling the cash grain immediately and purchasing March futures, the elevator eliminates price risk. As a third example, the elevator may offer a forward price contract in April for November delivery of soybeans. The elevator will hedge this contract because there is always the possibility of the price going down. Finally, various elevators do some trading on the basis.

Basis Pricing and Basis Trading

Recall from Chapter 10 that a short hedger gains when the basis narrows and loses when it widens. The converse holds, of course, for a long hedger. Some elevators and other grain traders make trading decisions according to their expectations as to the movement of basis. Thus, a trader who expects a narrowing of basis will try to be long in cash grain (which he hedges), whereas a trader expecting a widening of basis will try to be short in cash grain through contracting to sell cash grain for future delivery while buying futures. Although the basis often widens during the rush of harvest and then narrows soon thereafter, it does not always do so. Considerable basis profits (or losses) may be earned through such basis trading.

Imagine that traders A and B both buy and sell corn. On December 1, trader A expects a narrowing of the basis. She accumulates cash corn and hedges it by selling futures at a basis of 20¢ under. However, trader B expects a widening of the basis, so he contracts to deliver cash corn while buying futures as a hedge. If the basis narrows (strengthens) soon thereafter to 10¢ under, then trader A gains 10¢ per bushel, and trader B loses 10¢. However, if the basis widens (weakens) instead to 30¢, then trader A loses 10¢, and trader B gains 10¢. Note that both traders were fully hedged; their losses or gains were from changes in their bases.

Most pricing in the grain business is set in terms of basis. **Basis pricing,** a practice of making price offers or agreements about grain specifying a certain differential above or below the daily market prices of a nearby futures market, is related to but different from **basis trading,** which is an attempt by a grain trader to profit by taking long or short net positions according to his expectations about basis movements. As an example of basis pricing, a processor's daily price offers might be X cents below the daily market prices of a nearby futures contract. Processors and merchants extend such basis pricing bids to country elevators, which use them in establishing their daily prices.

Inventories in the Market Channel

It is possible to surmise from USDA data on market receipts and stocks that the trade buys from one-third to one-half of its year's purchases of corn, wheat, and soybeans in the three months near harvest. The rest of the purchases are spread somewhat unevenly throughout the marketing year. Although this information helps us see how these major annual crops flow through the pipeline, so to speak, they provide only indirect clues as to ownership or contractual commitments.

There are many owners of inventory within the trade and various paths of movement through the pipeline. One could visualize farmers selling to country elevators who, in turn, sell to interior merchants or to subterminal elevators, who then sell to terminal elevators, who sell to millers, crushers, and exporters. Some of this does happen, but products move by other paths as well (Exhibit 13.5). Flour millers receive large grain shipments directly from subterminals as well as from terminals. Because there is a considerable

13.5   Grain M–P channels and pricing points.

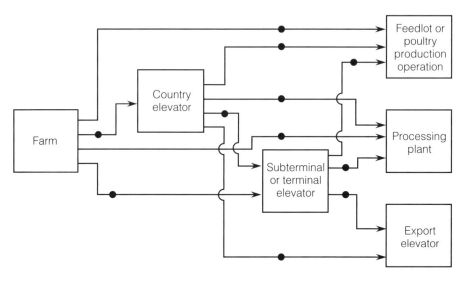

● Pricing point, except when establishments are vertically integrated.

Source: Mike Turner et al., *Who Will Market Your Grain?* Texas Extension Bulletin D–1057, March 1978.

amount of vertical integration in both wheat and soybeans, it is entirely possible that the processor and the country or subterminal elevator are part of the same firm, so that grain transfers after the farm sale take place within an integrated firm rather than through market transactions.

Processor Margins

Processor procurement prices for soybeans depend in the long run on export demand for soybeans and the market values of soybean oil and soybean meal, minus storage, transportation, handling, and processing costs. On a day-to-day basis, these relationships are variable because sellers differ in their eagerness to sell and buyers in their eagerness to buy. Because soybeans are a storable product, the day-to-day decisions of both buyers and sellers are influenced by their expectations; for sellers, storage is an alternative to selling, and for buyers, withdrawal from already purchased stocks is often an alternative to current procurements. With a storable, annually harvested product, inventory management and pricing are interrelated strategies involving all market participants.

The market prices of soybean meal and soybean oil have fluctuated greatly in recent years, and not always together. Even the annual average prices illustrate both these points (Exhibit 13.6). As illustrated by the **spot**

EXHIBIT

13.6 Soybeans, annual average value of products per bushel processed, and spot price spread.

	(1) Soybean Oil Value	(2) Soybean Meal Value	(1) + (2) Total Products Value	(4) Soybean Price*	(4) − (1 + 2) Spot Spread
1987/88	$2.50	$5.54	$8.04	$6.76	$1.28
1992/93	$2.27	$4.58	$6.85	$5.95	$0.90
1997/98	$2.76	$4.40	$7.16	$6.47	$0.69
2003/04	$3.20	$6.08	$9.28	$7.34	$1.95

*Price of No. 1 Yellow Soybeans, Illinois points.

Source: USDA, *Oil Crops, Situation and Outlook Report, July 1994,* Table 19, and author calculations from USDA data for 1997/98 and 2003/04.

spread in Exhibit 13.6, the crushing industry's average annual margins between its sales prices and its procurement prices have varied in recent years from $0.69 to $1.95 per bushel.

Financial results of individual firms vary from these industry spreads. Soybean processors have the unique opportunity of using futures markets for both their raw material and their output (meal and oil). These three futures markets give the processors great flexibility, but they also permit speculators to have short-term influence on processing margins. Thus, it is entirely possible for processors in, say, June to be able to hedge in a profitable processing margin (by buying bean futures and selling product futures) for several of the coming months but to face losses for other months. Processors employ a number of complex strategies in both the cash and the futures markets as they try to hold down risks while obtaining profitable crushing margins. Generally, processing margins work out better than the spot spreads indicate.[4]

Keeping the Wheels Humming

The grain and oilseed processors are motivated, like other processors, to keep their facilities busy. The strength of that motivation varies with the size of ongoing costs. The soybean crusher is probably most like the canner or packer, whereas the exporter is less bound by continuing costs. To a great extent, grain and soybean processors may acquire commodities and keep their storage and processing facilities busy while taking fairly small (but not zero!) risks by hedging in the futures market. Processors vary in the degree to which they avoid ownership risks. The larger firms generally have such information networks and such expertise in interpreting the information that significant portions of their earnings stem from the acceptance of ownership risks.

In determining the level of inventories they wish to hold, processors consider a convenience yield factor that reflects the value of keeping their facilities busy. **Convenience yield** describes the value of holding inventories, when storage does not pay. The cost of shutting down operations due to inadequate supply may be greater than the cost of holding stocks, hence holding inventories may be wise.

The entire channel for grains and soybeans is shaped by the important fact that the United States is a major exporter. Prices, therefore, reflect worldwide influences. Physical movement is generally from production areas toward export elevators, and the national pattern of prices reflects that direction of movement. Livestock and even canned vegetables are not entirely isolated from world trade, but their prices are not dominated by international concerns to the extent that grains and oilseeds are.

Market Intelligence

Grain and soybean processors obtain market intelligence both publicly and privately. Market prices (futures and cash) reflect a myriad of worldwide factors concerning happenings and anticipated happenings: the size of foreign buyers' orders, as well as weather, disease, and other natural factors affecting the anticipated harvests in each production area of the world. Additional factors include the production of substitutes, governmental policies affecting supply or demand, and transportation developments affecting cost or temporary timeliness of deliveries. (Substitutes include rice, millet, fish meal, palm oil, canola, and sunflower meal and oil.)

Large processors, and particularly the large exporters, have excellent private networks for gathering and interpreting information. Generally, they have had a particular advantage over farmers and smaller competitors in foreign markets. In the mid-1970s, the U. S. government tightened its requirements for reporting large sales promptly. However, the very nature of private negotiations almost ensures that exporters know more, and know it sooner, than anyone else.

A vast public system exists to provide public information. The National Agricultural Statistical Service (NASS) gathers and disseminates, at appropriate intervals, information on planting intentions, acres planted, anticipated yields, total crop and acres harvested, and total production. This information is estimated on the basis of samples, but the accuracy of these estimates is remarkably good, considering the low cost to users. The NASS also provides monthly data on size and location of stocks, disposition by major use (e.g., exports or feeding), and prices received by farmers.

The Federal–State Market News Reports, as well as private news services, cover market prices, demand, supply, commodity movement, price support activities, and other relevant information. Cash and futures closing prices at principal markets across the nation are reported daily and are carried on various wire services.

The USDA reports comprehensive analyses of the various aspects of supply and demand several times yearly in *Feed Outlook* for corn, in *Oil Crops Outlook* for soybeans, and in *Wheat Outlook* for wheat.

SUMMARY

1. A processor may select from five alternative procurement systems, ranging from purchase in the current market to producing the desired agricultural commodities with her own employees. Other alternatives are procurement by marketing or production contracts and purchase from a farm cooperative, rather than from individual producers.

2. The differing procurement alternatives give rise to important differences in the independence of farmers, the extent of capital investment and of risks assumed by processors, and the roles of marketing agencies and market news.

3. Processors generally assume the price risks of ownership of agricultural commodities. Processors in grain and oilseeds use the futures market to hedge some of those risks and also to try to enhance their returns through basis trading. Canners of vegetables face long-term price risks because of their production contracts and the absence of futures markets. Moreover, they share some production risks with producers—risks that are not shared by processors who do not use production contracts.

4. Market information is essential to advantageous trading. Generally, processors have market information that is as good as or better than the farmers or assemblers from whom they buy. Although much of the market data is generated by public agencies, the processors often supplement it with private sources and make their own analyses.

5. Descriptions of the typical procurement systems for cattle, hogs, canning vegetables, grains, and soybeans indicate differences in the systems and some of the reasons for those differences.

6. Procurement of canning vegetables is quite localized, livestock procurement is less localized, and procurement of grains and oilseeds is regional. The storability and inexpensive transportation of grain widens greatly the procurement area and increases the likelihood of intermediaries between farmers and processors.

7. Good timing is likely the most important factor in the successful procurement of grains and oilseeds, as processors compete in a market dominated by worldwide supply-and-demand factors.

Agreement Number: **XXXXXXXXXXXXXXX**
Originator: _____, _____, _____
Program Name: _____

2006 Low Linolenic Soybean Production Agreement
Bellevue, Ohio Area
Bunge North America (East), L.L.C.

Parties: Contractor   Bunge North America (East), L.L.C.
                            c/o Pioneer Hi-Bred International, Inc.
                            6900 NW 62nd Ave
                            P.O. Box 256
                            Johnston, IA 50131-0256

Grower   _____
         _____
         _____
         _____
         _____,_____
         _____

Agreement # XXXXXXXXXXXXXXXX

Elevator   _____,_____

READ THIS AGREEMENT CAREFULLY. It is a legal document between BUNGE and _____. This agreement sets forth, in detail, the rights and obligations of both you and BUNGE. IT IS THEREFORE IMPORTANT THAT YOU READ IT CAREFULLY.

This AGREEMENT is made between the GROWER and BUNGE. In consideration of the promises and obligations set forth herein, the parties agree as follows:

DEFINITIONS
a. **AGREEMENT** is this document.
b. **BUNGE** – Bunge North America (East), L.L.C.
c. **ELEVATOR** is _____. _____. _____.
d. **GROWER** is _____.
e. **IP LOW LINOLENIC SOYBEANS** – Identity Preserved Low Linolenic Soybeans are soybeans with a linolenic acid content of less than or equal to 3% and have been kept separate from other soybeans and other crops. In order to maintain identity preservation all seed/soybean handling equipment, including but not limited to, wagons, planters, drills, combines, augers, conveyors, legs, bins, and trucks, must be cleaned before use to remove other seeds/soybeans/grains.

(continued)

APPENDIX   Sample production agreement, continued.

f. **PHII** – Pioneer Hi-Bred International, Inc. BUNGE has given PHII authority to act for BUNGE in carrying out certain BUNGE obligations under this AGREEMENT.

Contacts:

Bunge North America (East), L.L.C.
c/o Pioneer Hi-Bred International, Inc.
[Name]
[Phone]
[Fax]

1. **ACREAGE AND SEED**
    a. The GROWER agrees to plant _____ acres of IP LOW LINOLENIC SOYBEANS.
    b. The GROWER agrees to purchase and plant the following Pioneer® brand low linolenic soybean varieties:

    Seed Company name and units display here.

    c. In the event that there is a shortage of seed due to germination or seed quality problems, BUNGE may void this AGREEMENT at no expense.

2. **DELIVERY**
    a. The GROWER agrees to deliver all of the IP LOW LINOLENIC SOYBEANS to the ELEVATOR, unless the ELEVATOR instructs that the IP LOW LINOLENIC SOYBEANS be delivered directly to Bunge North America (East), L.L.C., Bellevue, Ohio. The delivery period shall be:

    Delivery Windows and contracted amount display here.

    b. BUNGE may direct the GROWER to deliver the IP LOW LINOLENIC SOYBEANS to a different location and will reimburse the GROWER for any additional reasonable transportation costs.

3. **SAMPLING AND QUALITY SPECIFICATIONS**
    a. The ELEVATOR will sample and grade each load of IP LOW LINOLENIC SOYBEANS.
    b. IP LOW LINOLENIC SOYBEANS must meet the following minimum quality specifications or will be subject to the ELEVATOR'S discount schedule or rejection.

Moisture	13.0% or less
Splits	20.0% or less
Total damaged	2.0% or less
Heat damaged	0.29% or less
Foreign material	1.0% or less
Odor	Cool, sweet

(continued)

APPENDIX   Sample production agreement, continued.

   c. Each load of the IP LOW LINOLENIC SOYBEANS will be tested by NIR machine at the ELEVATOR or at PHII. IP LOW LINOLENIC SOYBEANS must have less than or equal to 3.0% linolenic acid content or be subject to rejection with no premium paid. If a load fails the NIR test, then the sample will be tested at PHII using the Gas Chromatograph (GC) method. If the sample passes the GC test, the GROWER will receive the premium for that load.

   d. IP LOW LINOLENIC SOYBEANS shall be of merchantable quality.

   e. The ELEVATOR'S weights and grades shall govern. The GROWER has the right to appeal any grade by submitting a sample to the Federal Grain Inspection Service (FGIS). The GROWER must pay for the cost of the official grade.

   f. If the GROWER has on farm storage, the GROWER will provide a sample of GROW-ER'S IP LOW LINOLENIC SOYBEANS if requested by BUNGE or its representative. BUNGE will provide sample bags and sample shipping instructions to the GROWER.

   g. IP LOW LINOLENIC SOYBEANS must be cool and sweet and must be suitable for storage. IP LOW LINOLENIC SOYBEANS with high moisture are *not* suitable for storage and may be rejected with no premium paid.

4. PRICING AND COMPENSATION

   a. This is a buyer's call contract. When BUNGE calls for the IP LOW LINOLENIC SOYBEANS, the ELEVATOR may require the GROWER to sign a Price Later Agreement (Credit Sale Agreement) or sell all or a portion of the IP LOW LINOLENIC SOYBEANS.

   b. Any storage or price later fees are between GROWER and ELEVATOR and not part of this AGREEMENT.

   c. The GROWER agrees to sell all of the IP LOW LINOLENIC SOYBEANS to the ELE-VATOR.

   d. The ELEVATOR is obligated to pay the GROWER the commodity soybean price plus any premium due using the scale below:

Premium Scale for Harvest Delivery to the ELEVATOR

Less than or equal to 3.0% linolenic acid content	$0.35 per bushel
Greater than 3.0% linolenic acid content	$0.00 per bushel

Premium Scale for Farm Stored Buyers Call Delivery

Less than or equal to 3.0% linolenic acid content	$0.40 per bushel
Greater than 3.0% linolenic acid content	$0.00 per bushel

   e. An additional $0.05 per bushel signing bonus will be paid on all accepted bushels delivered at harvest.

(continued)

f. An additional $0.10 per bushel signing bonus will be paid on all accepted bushels delivered on buyers call from farm storage.

    g. The ELEVATOR will pay any premium due to the GROWER at the time of payment for the IP LOW LINOLENIC SOYBEANS.

    h. For the purpose of obtaining payment from the ELEVATOR, the GROWER is a third party beneficiary of BUNGE'S agreement with the ELEVATOR.

    i. The GROWER agrees to look only to the ELEVATOR for payment.

    j. The GROWER agrees to inform the ELEVATOR of all liens placed against the IP LOW LINOLENIC SOYBEANS.

5. DISCLAIMER OF WARRANTY AND LIMITATION OF DAMAGES

NEITHER BUNGE NOR PHII MAKE ANY WARRANTY OF MERCHANTABILITY OR FITNESS FOR A PARTICULAR PURPOSE OR ANY OTHER EXPRESS OR IMPLIED WARRANTY. NO CLAIM OF ANY KIND, WHETHER OR NOT BASED ON NEGLIGENCE, SHALL BE GREATER IN AMOUNT THAN THE VALUE OF THE MAXIMUM PREMIUM PAYABLE TO THE GROWER UNDER THIS AGREEMENT. NEITHER PARTY SHALL BE LIABLE FOR SPECIAL, CONSEQUENTIAL, OR INDIRECT DAMAGES WHETHER OR NOT CAUSED BY OR RESULTING FROM THE NEGLIGENCE OF SUCH PARTY. NEITHER BUNGE NOR PHII MAKE ANY WARRANTY REGARDING YIELD OR PERFORMANCE OF THE PIONEER® BRAND SOYBEAN VARIETIES.

6. GENERAL PROVISIONS

    a. The GROWER is an independent contractor and nothing contained in this AGREEMENT shall make the GROWER an employee or agent of BUNGE or authorize him/her to act on BUNGE'S behalf. The GROWER shall indemnify and hold BUNGE and/or PHII harmless from all claims in any way connected directly or indirectly with GROWER'S operations pursuant to this AGREEMENT.

    b. This AGREEMENT constitutes the complete understanding between the parties and supersedes all other representations. The parties agree that no modification of this AGREEMENT shall be valid unless done in writing and signed by both parties.

    c. This AGREEMENT shall bind the parties, their heirs, administrators, executors, successors, and assigns.

    d. This AGREEMENT shall be subject to and governed by the laws of the State of Ohio. BUNGE and the GROWER agree that all disputes arising out of or relating to this AGREEMENT shall be settled by arbitration in accordance with the rules and regulations of the National Grain and Feed Association pursuant to such Association's grain arbitration rules. BUNGE and the GROWER agree that judgment may be entered upon any arbitration award in any court of competent jurisdiction.

    e. Written notices to BUNGE shall be by personal delivery or by postage paid letter addressed to Bunge North America at the above address.

(continued)

APPENDIX   Sample production agreement, continued.

f. BUNGE and its representative shall have the right to access fields, harvesting equipment, transportation vehicles, and soybean storage facilities used in the production of IP LOW LINOLENIC SOYBEANS. The purpose of such access is to inspect and/or sample the IP LOW LINOLENIC SOYBEANS.

g. BUNGE and its representative shall have the right to inspect and audit all of the records of the GROWER pertaining to this AGREEMENT.

h. The GROWER acknowledges that PHII is a limited agent of BUNGE for the purpose of organizing and managing the production of grain. The GROWER thereby agrees to RELEASE PHII from any harm or damages of any kind for the non-performance of this AGREEMENT.

i. The GROWER agrees to follow the identity preservation guidelines provided by BUNGE or its representative.

7. AGREEMENT TERM AND TERMINATION

a. The term of this AGREEMENT shall commence once signed by both the GROWER and BUNGE.

b. This AGREEMENT is in effect for the 2006 crop year only.

c. This AGREEMENT shall end when all of the IP LOW LINOLENIC SOYBEANS have been delivered and payment has been received.

GROWER and BUNGE agree to all the terms and conditions set forth in the AGREEMENT:

Grower Signature: _____   Date: _____

Bunge North America (East), L.L.C. (or its agent)

Signature: _____   Date: _____

® Registered trademark of Pioneer Hi-Bred International, Inc.

This form is used with permission.

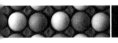

STUDY QUESTIONS

1. What are five alternative procurement systems for the private processor? What are some considerations a processor faces when she decides to "make or buy"?

2. Discuss the characteristics of the spot (current) market and some of its requirements as far as the processor is concerned.

3. What are some of the characteristics of procurement contracts? Discuss them from the perspective of processors, their purposes, requirements, and problems. What are the advantages and disadvantages of this method of acquisition? How do processors attempt to hold down risks and price competition?

4. Discuss the use by processors of production contracts.

5. Discuss procurement by labor contracts. How do the production contract and the labor contract differ?

6. How does a producer-owned ethanol cooperative impose the convenience yield? What are the costs of not being able to access corn stocks for ethanol processing?

7. How does the degree of commodity perishability affect processing methods and channels?

CLASS EXERCISE

For your group's agricultural commodity, interview a procurement person for one of the agribusinesses that buy the commodity. Your questions should include the following:

1. What methods (cash, contract, broker) are used to buy the commodity?

2. What logistical issues arise?

3. Is quality an issue in the buying decision?

4. What does a typical business day involve?

Your group should prepare to participate in a class discussion about the alternative procurement styles used by different firms for different commodities.

NOTES

1. It is more complicated than this; see the canned vegetable example in this chapter.

2. Much of the following is based on Gerald Campbell, "Grower-First Handler Exchange Arrangement in the Wisconsin Processed Vegetable Industry," *Coordination and Exchange*, NC-117, Monograph 2, 1976, pp. 29–42.

3. U.S. Department of Agriculture, *Cost Components of Farm–Retail Price Spreads for Selected Foods*, ERS Agricultural Economic Report 343, 1976, p. 56.

4. Thomas Hieronymous, *Economics of Futures Trading: For Commercial and Personal Profit*, 2d ed. (New York: Commodity Research Bureau, 1977), pp. 186–189.

14

PROCESSOR MARKETING

PREVIEW

- A processor's marketing mix includes four principal ingredients.

- Those basic concepts are applied to the marketing of numerous foods (especially dry groceries) by national brand processors.

- New products and the product life cycle are central to product marketing strategies.

- Promotion includes many facets.

- Pricing strategies vary among new and established products.

KEY TERMS

distribution center

Four Ps

marketing mix

new product

place

price

product

product life cycle

promotion

return on investment (ROI)

sales promotion

wholesaler–retailer (WR)

Processing will be treated conventionally in this chapter as food manufacturing. Mainly, we will examine the marketing side of processing to complement the procurement side discussed in the last chapter.

Food processing is big business. The processing cost share of U. S. foods reached $120 billion in 1994 and has continued to rise, reaching over $220 billion in 2004. The $220 billion figure refers to the value added in processing and is much smaller than total sales of processors. More value is added in food processing than is added in farm production.

Food processing is big business in another sense. The leading food manufacturers are very large firms. In addition, many of them are significant parts of conglomerate operations that are giants of the economy. Food and beverage manufacturing is a diverse business that varies by commodity (Exhibit 14.1).

About two-thirds of processor output goes directly to the consumer sector (retail stores and mass feeding institutions such as restaurants). Nearly one-fifth goes to other processors. For example, soybean crushers sell oil to refiners, who in turn sell to salad oil makers; crushers also sell soybean meal to feed companies. Similarly, a processor sells frozen fruit to other processors who make jams and jellies. The processor output not going to retail or to other processors goes to export, government purchases, and other uses.

14.1   Components of food and beverage manufacturing: Value of shipments.

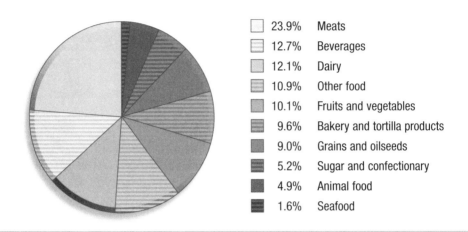

23.9%	Meats
12.7%	Beverages
12.1%	Dairy
10.9%	Other food
10.1%	Fruits and vegetables
9.6%	Bakery and tortilla products
9.0%	Grains and oilseeds
5.2%	Sugar and confectionary
4.9%	Animal food
1.6%	Seafood

Source: USDA.

Soybean oil sold to refiners is as much a commodity as soybean meal sold to feed manufacturers and as soybeans purchased from farmers. Because product differentiation does not exist, these processed commodities are traded much like other agricultural commodities; for example, there are futures markets for both soybean meal and soybean oil. These industrial-type commodities traded among processors will not be discussed further.

Although the retail store market is the larger market for processors, the mass feeding (food service) market is growing in importance. Between 1955 and 2006, the food service share of the consumer food dollar increased from 25% to 47.5%. These two markets differ significantly from each other. Processor brands are of limited significance to mass feeders, particularly the larger ones. Mass feeders are typically very demanding as to processed characteristics, and they frequently want the most convenience. They want frozen french fries and instant mashed potatoes rather than fresh potatoes. They want hamburgers that are uniform in composition and in sizes that weigh exactly 1.6 or 4.0 ounces. They want assurance of an absolutely adequate supply, regularly scheduled deliveries, and other services. Of course, they also want a competitive price. Processors compete on the basis of price and service for the mass feeding market, so their competition is somewhat similar to that in commodity markets. Although some processor promotion and advertising is essential, this market cannot be presold by mass consumer advertising stressing brand identification.

In a sense, two macrochannels exist between food processors and their largest market sector, the food stores.[1] In one macrochannel, organized by the core of very large processors, the processors market highly advertised and promoted branded items to all retailers, but particularly to the independent retailers. These processors dominate the marketing of some or all of their products as effectively as, or even more effectively than, they dominate the procurement of farm commodities from which those products are manufactured. In the second macrochannel, organized by the food chains, the chains procure specification products (generic or store brands) or relatively unadvertised processor brands from processors and especially from the small and medium-sized food manufacturers. These processors have so little control over their marketing that the channel, after processing, may be regarded as distributor controlled rather than manufacturer controlled.

We will give major emphasis in this chapter to the processor-dominated marketing channels. A more thorough discussion of distributor procurement will follow in Chapter 15. Many of the marketing channels concern items known in the trade as dry groceries (breakfast cereals and baby foods) and frozen foods.

The organization of the processor's marketing channel depends on his ability to presell products to consumers. This channel throbs with new products, new packages, cents-off deals, and all the excitement of modern merchandising. Although virtually all retailers participate in this channel, the smaller chains and the independents (usually wholesaler affiliated) are most receptive. Some of these retailers lack merchandising ability of their own, and they ride the coattails of the national processors. Others may be good merchandisers, but they are too small to organize a procurement effort, so they fit willingly into the processor-organized channel.

It might be argued that a reason for the continued growth of food processing is the existence of large food processors. That is, large food processors constantly scan the market to find areas where they can market more of their products or develop new products. Certainly, modern food processing involves more than technical expertise in food preservation. Large food processors frequently spend as much or more effort on marketing their products than they do on the manufacturing functions. Some of the large food processors are among the most skillful businesses in the whole economy in gauging and shaping consumer demand and in developing new products and new markets.

THE FOUR Ps OF THE MARKETING MIX

Successful marketing requires careful attention to a set of activities beginning with product design and including promotion, channel organization (place), and pricing. These activities, integrated and balanced to complement one another, are called a **marketing mix**.[2] This mix must be tailored to the particular firm's objectives and its market environment. The activities in the marketing mix are designated the **Four Ps**:

1. Product
2. Promotion
3. Place
4. Price

Product

Any marketer must cater to the needs of her potential customers. She is selling a set of satisfactions that revolve around the characteristics of the product, its packaging, and its general image. Generally, a marketer seeks to establish a unique image of a product, although typically several close substitutes are available (recall the discussion of monopolistic competition).

The **product**—the output of a firm that has some value added to the original raw commodity—is designed in terms of maximizing customer appeal against the real constraints of costs. For example, one does not design a Cadillac for a Chevrolet market, and vice versa. Nor does one try to market high-fat, premium ice creams to a health-conscious, inner-directed market segment (see Box 14.1). In a society geared to change and progress, it may be advantageous to introduce "new" products periodically. The marketer is thus motivated to keep developing new products or new versions of existing products.

MARKETING FINE-TUNES FOOD PRODUCTS — BOX 14.1

Food marketers are looking beyond demographic trends to lifestyle preferences for more information about what influences consumer purchasing decisions. Psychographics examine the sociological, political, theological, and economic factors that interact with personal histories and environments to form consumers' value and lifestyle preferences.

One development in psychographics is a value and lifestyle classification system (VALS) developed by the Stanford Research Institute (SRI) and explained in the book *The Nine American Lifestyles*. VALS formulation attempts to not only classify consumers' common lifestyle characteristics, but also to determine how individuals move between lifestyle categories as they age and mature.

The SRI system defines nine categories of consumers generalized into four groups that show the distinct marketing problems and prospects faced by retailers and manufacturers of mass-produced food products. Largest of the groups, made up of about 35% of the population, is the belongers. . . .

Belongers are generally traditional, conservative, conventional, nostalgic, sentimental, and unexperimental. Their central need is to fit in, not stand out. Belongers prefer brands and avoid experimenting with new foods and cooking methods. A typical dinner of meat, potatoes, and a vegetable projects the image of the diet.

The second-largest segment of the market, with 32% of the population, is the achievers. They are typically enterprising, hardworking, and hold values focused not only on the good life, but on a better one.

Achievers are mostly middle-aged, white, and working in successful managerial, professional, technical, or sales occupations. They are competitive, self-confident, and willing to try anything new, especially if it involves a technological breakthrough. Achievers prefer products and services that are top of the line and convenient. They own microwave ovens, shop in gourmet and specialty stores, and spend a significant portion of their food dollar on meals outside the home.

The third major group, inner-directed, shares qualities of affluence with achievers but is also significantly different. Since there are growing numbers of inner-directed consumers with more money to spend on food, marketers are concentrating on this group, along with the achievers.

Inner-directed consumers often come from achiever family backgrounds, are highly educated, and hold technical professional jobs. These consumers are very socially concerned, and they are often active believers in holistic health and inner growth. Their food interests tend toward the exotic. Freshness, appearance, flavor, and health and nutrition are all important characteristics they look for in products.

The final category, need driven, is composed of money-restricted consumers who have a few economic resources and are, therefore, driven more by need than by preferences. This part of the market, which represents about 11% of the population [in the mid-1980s], is characterized by extremely low or poverty-level incomes, greater numbers of minorities, high unemployment levels (especially among the young), and a high proportion of females.

The need-driven consumer segment is dominated by a sense of alienation, worry, and mistrust of authority, although the older members tend to be strongly traditional. Generally, price is the most important characteristic they look for in food items. They prefer private labels, shop for loss-leader items, use coupons, and often pay for food with food stamps, welfare check, or Social Security checks.

TARGETING WITH NEW PRODUCTS

To illustrate how knowledge of consumer lifestyles influences what we see on the grocer's shelves, consider the fruit and vegetable market. For the most part, processed fruits and vegetables are geared toward belonger and need-driven consumers because canned produce can be relatively less expensive and fits best into the traditional three-course-meal lifestyle. In addition, many of the need-driven consumers do not have access to freezers, so they purchase more canned fruits and vegetables.

To appeal to broader lifestyle segments, processors expanded product lines. Canned vegetables with no salt or fruits packed in light syrup and natural juice, for example, were designed to meet the inner-directed group's desire for more healthful foods. At the same time, these products have given the canned fruit and vegetable industry a much-needed boost. . . .

New kinds of frozen foods have also been a growth area for marketers. Products like Pepperidge Farm's Vegetables in a Pastry and frozen quiche are examples of manufacturers' attempts to match the achiever and inner-directed consumer's demand for healthful, quick, convenient, exciting, and nutritious foods.

Reprinted from Larry Hamm, *National Food Review*, NFR-29, 1985, pp. 25–26. Used with permission.

Promotion

Promotion is the communication of good, positive aspects of the marketer and his products to potential customers. Promotion includes *advertising*, which is nonpersonal communication through the mass media, mail, and billboards. Promotion also includes *personal selling*, which is face-to-face communication to potential customers. Personal selling is typically directed at retailers and any other intermediaries between the processor–marketer and his ultimate customers. Finally, promotion includes other forms of non-personal communication such as free samples, display materials, coupons, and contests; these are known as *sales promotion*.

As indicated in Chapter 5, communication with potential customers is essential to their purchase decisions. In a modern, industrial society, marketers rather than consumers take most of the initiative in trying to achieve that communication. Vigorous promotion is the norm.

Place

Channels of varying length and type carry goods to consumers (see Chapter 11). The marketer must develop a way for her product to reach consumers. Ordinarily she will rely on established channels, although she may consider alternatives such as door-to-door sales, catalog or TV-based sales, and marketer-owned or franchised retail outlets. Some marketers have achieved such tremendous consumer acceptance of their products that intermediaries need no persuasion to handle them. However, new or smaller marketers have to work hard to convince wholesalers and retailers to carry their products.

Thus, the marketing manager of a processing firm faces many decisions as she tries to develop the best conduit to her ultimate customers. Considering the nature of the products and the company's goals and resources, she must find answers to many **place** questions. She must organize a way through the channel to the final consumers. Should she seek intensive distribution—in every possible retail store—or a more selective distribution that aims at a more select market segment and builds a certain product image? Should she use existing channels or try to integrate vertically to retail? If she uses existing channels, should she develop a sales force or rely on brokers to sell to wholesalers and chain retailers? What sort of physical distribution system shall she develop to keep the product available to wholesalers and retailers while keeping down delivery costs? One can easily see that answers to these questions relate back to decisions as to the nature of the promotion mix.

Price

Price is obviously an important part of the marketing mix and is likely the most easily changed. Other things equal, lower prices attract more sales. However, the level of price also may convey an image of quality, and low prices can squeeze the margins of the seller. Thus, price must be considered carefully as an integral part of the marketing mix.

Unless the processor is vertically integrated to the consumer level, he probably cannot control directly the retail price. However, he generally can vary the retail price indirectly by changing the prices that are charged to intermediaries.

Pricing policy is complex. It is much different for a new, exciting product than for a "me-too" imitation of a dozen similar products in the market. Certainly, costs and potential profits must be considered carefully. However, unit costs often fall with higher sales, so demand projections at various prices should be tied to the cost estimates. In oligopolistic situations, possible competitive reactions may have to be calculated in setting price.

A marketing manager must integrate decisions on all of the Four Ps into a marketing strategy that works. Later, we will examine some of the particular problems that food processors experience in making decisions about their marketing mix.

THE MARKETING OF DIFFERENTIATED PRODUCTS BY LARGE, NATIONAL-BRAND PROCESSORS

To dominate a marketing channel, processors must do many things well. Their marketing strategy must identify appropriate target markets, and they must develop effective marketing mixes. They must have products that many consumers like. They must get those products on the shelves of thousands of supermarkets in an eye-catching, appealing package that shoppers will pick up. Processors must have a distribution system that ensures that those shelves are restocked as rapidly as the product sells. All this has to be done at costs that permit attractive prices to distributors and consumers and that garner profits for the processor. We turn now to examine how national processors handle the Four Ps in developing their food marketing mix.

Processors' Approach to Product

A food processor is selling much more than a set of calories or amino acids or the main course for a meal. She is selling a set of satisfactions that revolve around taste, eye appeal, quality, sanitation and healthfulness, convenience, packaging, positive and negative associations (Is it fattening? Is it popular with the beautiful people?), and nutrition.

Food is consumed in many different situations. The coffee break, the soft drink date, and the backyard barbecue are familiar examples of the many kinds of social situations in which food is consumed. In many such circumstances, the physiological needs of nutrition are farthest from the mind of the consumer; instead, psychological and social needs, such as belonging to a group and self-esteem, are more important.

The working parent may have concerns about the nutritional and physiological needs of her family as she prepares a quick breakfast of milk and cereal for her children. But she ordinarily chooses cereal rather than bacon, eggs, and hot biscuits because cereal is faster to prepare and clean up and the kids have absorbed so many cereal advertisements on TV that they usually insist on certain brands of cereals.

The weekday evening meal and the weekend meals are important opportunities for food processors selling through food retailers. Even on weekdays, the standard time for preparing a meal is probably only one-third as long as it was a generation ago. On weekends, the family pace may be a bit more relaxed, and there is time for preparing and consuming a rich variety of foods. The scents of the outdoor barbecue permeate suburbia on warmer weekends. In apartments, the more adventuresome singles may take a fling with the latest gourmet cooking. But for all of us some of the time and for some of us all of the time, food preparation is a tiresome chore, and cleaning up the kitchen and dishes is a pain.

Convenience

Is it surprising that convenience is a prime objective of the food processor as he designs foods for modern Americans? "Convenience sells" has been the lesson for more than 50 years.

Convenience has many facets. The rapid growth in ownership of microwave ovens (from less than 50% in the early 1980s to almost 100% today) has required the development of many kinds of products that can be cooked, warmed, or defrosted in the microwave. Children returning home from school can heat up their own Kid Cuisine frozen meals from ConAgra. Later, Mom or Dad may thaw a Healthy Choice or a Lean Cuisine (Stouffer) frozen meal. Then Dad may slip a Dial Foods Lunch Bucket in his brown bag for tomorrow's lunch at work. A late 1980's study by Pillsbury estimated that 1 out of 4 people subsisted on fast food, frozen dinners, and pizza.[3] On the other hand, the proportion of consumers who are retired people—with more time and more concern for healthful food—is growing. These people may set new trends.

Many other items are designed to help the cook who turns out conventional meals. Cake and pancake mixes assemble all, or almost all, of the ingredients in the right amounts. A macaroni package has the appropriate amount of cheese inside. Potatoes are available in various packages ready to be french fried or hash browned or heated as instant mashed. And salad in a bag became an everyday retail product beginning in the 1990s.

The Package

Convenience means more than saving the customer time. Packages of varying sizes provide the desired serving, whether it is consumed by a family or a single person.

Packaging is a very important part of product design and product competition for the food processor. Packaging began with the utilitarian objective of food preservation. Packages are necessary to prevent many foods from spoilage, from quality deterioration, or from contamination by insects, airborne bacteria, and handling. But there is far more to packaging than preservation of healthfulness and quality. Consumers demand packages that can be opened safely and easily. Today, pop-top lids and resealable bags are common. Packages are merchandising devices. In a self-service supermarket with thousands of items, each product is designed to attract the shopper's attention. Fruits, vegetables, soups and other foods are preserved in jars or cans and labeled with attractive print and mouth-watering photographs to sell them. The graphic design and the printing of a cereal box may be almost as costly to the manufacturer as the actual grain ingredients, and they may also be as important as the ingredients to the successful sale of the product. Since the 1990s, processors have been pressured to use packaging that is recyclable or otherwise less threatening to the environment, although current trends toward individual packaged portions run counter to this trend. Currently, dolphin-safe seals appear on most cans of tuna, and some organic corn chips are even sold in organic plastic bags made from corn co-products.

Package sizes are affected by various competitive situations. The half-pound lunch meat package was seemingly underpriced by competitors who sold a 6-ounce size. In time, the 6-ounce package has become the standard in lunch meats. The correlation between the apparent volume of cereal boxes and their net weights is fairly poor. Package sizes of certain products are sometimes reduced as a substitute for a price increase. For example, candy bar weights have increased and decreased over a considerable range during the economic changes of the past decades.

Highly Processed and Differentiated

It is no accident that most of the highly differentiated, successfully branded food products are highly processed packaged goods (dry groceries). These are the foods in which the large processor can exploit her processing and packaging skills—and in which she can build in convenience. These are the foods that the advertising department can sell as unique to the particular processor.

In contrast, processors of products other than dry groceries and beverages have had mixed results in establishing product differentiation. The frozen-food department has come along fairly well, with many similarities to dry groceries. Similarly, processors have found considerable branding success in cured items, sausages, lunch meats, and cheeses. Among the fresh, perishable items, there has been limited success with fluid milk and a very few produce items (e.g., Chiquita bananas) and success with fresh meats is only now occurring.

Success in processor product differentiation is not necessarily a once-and-for-all accomplishment. For example, some national processor brands of processed fruits and vegetables are encountering very stiff competition from retail brands in the other macrochannel. The competition between the dual channels is of a dynamic and changing nature.

New-Product Competition

A processor's product strategy is conditioned by general consumer receptivity to new products. In a technologically progressive society, a new product sometimes presents exciting satisfactions. Many consumers are geared to try "the new" because they perceive an enhancement of well-being. Besides, how many want to be known as the only one who has not experienced some new product or service?

What is a new product? Charles Post's development of Post Grape-Nuts cereal in 1898 began the dry breakfast cereal industry in America. Gail Borden's development of condensed or evaporated milk led to the development of a great corporation and a new industry. Nicolas Appert was recognized by Napoleon in 1809 for developing the basic process of canning foods. Clarence Birdseye began the experiments in 1923 with quick freezing of fish on which the frozen food industry is based. The newness of those products and processes during their time was probably generally accepted. But was a new kind of cereal, such as corn flakes, considered a new product? When a competitor imitated corn flakes by producing his own brand, was that a new product? If a processor sugarcoats corn flakes, is that a new product? What if she puts the corn flakes in a different-sized box?

There are many definitions of **new products,** of which close to 10,000 are introduced annually. One study suggests the following categories of new products:

1. Innovative items, which are obviously different from other products
2. Distinct products that are new to a firm
3. Product line extensions, such as new flavors, package sizes, and so on
4. Product improvements, including modification of ingredients, processing, and packaging.[4]

Most "new products" fall into one of the last three categories, and particularly the last two.

Most industry sources emphasize the great importance of new products. It is not uncommon to read a food processor's statement that half of its sales for a given year were of products it did not even have a decade ago. Such data generally depend on a broad definition of new products. It is more likely true that about 80% of the dollar sales of large food processors are "old-time" products, whereas 20% are from new products.[5]

Even the research and development departments of the biggest food processors seldom produce an item as innovative as Doritos Tortilla Chips or Kellogg's Pop Tarts. Truly innovative products cannot be produced on a schedule. The research and development departments can and do grind out the other three categories of new products. The research and development for a distinctly new product may require a year or more of effort, and perhaps $100,000 or more of investment. Then more time is required for product testing and test marketing. The test marketing may cost two or three times as much as the research and development. Then comes the big expense (usually much more than $10 million): all of the costs of promotion associated with obtaining first limited and then national distribution. One study of the profitability of such distinctly new products showed that less than half broke even in the first year of regular distribution; many required two or three years, and some were dropped without ever covering the development and introductory costs.[6]

The smaller product adaptations of the third and particularly the fourth categories in this list require less research and development effort and also may require less effort to introduce. If a firm simply chooses to replace a product with a slightly improved formulation or package, the market may accept it with little effort. However, the game is basically one of adding new items, and that always takes persuasion of consumers and of distributors.

Success Rate of New Products

It is not unusual to read that only 1 in 10 (or 20) new products is a success. On the other hand, it has been reported that the success rate of new products in the food processing industry is 30% to 40%.[7] The various quoted rates undoubtedly depend mainly on the definitions used. We have already explored the variety of definitions of new products. There are other complications. Does one count all the ideas tried in the research and development lab as new products or only those that are left after test marketing? Then what is success? Is it enough to make money by the second year and be dropped the third year, or is more continuity required?

Differentiation as a Marketing Strategy

Differentiated products are central to the marketing strategy of any large processor. The products are branded so that they may be obtained only from the processor that owns the brand. A further objective is to design in enough satisfactions that these products will be readily consumed at prices profitable to the processor and the intermediary handling firms. Then there must be massive advertising to make—and to keep—consumers aware of the product and its particular sets of satisfactions. Finally, the processor must promote the product and persuade retailers and other handlers to maintain an adequate supply pipeline to consumers. In some cases, retailers must be paid slotting allowances to add new products. Such allowances are often demanded on products that retailers consider less likely to succeed.

Large food processors, with a few exceptions, offer an immense array of products. Heinz has far more than 57 products. Using a definition of "new product" that excludes the fourth category (simple improvements), the number of "new" food products introduced annually rose steadily (Exhibit 14.2) from 5,600 in 1985 to 17,000 in 1995 and then dropped significantly between 1995 and 2000.

Various reasons exist for this outpouring of new products. A small minority represent something really new and so present the potential of building a large, new market for a processor. Most, of course, are me-too

EXHIBIT

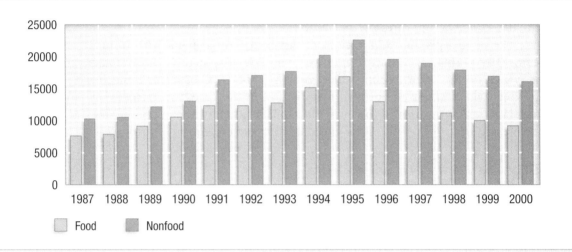

14.2   New food and grocery product introductions, 1987–2000. In recent years the number of food introductions has dropped significantly.

Source: USDA.

products. A processor that brings out a "new" product that imitates a successful innovation of a competitor may attract new customers. In terms of the economic theory of Chapter 2, truly innovative products may yield short-term monopoly profits, whereas me-too products may yield their makers small profits while eroding the monopoly profits of the innovator. As stated previously, from 1995 to 2000, many companies backed away from new product introductions. This decrease occurred because of the weakening economy and because most of the me-too food gaps had already been filled. Today, however, there appears to be a swelling of new food product developments in two areas: those that meet consumer health desires and those that fit consumer convenience trends.

The proliferation of new products is associated with and perhaps explained by oligopolistic competition among the large food processors. It was noted in Chapter 5 that the total domestic market for food expands slowly—as population grows, as incomes rise, and sometimes as tastes change. The typical large processor wants to grow faster than the total market. One strategy is to try to wrest markets from competitors by price competition, but that is too risky a business to be a dominant method. Another competitive method is to out-advertise and out-promote one's competitors on existing products; this is common but often ends in expensive standoffs. Perhaps the safest and most popular strategy of all is to bring out new products. If a new product is successful, it will likely take months for competitors to respond.

Yet competition by way of new products sometimes bears more than a little resemblance to a dog chasing its tail. Much (not all) of the market for new products represents a shift away from old products. These old products are likely to be the existing products of competitors. They could even be one's own old products! Thus, as all large food processors press forward with new products and attain new markets, they find that the markets for their old products often diminish. The near dominance of Campbell's premium frozen dinners with its LeMenu line was in turn displaced by Heinz Weight Watchers, ConAgra's Healthy Choice, and Stouffer's Lean Cuisine.[8] From a social viewpoint, some critics ask if all this proliferation and churning of products is worthwhile. Processors may insist that their survival is contingent on continuing the race.[9]

Certainly, new product competition would be much less if consumers were less responsive. ConAgra's Healthy Choice frozen entrees had sales of $190 million the first year.[10] Other big successes in the 1980s were Nabisco's Teddy Grahams, Hormel's Top Shelf entrees, and Heinz Weight Watchers. During the 1990s, per capita consumption of bottled water outpaced growth of any other food or liquid. Bottled water is a multibillion-dollar industry, and numerous brands compete in this market. All of these successful products possessed four basic consumer characteristics: convenience, taste, quality, and health. The first three characteristics have always been important, but health joined the group in the 1980s and has remained an important characteristic through today.

Product Life Cycles

Any product—food or nonfood—is thought generally to have a **product life cycle.** As a new product with a fine set of satisfactions, its sales rise when the market is opened; then sales grow for it and its rival imitations, and eventually its sales stabilize. Its sales may stay on a high plateau for a long time. But at some point another new product or set of new products comes along and replaces it in the consumption pattern of most or all consumers, so its sales decline. Perhaps it is eventually withdrawn from the market. The steam locomotive experienced such a life cycle, as did the horse-drawn vehicles of the nineteenth century.

The life-cycle concept makes sense in terms of supply-and-demand theory and the consumer-need concepts of Chapter 5. When a product is introduced, only the more venturesome of potential buyers try it and find that it meets their needs. When those buyers are satisfied, word spreads and demand expands. As output rises to meet the growing demand, average production costs are likely to fall, enabling price decreases and encouraging still more sales. However, this expansionary process must halt when all potential buyers have discovered the new product, as well as its new competitors.

Definitions, again, are important. Few would suggest that the product "food" has a life cycle. What about a specific food, such as potatoes? Per capita consumption of potatoes plateaued long ago. But consumption of processed potatoes is rising while consumption of fresh potatoes is falling. If the product is dehydrated potatoes or chips and shoestrings, per capita consumption has been rising impressively. If the definition is further narrowed to mean Sterzing's Potato Chips, then that product already may have gone through its entire life cycle. Individually branded items (narrowly defined products) may be expected to have life cycles.

Food processors use several concepts of life cycle in trying to understand and project their markets. Nestlé, a major pet food manufacturer, may watch carefully the total sales of dry dog foods, which are still growing. It also may watch carefully the growth (or decline) of the sales of each of its brands of dry dog food as it tries to project where each is in its life-cycle pattern.

The typical cycle of a branded, promoted food product is illustrated in Exhibit 14.3, which shows the pattern of both sales and associated profits. During the introductory period, with its heavy promotional expenses, profits are negative. Sales rise rapidly as distribution expands. Eventually, most potential markets are reached and competitors have responded with their own products; usually, profits level off and then so do sales. Decline eventually occurs as other kinds of new products attract consumers away from the old product. The life cycle illustrated in Exhibit 14.3 is a theoretical model. The actual life span of a branded item may be 10 or 100 times as long as that of another. The slope of the curves of actual products may differ considerably, and the curves may peak more than once. Although the irregularities of real life cycles, particularly after the first two stages, make their usefulness for prediction debatable, the fact of the quick mortality of many packaged goods after a few brief years is an important concept for product managers of processing firms to grasp.

Usually, the life cycle is as short as the product definition is narrow. Brands of pickles may come and go, but pickles seem to be here for a long time. Many products receive periodic facelifts in terms of packaging and promotion to extend their period of market maturity. They may be revived by a fresh advertising campaign or by introduction to new market segments.

EXHIBIT

14.3   Stages in a product life cycle.

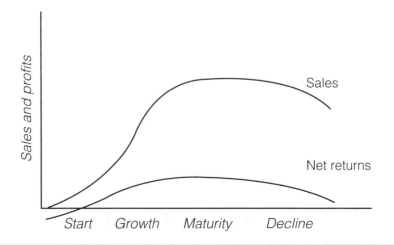

A firm may try to replace a product with a new one as soon as the sales of the old one begin to decline. Many retailers drop a product as soon as its sales start to decline, so a processor may find that he has little alternative to dropping a product that is in the declining stage of its life cycle.

Processors' Use of Promotion

The proportions of advertising, personal selling, and sales promotion will vary from firm to firm, but generally all three are essential to food processors in building and maintaining dominance of marketing channels.

Food is the most heavily advertised of all consumer products. In 1999 food marketing firms spent about $12 billion in direct consumer advertising, including electronic media, printed media, and coupons, and they probably spent about twice that amount for other retail promotions, such as trade shows, other discounts and allowances, and other incentives.[11]

Goals of Advertising

Some food processor advertising is institutional (with the objective of developing goodwill toward the firm), but most advertising is product oriented (the objective being to sell specific products). Some firms maintain firm identification with all or most of their products (e.g., Dole, Heinz, Hershey's, and Sara Lee). Other firms strongly emphasize the product brand. Did you know that Folger's coffee is a Procter & Gamble brand, or that Sanka and Maxwell House both belong to General Foods? Whereas brand-stretching can reduce advertising costs, an unpopular product can hurt the good name of the entire brand. Moreover, there are real limits; imagine Pepsi green beans or Hershey sausages.[12]

Effective advertising has specific goals. One way to categorize product advertising is in terms of the life cycle of the product.[13] During the introductory period of the life cycle, pioneering advertising is concerned with introducing the product to consumers and to intermediary handlers. Ads on TV and in magazines and newspapers *inform* potential consumers as to the existence and desirable attributes of the new product. Effective advertising causes consumers to ask retailers for the product if it is not yet on the shelves. It prepares the way for salespeople as they contact retailers to sell them on handling the new product.

The larger, national-brand processors have well-organized programs to get new products on retailer shelves. The retailers are faced with a coordinated program of introductory deals, consumer ads, and coupons that gives them little choice but to give the new product a try. Of course, they must usually evaluate the movement of existing lines and drop a slower-moving product to make room for the new product.[14]

Competitive advertising in the growth phase of the life cycle is designed to persuade consumers that the processor's brand is the best product in the group of such products competing for consumer demand. By this time, retailers and other intermediary agencies are already sold on the product. It is a matter of persuading more and more consumers to think of this particular branded product (e.g., to think of "Kleenex" when wanting a tissue). Such advertising on a national basis is so expensive that typically only large food manufacturers can finance it.

Every merchandiser would like to achieve *brand insistence*—so that consumers will buy no other brand. A lesser objective is to achieve *brand preference*. The first step on the ladder is to obtain *brand recognition*. Superior advertising may be sufficient to achieve brand recognition, but the entire marketing mix must be right to achieve that rarity, brand insistence.

Reminder advertising in the product maturity stage is concerned with keeping consumers reminded of the brand. Amid all the competing din of advertisers, the big firms know that they cannot take consumers and retailers for granted. Brands that cease advertising gradually lose sales. The jingles and slogans for well-known soft drinks are examples of reminder advertising.

Processors frequently provide *promotional allowances* to retailers. The allowance matches, in some specified ratio, the retailer's expenditures in advertising the processor's product in the retailer's market area. Through such allowances processors may get more local advertising for their money plus greater retailer interest in the product.

Large retailers may play off competing national brands in an effort to obtain more promotional allowances and deals. The strongest processors may be able to resist such ploys by concentrating on national advertising and consumer coupons. Because the promotional allowances amount to local price cuts, processors try to avoid heavy dependence on them. Most popular brands will receive a continuing series of deals and promotional pushes to keep retailers selling and consumers buying.[15]

Tasks of Salespeople and Food Brokers

Although advertising may "soften up" the retailer, it generally requires a sales call to get a retail group or chain to consider adding a new product. Whereas advertising "pulls" products through the channel, personal selling "pushes" them. The national processors generally have large sales staffs, although they sometimes make considerable use of brokers as well. Most retail chains and wholesale groups have an executive buying committee that decides regularly which of the numerous new products will be given a trial on their shelves.

Processor sales requires someone to work in the following ways with retailers:

1. Persuade the buyers for chains (and wholesalers) to try a new product
2. Check the retail displays to ensure proper merchandising
3. Obtain orders (more likely for perishable or fragile products than others)
4. Inform store managers and involve them in special product promotions, contests, and so on
5. Relay sales intelligence back to the processor

Food brokers are a vital link in this marketing channel, particularly for canned fruits and vegetables and frozen foods.[16] Depending on the completeness of the services desired by the processor, the broker may provide as many or more services than would be provided by the processor's own sales staff.

The smaller processors use brokers because they have insufficient volumes to justify a sales force. In some markets, large processors use brokers who do jobs superior to the processor's own sales force. Brokers charge commissions of 2% to 5%, depending on the sales volume of the account and the services furnished.

Sales Promotion

Sales promotion refers to those promotional activities that are complementary to advertising and salesmanship. Sales promotion includes the following:

1. P-O-P (point-of-purchase) displays
2. Sales contests among retail managers
3. Trading stamps
4. Sweepstakes
5. Bonus packs
6. Free samples
7. Cents-off deals on packages
8. Cents-off coupons distributed to customers
9. Exhibits at trade shows

It is estimated that the food-processing industry spends about twice as much on sales promotion and personal selling as it does on advertising.[17]

The cents-off deal is regarded as a good method of price cutting that stays under the seller's control; both customers and competitors regard the price reduction as temporary. The cents-off coupon is frequently used to introduce new products. In conjunction with mass advertising, it can be effective in persuading retailers that the product will move when put on their shelves. Like advertising, coupons are overdistributed.

Processor Decisions About Place

Processors develop channel systems to make their products available to consumers. Most food processors seek widespread distribution. There are exceptions, such as high-priced gourmet items, that processors seek to sell only in outlets catering to high-income people. A processor's sales depend in part on the number of retail stores carrying her products. Cost is obviously a limiting consideration—there are stores too far away from a distribution center or too small to justify the costs of servicing, and the processor acts accordingly.

The Wholesaler–Retailer Market

The larger segment of a typical national-brand processor's market is made up of affiliates. This segment, described more fully in Chapter 15, consists of various affiliations (such as Associated Wholesale Grocers, IGA, and Super Value) of wholesalers and retailers, tied together usually by contract and sometimes by ownership. Many local and regional chains are included in this segment. As indicated earlier, this segment has traditionally been much more receptive than has the big-chain segment to channel leadership by processors. The national and largest regional corporate retailer chains are also important customers of affiliates. They usually refuse to rely exclusively on national processors' brands of most products, but they generally carry them.

Because virtually all retailers are in some fashion connected very closely to a wholesaling operation, it is useful for certain purposes to think of retailers and wholesalers as a single entity. Most food products physically move from the processor to a wholesale or chain **distribution center** rather than directly to the retail locations. A *distribution center* is a transshipment warehouse that receives boxcars and truckloads of foodstuffs from many processors and then quickly sends trucks of assorted items to associated retailers. Selling to the wholesaler means that the processor has also sold to the retailer when the two are linked by ownership and often when they are linked by contract. To emphasize this vertical integration of wholesale and retail, we will use "WR" to mean **wholesaler–retailer**—the wholesale distribution center and the "connected" retailers. The term recognizes the contractual or ownership integration that typically links the food wholesale and retail functions.

Retailers generally emphasize volume; they are efficient handlers of tonnage. They are also managers of substantial shelf and floor space in which thousands of items are available for sale. Retail storage is very short term, as the focus is on high turnover of inventory. Retailers see themselves as selling a satisfactory shopping experience to thousands of customers, and the more customers the better. The affiliates are receptive to the national processors' products because these products carry national advertising and prestige, because they complement the merchandising image that the affiliates are trying to develop, and because the processors take the responsibility of providing exactly the volume wanted when the affiliates want it, at their warehouse or retail door.

At the same time, the affiliated WRs are not a pushover for every new product or even for the whole line of an individual, large food processor. Shelf space is limited. The WRs specialize in routine handling of tremendous tonnage. Each new product breaks the routine: a storage slot for it must be found at the warehouse; it must be added to the checklists and to the ordering system. For every 100 new food products added, 95 will have to be dropped.[18] The WRs are buyers for consumers, not sales agents for processors. They try to buy what their customers want to buy. If a particular item does not move at a profit, then it will not be around long.

The larger processor's task of organizing the channel (place) may be described simply, although the actual doing of it may be difficult. The processor uses her promotional resources (salesmanship, mass advertising, and sales promotion) to reach the several hundred WRs across the nation. She sells the WRs on carrying as much of her line of products as they can effectively merchandise. She sets up a physical distribution system that ensures prompt and adequate delivery to the WR distribution centers. She assumes responsibility for a continued flow of new products and for a succession of advertising campaigns and promotions that maintain her brands in the hearts and minds of the WRs' customers.

Efficient Physical Distribution

The large food processors have made giant strides in the difficult task of physical distribution—the job of getting products to WRs at an economical cost for a desired level of service. Customer service and low costs are competing objectives. Economies are generally associated with carload lots, slow delivery, and a few very large warehouses. Fast customer service does not fit those economies, so compromises (tradeoffs) must be made, and the whole physical distribution operation must be organized to reduce the conflicts between economies and service.

The management of physical distribution is a constantly changing and challenging aspect of processor marketing. One of the best selling points of a processor's salespeople to WRs may be the speed and adequacy of his supply service.

Vertical Integration of Processors and WRs

Why don't processors go into wholesaling–retailing themselves and avoid all the problems of selling to independent WRs? Some do, for a few product lines. There are dairy processors with dairy stores, candy manufacturers with candy outlets, and even an occasional meat market owned by a packer. But this is the age of the supermarket, incorporating many nonfood departments as well as foods. Thus, any food processor encounters the problem of mismatched assortments. No single processor manufactures even 5% of the great assortment of items available in a supermarket. A discrepancy of assortments does not absolutely prevent such vertical integration, but it certainly discourages it. There is virtually no ownership of supermarkets by processors.

Even though most national-brand processors lack the channel dominance of, say, the vertically integrated auto manufacturers, it should be clear that by developing a consumer franchise through modern customer services, they exercise effective channel leadership in their marketing channels.

Processor Pricing

Large, national-brand processors are price makers. They have considerable freedom in pricing their new products, have limited pricing discretion on their well-established products, and may be virtual margin makers on some old products that are in head-to-head competition with numerous competitors.

Pricing New Products

Processors have considerable discretion in pricing a product that is really new, but less discretion in pricing a carbon copy of an existing competitor.

General Foods is alleged to have had a pricing rule of thumb in its early history of one-third for manufacturing costs, one-third for marketing costs, and one-third for profits. Such a rule was cost oriented (the accountants must estimate, for a certain assumed volume of sales of each particular product, the costs of manufacturing), and it sought rather high initial profits. General Foods' policy is now more demand oriented, intended to keep price down to a level that generates higher sales volumes and does not encourage a flood of competitors.

Marketing people sometimes use such terms as *skimming the market,* for a policy of making large profits quickly or on new products, and *market penetration,* referring to pricing to obtain a mass market with the expectation that a large market share can be kept after imitators enter.

Effective pricing requires consideration of both costs and demand. To a considerable extent, both must be estimated on the basis of production and marketing experience. A firm will not go far into developing a new product unless its estimates show a satisfactory rate of **return on investment (ROI)**. Once the product is ready to be marketed, the firm certainly considers ROI in setting price. A simplified version of a formula for ROI is as follows:

$$ROI = \frac{TR - TC}{Investment}$$

where

TR = total revenue, which equals unit price times quantity sold
TC = total costs, which equals the unit cost times the number produced, plus fixed costs

The relation of quantity sold to price is obviously crucial to any estimate of ROI. Various aspects of a potential market affect a firm's estimate of the price–quantity (elasticity of demand) relationships. At what price level would middle-income Americans incorporate this food into their regular shopping budget? What sort of markup will be added by the WRs (so that probable retail prices can be estimated to match various manufacturer prices)? What are the retail prices of competing products? Would pricing, say, 20% above the nearest competitor enhance the quality image of this product, or is it more likely to price the product out of the market? It is a traditional rule in marketing that only 20% of people buy on the basis of the cheapest price.[19] However, any large price differential must be supported by a perceived quality differential. Would reducing the proposed price by a dime be as effective as spending that 10¢ on more promotion? Thus, pricing cannot be considered apart from other aspects of the marketing mix.

In a profit system, costs are important to pricing. Pricing obviously must cover costs. But even a high price may not cover costs if only a small volume is sold. Some businesspeople, therefore, like to calculate the *break-even point*—that minimum output at which total revenue (*TR*) finally equals total cost (*TC*). (Although neither *TC* nor *TR* is strictly linear, we make the usual simplification in rendering Exhibit 14.4.) Because the amount of profits depends on what happens after the break-even point, the break-even calculation does not indicate the particular price that will generate maximum profits. About all that a break-even point does is inform the price maker how much volume of the product has to be sold (per accounting period) at a particular price before it generates any profits. Note that both TR_1 and TR_2, associated with two different prices, generate break-even points.

Similarly, attempts to apply cost-plus pricing to a new product are not as simple as they first appear. Average costs depend on how much is sold. They may be several times as high at X sales volume as at 10X volume. The chosen average cost to which a margin is added is specific to a particular volume of output. Thus, it is necessary for WRs to estimate sales for various prices. The price decided on relates directly to the expected sales volume, and the sales volume and the underlying average costs may be substantially impacted by plant capacity. As a further complication, estimates of the overhead costs to be attributed to any particular one of the many products sold by a firm usually must be made quite arbitrarily. Moreover, a firm may allocate a lower burden of "costs" to a product known to be facing severe price competition than it does for a product facing less competition.

In short, there is no escape from estimating demand elasticities, sales volumes, and associated costs in pricing a new product. The estimates will not be as neat and precise as taught in the basic economics treatment of marginal revenue and marginal cost pricing, but those principles provide a point of departure.

EXHIBIT

14.4 Break-even point analysis.

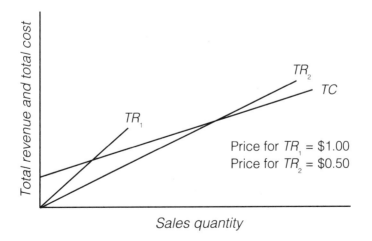

Price for TR_1 = $1.00
Price for TR_2 = $0.50

Pricing Tactics

Pricing is not a once-and-for-all event. There is rarely such a thing as "one price." Prices are changed over time. Moreover, different prices may be charged at any particular time to different buyers.

Prices change over time for various reasons. Processors change prices in reaction to changes perceived in demand or costs. Yesterday's optimum price is not today's optimum if input costs have changed materially or if new competition has rendered demand more elastic. The price of a highly processed, convenience consumer product often lacks much relationship to farm ingredient costs. The cost of the wheat in a box of Wheaties is so small that the processor does not need to adjust to most changes in wheat prices. The baker is less insulated and will react to smaller changes in wheat flour prices. The vegetable canner faces possible annual adjustments to the prices of his raw materials, depending on the size of the seasonal pack and movements in his costs. Processors have other costs—particularly labor, transportation, utilities, and supplies that escalate during times of inflation and that force the periodic reconsideration of prices.

Processors periodically lower prices on a temporary basis to promote WR interest and product sales, using various procedures. Promotional allowances were discussed earlier. A more direct method is to print a price reduction (such as 25¢ off) on the packages produced for, say, 30 days and reduce the price to WRs by the same amount. Another method is to put discount coupons for the product in the hands of consumers through newspapers, magazines, or direct mail. Although price concessions are a fairly reliable method of increasing sales, some experts warn against overuse. Repeated special deals may lead WRs and consumers to focus entirely on the price of the product.

These promotional price concessions may be used to introduce new products and to spark sales of established ones. Procter & Gamble first introduced Folger's coffee in Chicago with a mass distribution of coupons that enabled consumers to buy a can and get one free. The response was tremendous. Would the long-term effects have been the same if Folger's had been introduced at half the usual price and then raised after 30 days to its regular price?

Warning to Apprentice Decision-Makers

Numerous pricing traps await those who do not understand or who choose to ignore government regulations over pricing. Some of these matters are quite complicated, so we merely note the hazards. In other words, if you get into trouble five years from now, call the company attorney, not us. Still better, talk to her before you get into trouble.

It is permissible to charge competing wholesale buyers different prices under certain conditions. Generally, discounts, advertising allowances, and other concessions of value must be freely available to all competing buyers and must not be given secretly or under disguise. Discounts must be justified. For example, the Robinson-Patman Act of 1936 permits prices to differ to the extent that costs of producing and marketing the product differ. Thus, quantity discounts appear to be justified *to the extent* that it is cheaper to produce and sell larger volumes. A processor may sell an unbranded or store-branded version of a product to a WR cheaper than he sells a branded version, although it is not clear just how much cheaper. Robinson-Patman also allows a processor to sell cheaper to a particular WR if done in good faith to meet competition. Interpretation of those conditions is tricky for most laypeople and perhaps for some lawyers.

When competition is rough, situations may occasionally arise when it is tempting to set prices after consulting with one's competitors. The Sherman Antitrust Act, in rather sweeping terms, forbids any such conspiracy to fix prices.

Another trap is failure to recognize the many instances of oligopolistic interdependence (see Chapter 2). If your price cut reduces materially the sales of one or more of your few direct competitors, then he (or they) may retaliate. That, of course, is an important reason for making explicitly temporary promotional price concessions, because your competitors recognize their time limits. Too-frequent promotional price cuts, however, are likely to lead to aggressive price competition. A prime reason for emphasizing the nonprice aspects of the marketing mix—new products and promotion especially—is to reduce the number of head-to-head confrontations and to avoid price wars.

Final Comments on Price and the Marketing Mix

Remember that we have been discussing the pricing policies of large, national-brand processors, not of smaller firms. Pricing of the latter's products tend to be dominated by WRs, so discussion on that topic is in the next chapter.

Large processors have obtained varying amounts of dominance of their marketing channels. Such dominance is based on their building consumer acceptance for their products and on their economic power and ability to take leadership and get things done. Don Tyson has said that the marketing philosophy of Tyson Foods is "SCD": Segment, Concentrate, and Dominate. In other words, Tyson develops a product that appeals to a particular market segment, then concentrates promotion and marketing efforts until they achieve the 50% share essential to market dominance.[20] It is clear that many other large food firms have much the same philosophy. To organize the channel and to attract the attention of consumers is an ever-changing challenge. The nature of the marketing mix and many of the marketing tactics have changed considerably in the past quarter century. Expect the changes in tactics to be equally dramatic in the next 25 years.

SUMMARY

1. This chapter dealt with the elements of the marketing mix by which large, national-brand food processors organize their marketing to WRs. The prime examples include dry grocery items.

2. The concept of the marketing mix and of its four ingredients—product, price, promotion, and place—helps to provide a systematic explanation of how a processor can accomplish micromarketing objectives.

3. Organizing a marketing channel depends on adopting an effective marketing strategy and a balanced marketing mix. The national-brand processors have made a continuing stream of new products a central part of their marketing mix. Of course, promotion and pricing must be geared both to introduce and sell the new products and to persuade consumers to keep buying many of the old ones. There is a considerable element of creative destruction in this stream of new products. In other words, new products tend to drive out old products.

4. Promotion in all its aspects (advertising, salesmanship, cents-off deals, free samples, and contests) is an aggressive and expensive part of the marketing mix. Nationwide promotion is generally the province of the big national firms; it is too difficult and expensive for many processors.

5. The promotional ability of national processors to *pull* products through the channel by preselling them to consumers is a powerful aid in obtaining broad acceptance by WRs of processor products. Most processors also complement the pulling with an effective job of *pushing* products through their marketing channel by means of WR promotions, salesmanship, and effective physical distribution systems.

6. Pricing policies must fit the fabric of the rest of the marketing mix. New, really different products allow processors a great deal of pricing discretion. On the other hand, oligopolistic interdependence of older products with several competitors limits pricing discretion.

7. Farmers want their particular commodities merchandised by processors, and professional nutritionists want nutrition marketed, but national-brand processors are not sales agents for anybody else. They create and market those products that they believe will sell the best for them. They can profitably sell convenience and images of sociability and enjoyment. Merchandising is the name of the game for the national-brand processors.

STUDY QUESTIONS

1. Briefly describe the buyers to whom processors sell their products.

2. What is meant by dual marketing and microprocurement channels? Describe each of these channels. What is the difference between the processor's marketing channel and the retailer-organized procurement channel? Is there any overlapping? If so, where?

3. What is meant by the term *marketing mix?* What are the Four Ps?

4. How is packaging related to food marketing? Why?

5. Discuss new products in relation to the consumer and to the processors' product strategy. What is a "new" product? How many new food products are introduced annually? What is the success rate of new products? What are the four product characteristics essential to the consumer acceptance of a new food product?

6. Discuss product differentiation as a marketing strategy. What are the objectives of product differentiation? Why is there such a proliferation of product variety from the processors' point of view?

7. What is meant by product "life cycles"? Why do they exist? Can you recall a food product that was introduced in the past two years but is no longer obtainable?

8. Why is promotion so important in the marketing of food products? What is meant by "pulling" vs. "pushing" products through the market channel?

9. Discuss the pricing of new products. How much discretion do processors have in pricing new products? What is meant by "skimming the market"? By "market penetration"?

CLASS EXERCISE

New food products are introduced daily. For this exercise, your instructor will assign five different food categories (e.g., bread, cheese, sauces, cereal, and cookies). Visit a local grocery store and interview the appropriate manager to learn about food products recently introduced to the food category for that store. Ask about successes and failures of new products in the store, and why they succeeded or failed. Be prepared to participate in a class discussion as to why, or why not, the various products succeeded.

NOTES

1. Much of this section derives from the analysis in C. R. Handy and Daniel I. Padberg, "A Model of Competitive Behavior in Food Industries," *American Journal of Agricultural Economics* 53 (1971): 182–190.

2. F. J. McCarthy, *Basic Marketing: A Managerial Approach,* 5th ed. (Homewood, IL: Richard D. Irwin, 1975).

3. "Are Square Meals Headed for Extinction?" *The Wall Street Journal,* March 15, 1988, p. 35.

4. National Commission on Food Marketing, *Studies of Organization and Competition in Grocery Manufacturing,* Technical Study 6, Washington, DC, June 1966, p. 27.

5. *Prepared Foods New Products Annual 1989,* p. 36.

6. Ibid., pp. 32–39.

7. "The Hard Road of the Food Processors," *Business Week*, March 8, 1976, p. 52.

8. "The Campbell Kids Fight for the Middle of the Store," *The Wall Street Journal*, March 28, 1991, p. A19.

9. John Connor, "Food Product Proliferation: A Market Structure Analysis," *American Journal of Agricultural Economics* (November 1981): 612.

10. *Prepared Foods New Products Annual 1991*, p. 34.

11. USDA, Anthony Gallo, *The Food Marketing System in 1995*, p. 8.

12. "Brand-Stretching Can Be Fun—and Dangerous," *The Economist*, May 6, 1990, p. 77.

13. Much of this and the next three paragraphs is adapted from McCarthy, pp. 430–432.

14. Larry Hamm, "The Interactions of Food Manufacturer Advertising and Food Retailer Buying Practices: Some Implications for Food System Organization," in J. M. Connor and R. W. Ward, eds., *Advertising and the Food System*, NC-117 Monograph, University of Wisconsin, September 1981.

15. Dorothy Giobbe, "Newspaper Coupon Distribution Flat in 1993," *Editor and Publisher*, Nov. 19, 1994, p. 29.

16. Material in this paragraph is drawn largely from Daniel I. Padberg, *Today's Food Broker* (New York: Chain Store Age Books, 1971).

17. Anthony Gallo, *The Food Marketing System in 1990*, USDA Agricultural Information Bulletin 632, p. 8.

18. *Prepared Food New Products Annual 1991*, p.34.

19. Walter Kiechel III, "The Food Giants Struggle to Stay in Step with Consumers," *Fortune*, September 11, 1978, p. 53.

20. *Pigs-Misset*, June/July 1991, p. 9.

CHAPTER

15

WHOLESALE, RETAIL, AND FOOD SERVICE MARKETING

PREVIEW

- Wholesalers have evolved over time to become highly linked with food retail. The wholesale–retail relationship has evolved to the point of information sharing and long-term contractual agreements.

- Food retailing is often concentrated at the local level. However, nonprice competition is usually highly active; price competition became more intense in the 1980s with the growth of low-price formats and helped to hold food costs at or below the rate of inflation throughout the 1990s. Between 2000 and 2005, food price changes have been at or above the rate of inflation.

- Although some consumers shop for the cheapest prices, most are attracted by a set of attributes. Two main types of customers drive the utilization of two pricing formats, high–low and everyday low pricing.

- Aimed at various market segments are such different retail formats as warehouse stores, convenience stores, local grocery stores, super centers, and conventional supermarkets.

- Food is strongly advertised. The use of advertising and promotion helps develop a competitive image. Store and private label branding is becoming increasingly popular.

- Although the food service industry is still relatively unconcentrated compared to food retailing, the development of owned and franchised chains has been transforming the industry.

- Food service chains and restaurants have developed several concepts to serve different market segments. Evidence about the market orientation of modern food service operations shows that performance has been variable.

KEY TERMS

affiliate

chain

combination store

cooperative affiliate

everyday low prices
(ELP)

independent retailer

institutional food sector

institutional middlemen

price specialing

slotting fee

store format

superstore

variable price
merchandising (VPM)

We begin the examination of the marketing side of the food retailing and food service industries with a look at food retailers. Although our focus is mainly on food, you should recognize that few retailers sell only foods, and that some sell far more nonfoods than foods. Nevertheless, most food is sold by supermarkets or other stores regarded as food stores or by food service units.

STRUCTURE OF THE WHOLESALER-RETAILERS

The wholesaler–retailers (WRs) have many facets. Any description must include such concepts as chains, affiliates, independents, supermarkets, and convenience stores. Stores may be classified by the number of outlets owned, by the nature of their association with a wholesaler, by their individual sales volume, or by their function. First, a classification is made according to the number of stores owned.

Chain   = 11 or more food stores under one ownership
Independent = one store or as many as 10 under one ownership

Retailers may be classified by the nature of their wholesaler relationship. That relationship may be ownership, contract, or arms-length independence. A larger **chain** often owns a distribution center and does its own wholesaling, so chain ownership is a common WR relationship. An **affiliate** is an **independent retailer** or chain retail store that, along with other stores, is associated with a wholesaler by ownership or contract. There are two types of affiliate groups: voluntary and cooperative. The *voluntary* affiliates are more numerous; they are organized by wholesalers and contract to receive wholesaling functions. The first group of voluntary affiliates, the Red and White Stores, was begun by S.M. Flickinger Wholesale Grocery of Buffalo, New York, in 1921. Another example, IGA, is a federation of voluntary groups. IGA franchises wholesalers with the right to sponsor retailers as IGA stores. The second affiliate group includes the **cooperative affiliate;** here, retailers cooperatively own distribution centers that provide the wholesale function.

In addition to voluntary and cooperative affiliates, there are unaffiliated stores and wholesalers that do not have a contractual or ownership link. Presumably most unaffiliated retailers are independents. The unaffiliated independents are a rather heterogeneous class including a single, small mom-and-pop store in a village as well as a small group of supermarkets in New York City. Such complete independents shifted from having the majority of all sales to having a tiny minority by the last half of the twentieth century.

Geography of Distribution

The WRs are generally organized around the larger metropolitan areas. Some 53 distribution areas cover the nation.[1] In most metropolitan statistical areas (MSAs), 40% to 70% of the retail grocery sales are made by the top four firms. The typical area is served mainly by ten or fewer chains and affiliate groups, of which several likely have a wholesale distribution center through which most of their tonnage is funneled.

The operation of wholesale distribution centers achieves important economies of scale. Computerized automation of these centers has been quite successful. The economic factors limiting size for most warehouses include the delivery diseconomies associated with traveling farther and farther to serve more stores. An obvious "remedy" is to increase the number of stores served within a reasonable radius of the distribution center. One study suggested that 32 warehouses could serve the nation optimally. The number of warehouses has been falling steadily for the last four decades.

The chains were leaders in developing efficient distribution centers. The affiliates have largely caught up. Many wholesalers (affiliate and unaffiliated) serve one or more corporate chains among their customers.

The vertical integration of the WR relationship is not one size fits all. Ownership, contractual, and even independent and informal relationships still prevail. Much is in a state of flux. Nevertheless, the vertical relationships of WRs, whatever their legal variations, promote the efficient handling of a vast tonnage of foods and the expeditious supplying of a vast variety of items. Because of cooperative ownership of distribution, operators of small-chain and even single-unit supermarkets now have access to efficiencies that were once an important competitive advantage of the national chains.

Wholesale–Retail Margins

Margins (the difference between selling price and invoice cost expressed as a percentage of selling price) for WRs have generally been somewhat higher on private-label than on processor brands. At the same time, consumers' prices have usually been higher on processor labels. For example, Hormel Ham is premium priced to store-brand ham by $.70/lb, holding all other factors constant.[2]

Given that private labels benefit retailers with wider margins and consumers with lower prices, one might wonder why they have not obtained a much larger market share. Lack of consumer confidence in the quality of WR labels seems to be the primary reason they don't hold a larger market share. In some cases, the perception that some retailers' private brands are not equal in quality to the national brands may be justified, in others it may not. Equally important has been many consumers' national-brand allegiance, based on several of the factors discussed in Chapter 5, such as beliefs that higher price means higher quality. These favorable consumer evaluations are reinforced by heavy processor promotion.

Private-label items are not necessarily more profitable to WRs simply because they carry wider margins. A brand with a 15% margin that sells three cases a week is almost certainly more profitable than another brand with a 20% margin that sells half a case a week. But private-label items have an attraction beyond their immediate profitability. Larger retailers have liked them because they help to develop consumer loyalty to the store rather than a processor, they attract a market segment that shops for low prices, and they are a keystone in prying some market power away from the processor. Daniel Padberg of the NCFM concluded that the playing off of one supplier against another to furnish a WR-label product strengthens bargaining power.[3]

Procurement Pricing

Are WRs price makers or price takers in their procurement? They are some of both; it depends on the products and the WRs. The smaller WRs are price takers for virtually all products because they do not have the buying power or the private-label brands with which to bargain over price. The larger WRs are essentially price takers when dealing with the large processing oligopolies with highly differentiated products. The makers of national brands can name their prices. However, in dealing with the processors of commodities such as fresh meats and with the makers of their private brands, the larger WRs likely have as much or more bargaining power than the processors. Large WRs have found that they can use private brands effectively in increasing the price competition among processors to obtain their business.

As we have emphasized, the main forces affecting the level of the price of flour or bacon or canned vegetables arise from basic supply and demand. No WR is big enough to set the price of flour or canned peas at a certain level for the next two years. But within that context of the interplay of basic supply-and-demand forces, the large WRs do negotiate prices for particular products. They are price negotiators if not price makers.

LOCAL RETAIL MARKET STRUCTURE

On the whole, retail structure is concentrated at the local level. Most consumers shop for food within three miles of home. It is typical for a few chains (national and local) to have half of the sales within a metropolitan market. For all metropolitan areas (MAs), the four largest retailers' joint market share is typically greater than 40%.

Does oligopoly exist in food retailing? We certainly have an oligopolistic-type structure in most metropolitan areas and even more so in the restricted geographic areas in which most consumers shop. Although the difficulties of entry differ with the size of market, the strategy of existing competitors, and the competence of entrants, entry is usually not frequent and is not easy. In other words, entry conditions are often more like oligopoly than like other market models. We see evidence of price leadership and other types of oligopolistic behavior in a number of markets. However, one may find that store services differ and products are virtually identical. Yet, entry into this industry is quite difficult because of large capital costs and the need to develop relationships with wholesalers and distributors. We should not be surprised that the realities of this dynamic industry fit best in a gray area between monopolistic competition and oligopoly, possessing characteristics of both.

Chains have often been accused of "predatory practices," such as price cutting their way into a new market while subsidizing their losses from an area where they are well established. The National Food Commission found evidence of such activity in a few cases, particularly in the earlier period when chains were largely competing with small independents. Now that chains are typically competing with other chains or large affiliates, such predatory price cutting holds fewer attractions. It is expensive and risky. Of course, one of the advantages of a large regional chain is that losses in any one area will be balanced by better conditions and profits in other areas. A chain's financial strength, its buying power, and its continuity are more important competitive advantages than its use of predatory price cutting.

COMPETING FOR CUSTOMERS

A food retailer has no assurance of a market for her services. Her success depends on attracting the necessary volume of customers. When population and incomes were growing very fast in the 1950s and early 1960s, volume for most retailers was obtained relatively easily. Since then it has been a different story.

Attracting customers is an art that does not allow neat dissection. Important ingredients are the type of store, location, shopping atmosphere, merchandising skills, product mix, services, and pricing. A successful marketing mix must be responsive to the shifting social and economic environment.

Now, as in past decades, shoppers seem to indicate they desire such characteristics as economical prices, a pleasant shopping experience, sufficient variety for one-stop shopping, nearby location, sufficient parking, speedy shopping and checkout, long open hours, and specialty departments such as delis and bakeries.

All of these features are provided in a single **store format** at a Wal-Mart Supercenter, for example. A store that provides the ultimate in amenities and variety of selection will have above-average costs and prices unless it has exceptionally high volume. Wal-Mart Supercenters are driven by volume. Such a large store is not very convenient for the drop-in shopper who wants one or two items. The store that can provide the lowest prices is likely to omit some of the amenities associated with a pleasant shopping experience.

In the 1930s, the first supermarkets emphasized economy. They were similar to what we now call warehouse stores, with few amenities but a large selection (compared to the typical small stores of the time), drive-in convenience, and low prices. Over the next 40 years, the conventional supermarket gradually evolved into a larger store with better atmosphere and more departments, more selection, and a bit less emphasis on economy. The changes were consistent with rising real incomes. However, some market segments were neglected.

New Formats

Chains of convenience stores began to develop in the 1950s. The number of grocery stores fell by over half (400,000 to 128,000) from 1950 to 1995,[4] and this trend has continued as ever-larger supermarkets crowded out small stores and the older, smaller supermarkets. Developers of convenience chains perceived a market opportunity for a new type of small store with limited variety and speedy shopping, conveniently accessible to many people and open 24 hours. Inevitably, costs and prices were generally higher because of low volume and low-dollar transactions. Obviously the convenience store format cannot appeal to a major segment. Tobacco, dairy products, beer, and soft drinks are the biggest sellers.

The next invasion of the territory of the conventional supermarket grocery store was by the limited assortment (warehouse) store. A German firm, Aldi, brought the concept to Iowa in 1976. Its target was the market segment most concerned with price. To provide low prices, the box store carries only 500 to 1,500 items, mostly private label, in an austere environment. The importance of the box store was not in the market share it gained but in its demonstration to food retailers that a price appeal would work.

The original warehouse store was a large box store with 1,500 to 7,500 items. It was close to being a discount supermarket but offered fewer amenities. The emphasis was on buying and selling cheaper. Often it carried whatever national brand it had been able to buy that week on a special deal. The superwarehouse store, developed in the early 1980s, has more departments and a larger assortment of items, in a discount format that is sometimes nicer in decor than the warehouse store.

At the other end of the amenities spectrum, the market of the conventional supermarket has been eroded by still larger stores (minimum of 30,000 square feet) with a large component of nonfoods and a huge variety of foods and special departments. At the extreme of these superstores is the supercenter with more than 100,000 square feet of space. The best example today is likely the Wal-Mart Supercenter. The more typical jumbo or **superstore** is one-third to one-half the size of the supercenter. (See Box 15.1.) In recent years, the superstores' share of supermarket sales has climbed rapidly. A *warehouse club* is a membership wholesale club such as Sam's Wholesale Club, PACE Membership Warehouse, and Costco. These include substantial food sections.

Another food retail format is the so-called **combination store,** which essentially combines a supermarket and a drugstore and stocks more than 20,000 items. Such stores may also house dry cleaning, fast food, and banking outlets within the store to appeal to those interested in "one-stop shopping." Such stores have volumes in the $10 to $40 million range, and they quickly became successful in numerous locations. An example of a combination store is Walgreens.

For management planning a new location, the type of store is a basic decision that cannot be altered easily. Thousands of small stores and convenience stores find niches in the marketplace. Should a supermarket be conventional, a huge superstore, or a combination store? Should it be freestanding or in a shopping center?

Supermarkets (including the larger versions) account for only one-fifth of retail grocery stores, but they make nearly three-fourths of the sales (Exhibit 15.1). At the other extreme, there is still a large but declining number of small stores (under $2 million volume) in small towns and tucked away in large

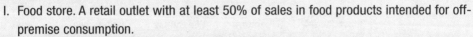

USDA CLASSIFICATION OF FOOD RETAILERS   BOX 15.1

I. Food store. A retail outlet with at least 50% of sales in food products intended for off-premise consumption.

   A. Grocery store. A food store that sells a variety of food products, including fresh meat, produce, packaged and canned foods, frozen foods, other processed foods, and nonfood products.

      1. Supermarket. A grocery store, primarily self-service in operation, providing a full range of departments, with at least $2.5 million in annual sales (1985 dollars).

         a. Combination food and drugstore—A supermarket containing a pharmacy, a nonprescription drug department, and a greater variety of health and beauty aids than that carried by conventional supermarkets. . . .

         b. Superstore—A supermarket distinguished by its greater size and variety of products than conventional supermarkets, including specialty and service departments and a considerable inventory of general merchandise products.

         c. Warehouse store—A supermarket with limited product variety and fewer services provided, incorporating case lot stocking and shelving practices. Superwarehouse stores are larger and offer expanded product variety and often service meat, delicatessen, or fresh seafood departments.

      2. Convenience stores. A small grocery store selling a limited variety of food and nonfood products and typically open extended hours.

      3. Superette. A grocery store, primarily self-service in operation, selling a wide variety of food and nonfood products with annual sales below $2.5 million (1985 dollars).

   B. Specialized food store. A food store primarily engaged in the retail sale of a single food category, such as meat and seafood stores, dairy stores, candy and nut stores, and retail bakeries.

Source: USDA, *Food Marketing Review, 1992–93,* Agricultural Economic Report 678, 1994, pp. v–vi.

cities. In the past few decades, the total number of grocery stores has dropped significantly but the number of convenience stores has increased.

A supermarket must be big enough to carry what shoppers want but small enough for convenient shopping. The retailers' idea of that proper size balance has been growing and likely will continue to grow.

Overall, the trend has been toward larger size. The average supermarket that opened between 1973 and 1975 was slightly over 25,000 square feet, with a selling area of 19,000 square feet, whereas stores that closed were less than two-thirds as large. The typical supermarket opening in 1991 had nearly 50,000 total square feet and was either a combo or a superstore.[5]

EXHIBIT

15.1

Distribution of number and total sales of supermarket stores by type, 1990 and 2000.

	Conventional	Superstore	Warehouse	Combination	Other
Number of stores (000s)					
1990	13.2	5.8	3.4	1.6	0.5
2000	9.9	7.9	2.4	3.7	0.7
Total dollar sales ($ billion)					
1990	92.3	87.6	33.1	29.3	19.4
2000	63.4	142.4	22.0	81.8	27.7

Source: Kaufman, P. R. "Food Retailing." U.S. Food Marketing System, 2002, USDA Economic Research Service.

Shopping Location, Merchandising, and Atmosphere

There is no precise measure of what amenities attract customers to stores. The customers themselves probably cannot articulate all the reasons they select one store over another. When asked, they usually emphasize convenience of location, helpfulness and friendliness of store personnel, and quality and freshness of meats and produce. All those factors and more are important, but there is no precise formula for adding them up or making trade-offs.

A top manager can usually make a success out of a mediocre location. However, good locations have made many mediocre managers look good. A good location is one that gives plenty of potential customers more convenient access to that store than to any others. The more desirable locations in relation to a particular housing and street pattern can be ascertained fairly readily. However, things can change rapidly due to new streets, changing neighborhoods, and new competitors.

Good merchandisers differ as to how they attract customers. Some try to add excitement to the shopping experience by means of huge displays of seasonal items (e.g., fresh produce or turkeys during the fall holidays), screaming ads, banners and posters plastered all over the store, and a friendly bustle of activity. Other merchandisers are strong on friendliness, a full variety of items, and services in a more gracious and sometimes luxurious atmosphere. The appeal of either approach is affected by the type of neighborhood. However, some proponents of either approach are good enough merchandisers to make it succeed in a wide variety of neighborhoods. Merchandising is an art, and there are a few outstanding merchandisers in large cities who can acquire a store that has failed and turn it into a success.

Most supermarkets choose to emphasize nonprice attributes. Certainly, they try to maintain an image of reasonable or competitive prices, but most of them try not to rely on simply being cheaper. However, supermarkets with a warehouse format and some with a conventional format focus on a low-price image, with names like Price Chopper or Food-4-Less. It is extremely important to identify and emphasize the attributes, whether cost or amenities, that are important in a particular location.

In supermarket nonprice competition for customers' loyalty, some characteristics are common. The shopping experience must be a pleasant one. This requires well-stocked shelves with a minimum of stockouts, especially of items in ads. It requires a clean, air-conditioned, attractively decorated, well-lighted store with a convenient parking lot that can be reached safely and conveniently from nearby main streets. It requires courteous service, ready help in the produce and meat departments, quick checkouts, and pleasant and quick check cashing. Other services and techniques are often added to the kit of competitive tools (Exhibit 15.2). An in-store bakery or florist is often added for its expected contribution to the store atmosphere, even though sales may hardly cover costs. New, larger stores typically offer many drug-store items. Some stores offer carry-out groceries, free coffee, or a "Kiddie Korner" for children. Of course, services and amenities may be omitted if the main emphasis is on everyday low prices. Even so, the shopping experience cannot be an unpleasant one, if the supermarket wants repeat business.

One might suppose the more departments the better, but it is not that simple. It takes a considerable sales volume to run a good bakery, deli, salad bar, floral department, or restaurant department. The demand is not always there. However, as stores become larger, these departments are more likely to be standard. Forward-looking retailers in the 1990s placed more emphasis on freshly prepared foods in delis and salad bars, perishables, and customer services.[6]

EXHIBIT

15.2   What's in the stores.

Lines and Services Offered	% of Stores
Retail and food stores with a deli	95.2
Fresh, prepared foods for takeout	94.0
Butcher to cut fresh meat to order	92.9
Greeting cards	89.3
Ethnic offerings	89.3
Floral departments	85.7
Fresh seafood	85.7
ATMs	85.5
Pharmacies	63.1
Separate organic/natural food aisle	57.1

Source: Food Marketing Institute, *Food Marketing Industry Speaks,* 2006.

Promotion

Advertising helps to create a store's image. Stores that are not very price competitive often rely on advertising to build the image that they are. Advertising can contribute to a desired image of friendliness, quality products, great variety of items, or excitement.

Over the past 50 years, retail advertising almost invariably has relied heavily on weekly newspaper ads, listing many prices. The weekly newspaper or circular ad—ranging from one to several full pages, listing many items with splashy color pictures to highlight items—is a standard in almost every city. There are substantial economies of size in advertising in large metropolitan markets, particularly in the use of TV and newspaper ads. Even stores adopting an everyday low price format use circulars to attract customers. Warehouse stores may limit mailings to members or rely on in-store promotions.

Advertising costs at retail are substantial. Whereas supermarkets' advertising costs are only about $0.7¢$ of the sales dollar, they are nearly 4% of the retailers' gross margin.[7]

Historically, conventional supermarkets typically spend time and money on posters and store decorations. Today, promotions are often paid by the company supplying the product, and it is common for retailers to charge **slotting fees.** Product suppliers pay slotting fees for the right to put products on the retailers' shelf. Furthermore, some stores have gone to the next level by asking suppliers to manage inventory, which is monitored through a complex electronic inventory management system seen by both the retailer and supplier.

Some merchandisers emphasize price. Others simply try to make the atmosphere appealing—the longer customers stay in the store, the more they buy. The supercenter stores usually combine a very attractive perimeter of perishables (produce, meat, dairy, and bakery) with a middle section of groceries and nonfoods stacked high on racks—the very image of savings. In fact, designers of economy format stores are wary of hurting their low-price image by making the store appear "too nice."

Promotional devices were more popular in the past. Such devices as trading stamps, games, premiums, vacation trips, contributions to your favorite charity, and coupons come and go, but there is seldom a long period when one is not around. Retailers sometimes offer double couponing, when they match the discount of any processor's coupon. Frequently the innovator in a market area takes on a new gimmick (say, double coupons). The practice costs the merchant a significant amount, but sales volume jumps so much that he does not have to raise prices to maintain profits. Soon competitors respond with their own double or even triple couponing program to protect or regain their volume. When almost every merchant is double or even triple couponing, the costs have to be recognized, because the practice cannot raise sales for *everyone*, only for the innovators, before they were extensively imitated. Merchant enthusiasm for the practice dies as soon as it covers the market. Either prices have to be raised or the practice has to be reduced or stopped. However, it may take a while to stop. Perhaps the first merchant to stop double couponing will be an innovator of some other promotional device—say, a bingo game or amusement park discounts.

Pricing

Marketing experts used to say that only 20% of customers buy on the basis of the cheapest price. There is considerable evidence that two groups of consumers are emerging: convenience shoppers and bargain shoppers. Bargain shoppers chase deals and buy whatever is on sale, whereas convenience shoppers go to the store with a list and desire fair prices and good quality. It appears that currently there are more convenience shoppers than bargain shoppers. Nonetheless, the competition of the low-priced format cannot be ignored by the other supermarkets.

The typical independent supermarket prices 25,000 items, and the typical chain supermarket prices 40,000 items. A supercenter or a large combination store prices twice that many. Management gives considerable thought to the overall gross margin and overall price image, but it obviously cannot give much thought to the pricing of any individual item. Among individual items, the most regular attention is given to those items that are traditionally the price special in the local market.

A loyal customer looks at the pricing of her entire basket of groceries rather than noting that she could save 20¢ on items A, D, and M in other stores this week. In contrast, the "cherry picker" (bargain seeker) spends some of her energy and gasoline by shopping the specials of several stores each week.

The art of pricing is to keep loyal customers happy and procure cherry-picker patronage at minimum cost, while managing to cover store costs and make a profit. Obviously, managers give considerable thought to firm demand in setting storewide margins. In a growing suburb with few competing stores, the margin is likely to be a bit fuller than in an area with many stores and no growth (as in older neighborhoods). If a new chain is trying to buy its way into a metropolitan area, margins may be tighter than normal. In areas that are over-stored, profit margins are under pressure.

Pricing involves variable markups. Some of the markup variation among items is explained by costs. The markup in bakery or produce must be higher than in groceries because of higher labor costs and greater spoilage. Thus, there are large differences in margins among departments and even among items within a department because of estimated costs. However, one should never attempt to explain markups solely in terms of costs. Retailers are beginning to use some systems of cost accounting in terms of individual products, but until recently they have operated with very little information of that type. Nor have they been terribly interested in individual product margins. They have seen themselves as selling a total mix, not individual products. No more than one-third to one-half of their costs can be considered variable, and it is difficult to assign even those variable costs accurately to individual items. However, Wal-Mart has become an industry leader in implementing cost accounting at the product level. Computer and web technologies and tracing of scanned data are stimulating advances in this area.

The variation in markups among items depends on crude cost and income estimates, tradition, competition, the general pricing image desired, and suggestions from the wholesaler or processor. One study concluded that variations in the markups of many products were essentially random.[8] In the meat department, for example, markups and profits tend to be much higher for lunch meats than for any other items. Why? Partly because more product differentiation exists in lunch meats but partly because of tradition.

Price levels of retail competitors generally reflect closely their overall costs of doing business. Profit margins as a percentage of sales are so small that variations in profits can seldom have more than a 1% or 2% influence on price levels.

Supermarkets have traditionally used one of two general pricing strategies. The continued manipulation of the prices of numerous items characterizes the strategy of high–low variable prices, often called **variable price merchandising** (**VPM**). In the weekly ad, specials on a strategic set of items drawn from various departments of the store provide very low prices. Thus, the store tries to present a low-priced image even though its margins are much higher on most items not in the ads.

In the VPM strategy, the prices and margins of a small fraction of all products are varied frequently. **Price specialing** (temporary price reductions or sales) rests on the premise that the store can increase traffic and increase its sales of many products by offering bargain prices on a few items. The premise is likely true in some limited sense. For example, it may be true that it is difficult to build good traffic without any specials *when your competitors have them*. Research on the impact of temporary price cuts on the sales of an item show that such price cuts generally yield a larger-than-proportionate increase in sales, that an advertised price cut usually generates more sales than an unadvertised one, and that the use of special displays or point-of-purchase (POP) materials usually further increases sales response.[9]

The fluctuating sales associated with VPM present many inventory management problems, especially for the perishable products. The **everyday low pricing** (**ELP**) strategy is easier to manage. This approach also advertises a set of items with low prices, but not cut as deeply as in the VPM approach. Wal-Mart uses the ELP strategy. For items of high turnover and popular appeal that normally carry fairly high margins, price reductions are repeated week after week to build the image that store X almost always seems to have cheap chicken, apples, and milk. There is considerable incentive for the conventional or extended supermarket to focus on many of the items carried by a competing economy format to create the impression that its prices are as low as the discounter's.

The VPM strategy, when used vigorously, can attract more attention than the ELP strategy. It is frequently used by a new competitor trying to obtain market share or by an old competitor trying to reverse a decline in market share. The ELP strategy has received considerable attention in all areas of retailing as Wal-Mart has successfully used the strategy during its expansion.

If specials were used to move temporary gluts of particular farm commodities, they would perform a real service for farmers and probably for society. Although such timing sometimes occurs, the more typical special has no relation to temporarily enlarged supplies. Thus, specials are a disequilibrating force in the market. They lead to sudden surges in sales of specialized items while often reducing slightly the sales of many competing items. From the viewpoint of producers and the whole marketing system, specials often distort the orderly processes by which products flow. The problem would not be important if each of many thousand stores independently chose its specials. However, when the hundreds of large supermarkets in a large chain act together, the impact is perceptible in the marketing system. Moreover, specials involve extra market channel costs in planning for and handling the surge of sales that accompany them.

THE FOOD SERVICE INDUSTRY

Food service is an industry of many facets, consisting of two major sectors: the public eating places sector and the **institutional food sector**. The latter is estimated by the USDA to be about one-third of the sales volume of the commercial eating places sector. Food service is sometimes referred to as HRI, an acronym for "hotel, restaurants, and institutions."

Both sectors include many different outlets. Restaurants, as separate eating places, including everything from the white-tablecloth type to fast-food venues, have a majority of the volume of the public eating places. Many public eating places are associated with other business units, including retail and drugstores, hotels and motels, bars, amusement places, clubs, factories, and office buildings. Schools, colleges, and the military services are the biggest segments of the institutional sector, which also includes hospitals, care homes, prisons, homes for people with disabilities, and other types of institutions.

The market for commercial food services is very broad. Virtually everyone eats meals away from home—some occasionally, some frequently, and a few almost always. Single individuals eat out more frequently than families.

Individuals of all age and income groups eat out. Not unexpectedly, those in higher-income groups eat out a little more frequently and spend considerably more than those in low-income groups.[10] Economic analyses generally indicate that expenditure elasticities for food away from home are considerably larger than for food at home. Thus, in a macro sense, food service and food retailing compete very directly—when people eat out, they are not eating groceries at home. The most direct competition is providers of "food to go"—food that is eaten off-premises, often at home. Supermarkets, convenience stores, and fast-food outlets are rapidly expanding deli sales, drive-through sales, and delivery sales. The food service industry over the past few decades has rather steadily eroded the market share of food retailers.

Franchising

Franchising has become the most important institution in food service. The *franchiser*—owner of a trade name and concept (such as Taco Bell)—licenses individuals or firms as *franchisees* to operate under the trade name and format. For access to the chain's name, advertising, merchandising, and operating techniques, and perhaps to supplies and services sold by the chain or its subsidiaries, the franchisee is required to follow the chain's standards of operation and to pay fees. Many chains involve large proportions of franchised units. Exhibit 15.3 gives a list of the largest food service businesses (all franchises) and their sales volume.

Franchisees typically pay royalty fees of 3% to 5% of gross sales. If they lease property, the rent payments are often an additional 4% to 8%. Generally, franchisees must contribute 1% to 4% of gross sales to a joint advertising and promotion fund. In addition, there is a substantial initial franchise fee.

One tends to think of the franchisee as an individual or small business operating as a single unit. There are many of those, but there are also many firms operating as multi-unit franchisees. These are becoming more popular among franchisers, because the multi-unit operations tend to have successful management. It is common for franchisers to own and operate some units while franchising others. The franchiser often has the right of first refusal in case the franchisee wishes to sell his operation.

Procurement

Such a heterogeneous industry as food service defies any simple summary of its structure and particularly of the degree to which there is concentration in procurement. The largest buyers include various parts of the government, such as the USDA buying for school lunches, each of the military services buying for their personnel, the New York City School Board,

EXHIBIT 15.3   Largest food service businesses (all franchisers), 2000.

	2000 sales ($ millions)	Ownership
1. McDonald's	19,573	McDonald's Corporation
2. Burger King	8,543	Diageo PLC
3. Wendy's	5,757	Wendy's International, Inc.
4. Taco Bell	5,100	Tricon Global Restaurants, Inc.
5. Pizza Hut	5,000	Tricon Global Restaurants, Inc.

Source: Price, C. "Food Service." U.S. Food Marketing System, 2002, USDA Economic Research Service.

and the Los Angeles Unified School District. A growing number of large restaurant chains typically concentrate their purchasing in groups larger than the individual unit but smaller than the entire chain. Such firms qualify as large buyers. Although the trend is definitely toward a more concentrated industry and procurement by a small number of buyers, as much as one-half of food volume is still purchased by relatively small businesses. Most of their purchasing is by supplier service and brand reputation and not by buyer specifications. Most food is typically marketed to these smaller food service operations rather than being procured by them.

Institutional Middlemen

Institutional middlemen are the principal suppliers of the food service industry. Processors typically use brokers in selling to those middlemen. These intermediaries include firms that supply almost everything that a unit could want, from canned peas to pottery. They also include firms that handle a single line, such as meat, produce, or fluid milk. The trend is toward a more complete multiple-product, one-stop service, particularly of nonperishables, and away from service by numerous single-line wholesalers. Because the costs of delivery generally consist of a flat fee per delivery and a small per-case fee (for example, $40 overall fee plus $1 per case), the average delivery cost per case falls rapidly as more cases of more items can be delivered to a particular customer. That is the basic economics behind multiple product service. This sector has undergone considerable concentration over the past decade and today is highly concentrated.

A number of large food processors operate special institutional wholesale units that provide a wide array of special products for food service outlets. For example, Kraft has developed a strong national network of food service distribution centers. Kraft will ship direct from the factory to large chains.

Meats are a very large component of the food service business. Meats are wholesaled by a wide variety of handlers. The terms *meat purveyor* and *meat broker* are often applied to wholesalers who usually buy primal cuts (or carcasses) and then fabricate cuts, grind ground beef, and provide other services including regular deliveries. *Fabricator* might be a better term to describe what some purveyors are now doing. Most customers are demanding portion-control cuts, and some are demanding pre-cooking of certain cuts as they try to reduce their kitchen labor requirements. Some purveyors are essentially job-shop operations cutting to customers' specifications, whereas others sell mainly standardized items. Several of the larger meat packers have acquired institutional wholesalers or purveyors.

Procurement by Large Buyers

The larger buyers and particularly the fast-food chains have organized procurement systems, much as the retail chains did. A regional group of units of a fast-food chain is sometimes formed to purchase on contract bids according to tight quality specifications. At minimum, most purchases of groceries, meat, and poultry are at the top corporate level. Chains are willing to guarantee a certain volume of purchases from a seller in return for price concessions and service and quality guarantees.

Chains with distribution centers or commissions report that the advantage is greater control of purchasing and particularly of quality. Such facilities, however, require considerable volume to be competitive, and they require capital, which a fast-growing chain may prefer to use in expansion of outlets.

As discussed earlier, many units of restaurant chains are not owned by the chain but are franchised to individual owners. The franchise relationship has some parallel to grocery store affiliation of wholesalers and retailers; franchising, even more than affiliation, complicates central control over procurement. The chains vary in their practices—some have centralized procurement, some have units cooperating in regional procurement groups, and some units buy on their own. Generally, chains provide a list of approved suppliers from whom their franchisees can buy.

The procurement practices of some restaurant chains are much like the practices of retail chains. They have the expertise and the mass buying power to set tight specifications and to buy many items on competitive bid. They tend to concentrate their business with a few sellers. Moreover, large processors lack an advantage that they possess in grocery retailing, where they are able to persuade stores to handle their products because of massive consumer advertising. Because few products reach food service consumers in processor-branded form, consumers do not ordinarily know or care whether they are eating chicken and noodles supplied by Kraft or Green Giant or Campbell. Thus, food processor promotion is aimed directly at food service operators in terms of the array of available services, the dependability of services, and the quality of products. A medium-sized processor can probably deal as effectively as a large national processor with large food service buyers. A small processor, however, probably lacks the technical ability, the volume, and the dependability to service large buyers.

Procurement Pricing

Are the restaurants price makers or price takers in their procurement? The smaller firms, still constituting the bulk of the industry but less than half of the sales, are price takers; the larger chains, to the extent that they have centralized procurement, are sometimes price negotiators rather than price takers. Thus, they are in the same position as the larger WRs discussed previously. The large buyers benefit from volume discounts and from more reliable supplies than the smaller ones receive. It should be emphasized, however, that the restaurant industry is considerably less concentrated than food retailing. Thus, passive price taking is much more common in food service than in food retailing.

The weaker bargaining power of most smaller food service units than of most retailers is quite visible in the very important category of meat. Meat distributors selling to the independents and smaller chains in the food service industry typically report that they use price lists and set their prices on a cost-plus basis. The packers selling to retailers report that pricing is a matter of supply and demand, and they typically deny that they are able to set prices.

Purchasing through competitive bids is a fairly standard practice in publicly operated institutions. Otherwise, procurement pricing is much the same for these institutions as for public eating places.

SUMMARY

1. Wholesaler–retailers (WRs) and particularly the larger chains have developed important procurement systems for many food categories, including fresh produce, meats, bread, and milk.

2. For several foods, there are dual channels of distribution, as the procurement system of retailers exists side by side with the marketing system of processors. The WRs have more bargaining power with suppliers when their own procurement system predominates, a little less bargaining power when dual systems exist, and the least bargaining power when faced with a processor marketing system alone. Key to the bargaining power of larger processors is the acceptance of their brands. That is why the typical national brand is supported by millions of dollars of promotion as processors try to build and reinforce consumer demand.

3. Most of the food service industry is served by a processor marketing system that includes processors selling through independent institutional middlemen, processors selling through their own wholesale units, and large processors owning food service chains.

4. A procurement system is developing in some parts of the food service industry, especially among the larger chains. As food service buyers become larger, they can be expected to develop effective bargaining with their suppliers. One of their advantages is that processor brands do not carry through to consumers in the restaurant; thus, the processors lack the important strength of being able to build consumer demand for their particular brands.

5. Food retailers and restaurants have traditionally been smaller family businesses, much akin to the family farm. However, supermarkets and chains have acquired the bulk of the retailing market. A trend toward similar "bigness" of owned and franchised chains is evident in food services.

6. Food chains are multi-plant firms that have some advantages in merchandising as well as in volume procurement. The uniformity of chains has merchandising strengths. Over the past decade, electronic communications, linked databases, and consolidation have allowed large chains to become even more efficient.

7. Attracting retail customers is an art, not a science. Doing one or two things well is not enough to be competitive. The successful supermarket does many things well—it provides a pleasing shopping experience that includes the location of the store, its physical appearance and upkeep, the effectiveness and demeanor of the clerks, the "extra" services such as check cashing, the completeness and attractiveness of the product mix, prices, premiums, and so on. The perceived image of the store may be affected considerably by the astuteness of its advertising.

8. Food advertising tends to emphasize price competition, but there is usually more competition among ads than among stores. The huge variety of products in a supermarket permits strategies that give the appearance of price competition without usually leading to actual head-on price competition. Food retailers strive hard to differentiate their services so that they need not rely on price alone as a drawing card. However, the growth of economy formats such as warehouse stores has accentuated price as a competitive variable.

9. Food retailers are margin setters, as are many other kinds of agribusiness; the difference is that their business margin is the composite of the margins of as many as 40,000 items. They have latitude in setting the margins on many of the individual items. There is some rhyme and reason to margin setting, but much of it seems to be arbitrary.

10. Over the past decade, larger grocery store formats have developed store brand products. Stores leverage their identity on products. In turn, stores do not need to spend large sums of money on advertising or packaging. Thus, store brands are sold at lower prices.

11. Food service establishments tend to be more differentiated than food retailers. The differences between a McDonald's, a Pizza Hut, and a fancy steak house are so considerable that the price cross-elasticities among the demands for their services must be small. Price competition is more direct among eating places of the same type, such as the fast-food chains that feature hamburgers.

12. Franchising has introduced some standardization of merchandising and production techniques into food service. Generally, franchised operations operate efficiently by using standardized operations and decor and limited menus. Fast-food franchises are uniquely American, but they now exist in many other nations.

13. In a broad sense, food retailers and food services compete for the consumer food market. Food service has been gaining, although it still has a smaller share. Considerable "food to go" is now take-home food to be consumed at the end of the family's working day. Food retailers and food services compete directly for this take-home market.

14. Developments in food retailing and food service often have a considerable impact on farming because they may affect the derived demand level for particular farm commodities.

STUDY QUESTIONS

1. Is retailing or food service usually more concentrated at the local level? Is competition among retailers vigorous in your hometown? Among food service firms in your town? Explain why or why not.

2. At the national level, has concentration in either food retailing or food service been growing? Which has a higher concentration?

3. Price is only one facet in the differentiation process. Name several examples of nonprice competition in food retailing and in food service.

4. "Promotional devices such as amusement park discounts will eventually raise costs for all participants." Is there validity in a statement such as this? Explain why or why not.

5. What interrelationship might variable markups have to pricing and advertising? How does this practice relate to retail price wars?

6. A corporation president once said, "The superstore of the future will encompass a truly one-stop store in which one can fill all of his or her needs including the cauliflower for the evening meal, a washer for the bathroom sink, and a light jacket for a crisp autumn evening." Explain some of the advantages and disadvantages of superstores and warehouse stores. Do you think either of these will drive most conventional supermarkets out of business?

7. Assume that you are the owner–manager of a new supermarket in a medium-sized city. Explain in some detail your merchandising strategies for the first six months of operation. What possible competitive reactions might cause you to change your strategies?

8. What are the current trends in restaurant concepts and menus? How would you explain them?

9. Compare the advantages and disadvantages in franchising from the franchisee's point of view and from the franchiser's point of view. How would you evaluate the performance of franchising?

10. Compare the promotions and merchandising efforts of supermarkets in your community. What are some similarities and differences? Why are there differences?

CLASS EXERCISE

For this exercise, your instructor will assign a different restaurant to each group. Your group should then visit the assigned restaurant and prepare a report that includes the following information:

1. Marketing style
2. Atmosphere

3. Clientele
4. Food types served
5. Pricing

While at the restaurant, your group should speak with a member of management and ask about the following:

1. How the restaurant is supplied
2. How procurement decisions are made, by whom, and how often
3. Whether the restaurant buys locally, and why or why not

With your group, prepare to participate in a class discussion as to how restaurants cater to different customers' desires and why supply chains differ.

NOTES

1. *Progressive Grocer,* Mid-April 1990, pp. 62–63.
2. J. L. Parcell and T. C. Schroeder, "Determinants of Pork Brand Price Premiums." Presented paper at NCR-134 Conference on Applied Commodity Price Analysis, Forecasting, and Market Risk Management, ed. S. Koontz (2003). Published on-line at http://agecon.lib.umn.edu/cgi-bin/view.pl.
3. Daniel I. Padberg, *Economics of Food Retailing* (Ithaca, NY: Cornell University, 1968), p. 259.
4. *PG,* April 1996, p. 13.
5. *The Super Market Industry Speaks, 1975* (Chicago: Super Market Institute), p. 9; *Facts About New Super Markets Opened in 1975* (Chicago: Supermarket Institute, p. 5; *The Food Marketing Industry Speaks, 1984,* p. 14; *Food Marketing Review, 1989–90,* p. 34.
6. *PG,* Mid-April 1990, p. 30.
7. *PG,* May 1996, p. 39.
8. Lee Preston, Reed Hartford, and Jan Gruettler, *Profits, Competition and Rules of Thumb in Retail Food Pricing* (Berkeley: University of California Institute of Business and Economic Research, 1963), p. 40.
9. V. James Rhodes et al., *Customer Responses to Retail Meat Prices and Ads,* Missouri Agricultural Experiment Station Research Bulletin 1006, 1974; and *National Food Review,* Summer 1980, p. 8.
10. *R&I,* August 22, 1990, pp. 37ff.

GLOSSARY

Acceptable risk Because zero risk is impossible, the amount of risk in food products we are willing to have.

Adequate volume The key to the profitability of any processor is achieving sufficient volume to achieve low, if not minimum, average costs.

Affiliates Retailers (independent or chain) that, along with other stores, have a contractual or cooperative relationship to a wholesaler. A voluntary affiliate is a contractual relationship organized by the wholesaler.

Agribusiness Any firm involved in the marketing of agricultural products or supplying farm inputs. Examples include grain elevators, meat packers, ice cream makers, and restaurants.

Allocation of decision rights Who is going to do what to meet the characteristics of the terms of trade.

Allocation of risk Value is subject to uncertainty.

Allocation of value Distribution of gains from trade.

Alterable supplies The situation when the rates of production of particular qualities of a commodity can be controlled, either entirely or to some extent.

Arbitrage The process whereby a commodity or product is simultaneously bought and sold in two separate markets to take advantage of a price discrepancy between the two markets.

Assembler An intermediary that collects many small shipments of producers into larger-volume units for sale and shipment to processors or to wholesalers. Assemblers may be merchants, dealers, or cooperatives or may be vertically integrated into a processor.

At-home market Consumers purchasing food for consumption at home.

Away-from-home market Consumers buying food for consumption away from home (in restaurants, autos, workplaces, and so on).

Back-haul The return of a transport vehicle to its origin after delivering a cargo. Because the costs of returning loaded are not much higher than the costs of returning empty, back-haul rates are often cheaper.

Bargaining association A cooperative that represents its members by collectively negotiating terms of trade but does not engage in the physical side of marketing.

Basis The differential between the specific cash price and the particular futures price for a commodity.

Basis, inverted When the specific cash price is above the specific futures price for a commodity.

Basis pricing A practice of making price offers or agreements about grain specifying a certain differential (basis) above (or below) the daily market prices of a nearby futures contract.

Basis trading A grain trader taking long or short net positions according to his expectations about basis movements; a form of speculating on the basis.

Behavioral systems approach A study of marketing that focuses on the interdependence and coordination of all key participants and their marketing activities. Markets and prices play key coordinating roles in marketing systems.

Biological lag The period between a decision to produce and the actual harvest or collection of output. For example, there is a lag of about 30 months between the breeding of a cow and the slaughter of the fed animal born from that breeding.

Blending The mixing together of two or more lots of grain that have been downgraded for various reasons with the purpose of producing a combined lot of higher grade and value.

Blend price The average price (before adjustments for quality, hauling, and so on) paid producers within a marketing order (MO) for their milk; it is based on the average usage of the total milk in the MO in the two or three price classes.

Boxed beef The marketing by packers of primal (wholesale) cuts of beef in boxes. This change from marketing in quarter or half carcasses led to many changes in beef marketing.

Brand name A word or group of letters that can be spoken and is used in branding; the identifying to buyers of a particular product or service for commercial purposes.

Break-even point The minimum volume of sales for a firm at which total receipts match total costs.

Brokers Intermediaries that arrange transactions for a commission but do not take ownership or finance customers. Brokers handle trading of futures contracts. Food brokers handle many sales by manufacturers to wholesalers or retailers.

Business logistics The process of planning, implementing, and controlling the efficient, effective flow and storage of goods, services, and related information from the point of origin to the point of consumption for the purpose of conforming to customer requirements.

Call option Gives buyers the right to buy shares of an underlying security at a fixed price before a specified expiration date. Call buyers hope that stock price will rise while sellers hope that the price will remain the same or fall.

Capper-Volstead Act Federal legislation in 1922 that provided certain antitrust immunities to associations of farmers operating cooperatives under specific restrictions.

Carrying charge The amount earned for the service of storage.

Carryover The volume of inventory (holdings) of a crop at the end of its marketing year (at the beginning of the next harvest).

Cartel An explicit agreement among sellers of a commodity that restricts their competing in certain ways; for example, it may restrict price competition or allot sales territories. Cartels are ordinarily illegal in the United States.

Cash grain position For a trader, the sum of grain inventory owned plus grain purchases contracted minus grain sales contracted. This position may fluctuate widely from day to day, so many traders use futures transactions to offset large changes in it.

Caveat emptor Latin phrase meaning "let the buyer beware."

Centralized cooperative A cooperative whose various regional and local facilities are all owned by the total membership.

CFTC Commodity Futures Trading Commission; regulates futures trading.

Chain Eleven or more food stores under one ownership.

Channel leaders Those firms in a marketing channel that initiate changes in products, procedures, practices, promotion, and even prices.

Checkoff The small part of the sale price of a commodity that a producer contributes to the promotion of that commodity via an industry board set up under government auspices.

Cobweb model A theoretical description of how prices of a commodity could cycle even though its demand and supply curves are stable.

Combination store A large supermarket that includes a nearly complete drugstore line.

Commission The fees paid for executing a transaction.

Commodity An economic good such as corn or wheat that can be legally produced and sold by almost anyone. A commodity contrasts with a differentiated product, which belongs to a specific seller and may often be trademarked as her exclusive property.

Commodity basis The difference between a local cash price and the relevant futures contract price for a specific time period.

Commodity handling The marketing of commodities, such as fresh meat or vegetables, tends to be highly price competitive because the commodities offer few or no profitable opportunities for advertising and promotion. *Cf.* Product marketing.

Common carrier A transporter, such as a railroad or a truck line, that provides regular, scheduled services at published rates to all who wish to use them.

Concentration ratio The percentage of industry sales (or purchases) made by its four largest firms. Data on concentration ratios are provided by the U. S. Census and are widely used as one measure of industry structure.

Conglomerate A firm doing business in several (or many) unrelated markets. For example, Altria is a major player in cigarettes, beer, groceries, cheese and ice cream, baked goods, coffee, breakfast cereals, and many other manufactured items.

Conglomerate merger The combining of two or more firms in unrelated markets into a single firm. An example is the merger of a shoe manufacturer and a food processor.

Consumer decision making The process of consumers valuing the attributes of products relative to any perceived costs in selecting one over another.

Consumer perceptions Notions or understandings developed by a consumer, often based on skimpy data and information.

Consumer sovereignty The concept that each consumer decides independently what to buy and that the collection of all these individual decisions directs all production and marketing activities in the economy.

Contract carrier A transporter, such as a railroad or truck line, that agrees with one or more shippers to provide certain transportation services on a regular basis. Rates are negotiated with each customer and are not published.

Contractual exchange Involves (1) any sort of sale–purchase in which it is agreed that one or more phases of a transaction, such as delivery or pricing, occur later than other phases, and (2) production contracts. *See* Production contract.

Convenience stores Small self-service stores that offer a limited assortment of items and long hours of operation.

Convenience yield The value that motivates a processor to store or offer incentives for input suppliers to store or market a product, even though there is a negative expected return to storage.

Cooperative (coop) A user-owned and -controlled business from which benefits are derived and distributed equitably on the basis of use. This is an idealized definition, and some firms that are called coops fall short of some of these characteristics.

Cooperative affiliate A food retailer that in association with other retailers owns cooperatively their wholesaler.

Data Facts, evidence, opinions, and news that can be gathered.

Decentralized, individual negotiation (DIN) A price discovery system operating outside of an organized market in which a buyer and a seller negotiate an individual transaction.

Deceptive advertising Advertising that misleads all but the most careful reader or viewer.

Delayed price rise The increase in retail price that tends to follow the introduction into an urban market of a promotional gimmick such as double coupons.

Delivery month The period (involving most of a month) when an open futures position must be terminated by an offsetting transaction or, in rare cases, by delivery of the actual commodity.

Delivery point The place where delivery can be made in the delivery month to satisfy a short futures contract. This location is usually in the city where the futures exchange operates, but it may be at specified other points.

Demand The set of alternative quantities that would be purchased at alternative prices.

Demand, cross-elasticities Measures the relative impact on the sales of one item of a change in the price of a related item by comparing a percentage change in the amount sold to the percentage change in price. Goods that are substitutes have a positive cross-elasticities demand—an increase in the price of item i increases the sales of a substitute item j because the latter is now relatively cheaper.

Demand for marketing services Whereas much of the demand for commodity marketing services (such as meat packing and retailing) depends ultimately on consumer income and preferences, the short-term variations in that demand are highly associated with changes in the volume marketed by producers of the commodity. Thus, larger hog marketings demand a larger volume of hog marketing services.

Demand, income effect An increase in the price of any item thereby reduces the purchasing power of its buyers and usually reduces the amount demanded of that item.

Demand, income elasticity The relationship between a percentage change in income and the percentage change in quantity demanded of (or dollars spent on) a commodity or specific product. If, as usually happens, the second percentage is smaller than the first, then the income elasticity of demand is inelastic.

Demand, inelastic The observation that in the short term, buyers of many foods resist changing their rate of purchases. Consequently, a 10% change in the tonnage of a commodity sent through the market will force a change in price of more than 10% in the opposite direction.

Demand, law of downward sloping An observation that buyers will ordinarily buy more at lower prices than at higher prices, other things held constant. For farmers, this law means that a bigger crop thrown on the market will ordinarily force prices down.

Demand, own-price elasticity Measures the responsiveness to price changes by comparing the percentage change in the quantity sold of an item to the percentage change in the price of that item.

Demand shifters Factors changing the number or incomes of buyers or their evaluations of a product and thus changing their demand schedule.

Demand, substitution effect An increase in the price of any product leads to some replacement by other products that are now relatively cheaper and thus leads to a reduction in the amount demanded of that product.

Demurrage User costs for not utilizing rail cars within a specified period of time.

Dietary guidelines A set of guidelines issued by the USDA for healthful diets. Because they suggest reduced intake of sugar and animal fats, they have been resisted by some farm groups.

Diseconomies of size A condition of average costs falling to a minimum and then rising with output in the long run. Because such rising average costs limit the expansion of a firm, the particular size generating diseconomies is an important influence in any specific industry on the number of firms.

Disequilibrium A set of prices that keep changing over time even though the basic supply and demand schedules are stable.

Distribution center The warehouse used to assemble food from processors and to distribute it to retailers.

Divestiture A breakup of a corporation or sale of parts of it compelled by the courts as a result of an antitrust case.

Dumping A form of price discrimination in international trade in which products are sold on the world market at prices below the cost of production (and below normal domestic prices).

Economies of size The economic concept that cost per unit of production decreases as the size of the business increases.

Electronic markets Organized markets in which potential buyers and sellers communicate by electronic means, such as at telephone auctions, rather than face to face.

Engel's Law An observation that the percentage of a family's (or a nation's) income spent on food declines as its income rises.

Everyday low prices (ELP) A practice, in contrast to variable price merchandising, in which a price competitor image is sought by advertising a set of food items at low prices for long periods.

Exchange rates The price of one nation's currency in terms of another's. For example, a euro may cost 75¢ (U.S.).

Expected prices *See* Price, expected.

Fallacy of composition The error of assuming that what holds true for one member of a group will necessarily hold true for the entire group.

Farm value The share of consumer food expenditures going to farmers.

Federated cooperative A regional cooperative owned by member cooperatives (ordinarily locals).

Firm A business organization involving one or more people. A firm should not be confused with a set of firms, which is called an industry. A firm usually operates one or more facilities (factories, farms, or retail stores) that are called plants.

Flow commodities Those commodities such as eggs and livestock that are produced daily rather than in a seasonal harvest.

Food service concept Those variations in the building, furnishings, menu, prices, promotion, and service that make a Burger King, for example, so distinctly different from an Olive Garden. A concept embodies a specific choice of a target market and marketing mix. *Cf.* Market segmentation.

Food service industry The set of firms providing ready-to-eat food and usually the surroundings in which to eat it. This industry includes the public eating places sector (fast-food shops, restaurants, bars, clubs, and so on) and the institutional sector (which provides food as part of a larger service or activity, such as schools, colleges, care homes, the military, and prisons).

Formula pricing A pricing system in which a buyer and seller agree that transaction prices will be based on a quoted market price occurring just prior to or at the time of their periodic commodity transfers.

Forward pricing The established future price today for delivery in the future.

Four Ps Product, promotion, place (channel organization), and price. The term describes a marketing mix that a firm develops to obtain its marketing objectives.

Free rider A person or firm who shares in the benefits of a group effort while not sharing in the costs.

Functional approach A study of marketing organized around a classification of activities such as buying, selling, storing, transporting, processing, standardizing, financing, information gathering, and risk bearing.

Futures contract A legal agreement to make or take delivery of a standard quality and quantity of a specific commodity in a specified future month at a specified price.

GATT Stands for the General Agreement on Tariffs and Trade (signed by many nations) and for the international agency that used to administer this multilateral treaty. It is the predecessor to the WTO.

Generic promotion The promotion (by advertising, coupons, and selling) of an agricultural commodity financed collectively by its producers.

Grade-and-yield buying The practice of buying livestock on their carcass value.

Grades A grouping or classification of a commodity that has been sorted by likeness in quality.

Grading The sorting according to federal standards of units of a commodity into quality groupings (grades).

Group negotiation A collective bargaining process that may determine prices and other terms of trade.

Hedge The taking of opposite ownership positions in cash and futures markets.

Hedge, buy The buying of futures contracts to offset the risk that market prices may rise before one can buy a commodity (a long hedge).

Hedge, sell The selling of futures contracts to offset the risk that market prices may fall on a commodity owned in storage (a short hedge).

Heterogeneous demand When two or more groups of buyers disagree on the ranking of various qualities (grades) of a commodity.

Homogeneous demand When buyers agree on the ordinal relationships of the various qualities (grades) of a commodity. For example,

buyers may agree that grade X is better than grade Y.

Horizontal merger The combining of two or more competing firms into a single firm.

Imports, competitive Imported items that substitute directly for similar items produced domestically.

Imports, complementary Imported items that are not produced domestically; examples are bananas and coffee.

Independent retailer Ten or fewer retail food stores under one ownership. An independent often has only one store.

Industry A set of competing firms producing similar products or a commodity; it is the seller side of a market. For example, Burger King and McDonald's are two of many firms competing in the fast-food restaurant industry.

Inelastic supply A supply curve is defined as inelastic when a 10% increase (decrease) in price yields a less than 10% increase (decrease) in the volume offered for sale. Remember that a supply curve that is inelastic for the first crop season after a price change may become elastic in later seasons as farmers have more time to adjust their production.

Infant industry argument A claim that trade barriers are necessary to allow a new home industry to grow large enough to compete.

Institutional approach A study of marketing featuring the key institutional players, such as processors and retailers, and key institutions (established practices), such as cooperatives, futures markets, and marketing orders.

Institutional food sector *See* Food service industry.

Institutional middlemen A set of firms that purchase from processors and distribute one or many lines of food products to the food service industry.

Interstate Commerce Commission (ICC) The federal agency charged with the economic regulation of interstate transportation.

Replaced in 1996 by the Surface Transportation Board.

Intrinsic value The value of an option relative to the underlying futures price.

Investor-owned firm (IOF) A firm owned by investors with ownership rights and dividends proportional to ownership. *Cf.* Cooperative.

Law of demand An observation that buyers typically will buy more at lower prices than at higher prices, other factors held constant.

Law of supply An observation that sellers will ordinarily offer more at higher prices than at lower prices, other things held constant.

LDCs Less developed and thus poorer countries.

MA A Metropolitan Area as defined by the U. S. Census Bureau is an area (often a county) of at least 100,000 population including at least one city of 50,000. These areas include three-quarters of the U. S. population and of the market for food.

Maintenance margin The set level below which a margin account cannot drop.

Manufacturers' brands The branded products of the larger food manufacturers; the better-known ones are often called national brands.

Margin The amount of money deposited with a broker to finance a futures contract. It is a considerably larger amount than the broker's fee but ordinarily much less than the value of the contract. The same margin is required whether the initial transaction is a purchase or a sale.

Margin call A signal that a contract holder must add funds to her account to the level of the initial margin.

Margin maker Those commodity handlers that have little or no power to set their sales prices may focus on maintaining a margin, or specific differential, between sales prices and purchase prices. For example, a grain elevator may set its offer prices to farmers by subtracting a margin from the daily futures closing price.

Margin money Earnest money placed in a brokerage account to cover potential losses.

Market (1) All of the possible buyers and sellers of a product or commodity. Usually involves firms as sellers and firms or consumers as buyers. (2) In the eyes of a seller, the potential buyers and their potential demand for the seller's product or commodity.

Market basket A representative group of domestically produced foods (excluding fish and beverages) that is sold in food stores.

Market clearing The process of market price adjusting so that all buyers and sellers currently wishing to trade at that price can do so. The more perishable the commodity, the less able sellers are to wait for a better price.

Market conduct The behavior of competitors within a market; such behavior may vary from predatory pricing to tacit collusion.

Market intelligence The data about current volumes of sales, current and futures prices, and events (such as disturbances in weather or in politics) that may influence upcoming prices and sales.

Market model A simplified representation of a real market, just as a toy airplane may resemble a Boeing 747.

Market segment An identifiable group of buyers within the larger buying side of a market facing a seller or sellers.

Market segmentation The process of a marketer identifying and targeting (focusing on) a specific group of buyers and potential buyers.

Market structure Those characteristics of a market, such as concentration, entry and exit conditions, and product differentiation, that affect the type of rivalry among competitors and thus marketing strategies.

Marketing bill A USDA measure of the total consumer food dollars going to agribusiness rather than to farmers.

Marketing channel The set of firms that move a commodity from the farm to the consumer.

Marketing, macro The performance of all business activities involved in the forward flow of goods and services from producers to consumers.

Marketing, micro The performance of business activities that direct the forward flow of goods and services to customers and accomplish the farmer's or the agribusiness firm's objectives.

Marketing mix A set of activities—sometimes called the *Four Ps*—beginning with designing and packaging a product and including promotion, channel organization (place), and pricing.

Marketing orders An institutionalized, self help program for orderly marketing used by producers of certain specific commodities under the direct supervision of the USDA.

Marketing plan A management strategy for timing throughout the year the pricing and marketing of a producer's output to accomplish such purposes as the timing of pricing and the management of price risks.

Marketing year The 12 months between harvests of annual crops. The USDA reports data for several crops on a marketing year rather than on a calendar year.

Market-oriented processing Manufacturing activities, such as baking fresh bread, near to its final market to minimize transport costs.

Marketing–pricing alternatives Various pricing arrangements open to producers allowing them to time their pricing, delivery, and transfer of ownership separately for a commodity when the normal simultaneous carrying out of those phases of a transaction does not appear to be advantageous.

Marketing–procurement contract *See* Contractual exchange (definition 1).

Maslow's hierarchy of needs Maslow's ranked list of physical and psychological needs that influence personal choices.

Merchants Intermediaries that buy and sell, ship, hold inventories of commodities and products, and even finance sales. Examples include wholesalers and retailers.

Micro procurement The performance of business activities that direct the flow of agricultural commodities to a firm to satisfy its objectives.

Monopolistic competition A market of many firms with each competing to sell a product or service slightly differentiated from the others. No competitor is large enough to dominate the others, so monopolistic competition is more competition than monopoly.

Most Favored Nation Clause A promise to a nation that the trade regulations and tariffs applied to it will be as favorable as those applied to any other nation.

Motor Carrier Act A federal law, passed in 1980, that reduced greatly the economic regulation of trucking.

NAFTA North American Free Trade Agreement, a treaty among the United States, Canada, and Mexico.

New product More than 10,000 new food products are introduced annually. Most are simple product extensions (new flavors) or improvements (more convenient packages or less fat); some are products new to a firm but much like competing products, and a very few are innovative items.

Nontariff barriers Include import quotas, state trading, biased health standards, and other regulations aimed at hindering or stopping trade.

Offer–acceptance pricing A pricing system in which numerous sellers make regular offers to a large buyer that regularly (say, weekly) accepts those offers that, in total, fill his needs.

Oligopoly A market of only a few firms of fairly similar size; each firm considers the possible reactions of each of its rivals in making pricing and other strategic decisions; entry is usually difficult; product differentiation often exists.

On-track buying The trade practice of a grain purchaser paying today's market price for grain that is, or shortly will be, loaded on rail cars at the seller's elevator; also known as *track country station.*

Option A particular futures contract that gives the buyer the right, but not the obligation, to take a position in a specific futures contract at a specific price at any time during the life of the option.

Option premium The value that a hedger pays for the right to take a futures position later.

Organized market A place in which all potential buyers and sellers have public access to one another as they discover prices. Examples vary from ancient peasant village market days to the futures trading pit at the Chicago Board of Trade.

Outlook information Data and projections about market demand, supply, and prices provided by private or public agencies.

Patronage refund Distribution of a cooperative's earnings to its patrons in proportion to their business volume.

Perfect competition A market of many competing firms selling a commodity; each firm is too small for its decisions alone to influence perceptibly the market price. Often called *pure* or *atomistic* competition in principles texts.

Perishability The quality of a food that loses its desirable characteristics (thus its value) over time. The speed of such quality deterioration varies among commodities and among methods of handling.

Piggyback The hauling of truck trailers or containers on railcars to combine the dock-to-dock flexibility of truck accessibility with low-cost, long-distance rail.

Place Refers to a marketer organizing a way through the channel to final consumers. For example, a food processor needs to convince brokers and retailers to sell its products.

Pooling A producer consigns a commodity to be marketed along with that of other producers by a cooperative or other agency. Most milk is pooled.

Price The value upon which a buyer and a seller decide to transact business.

Price cycle Long-term repetitive movement of prices.

Price discovery The process of buyers and sellers arriving at prices for a commodity when market conditions do not permit either group to set prices.

Price leader A competitor that ordinarily initiates price changes in an oligopolistic industry where all of the rivals tend to change prices at about the same time.

Price maker A firm that sets price or negotiates it with those on the other side of the market. Firms in monopolistic and oligopolistic competition are price makers.

Price specialing Large but temporary price reductions to increase store traffic. *See* Variable price merchandising.

Price spread The USDA term for the difference between the prices farmers receive and those that consumers pay for equivalent amounts of a food. Formerly called the *marketing margin*, it is computed for retail sales and would be larger if it also covered food eaten away from home.

Price taker A market participant that buys or sells such a small part of the market's total that it accepts price as a given. Consumers are usually price takers. Firms in competitive markets are price takers.

Price, expected The price that a seller estimates he can obtain at some later date. Because of biological lags, farmers typically make production decisions on the basis of prices estimated several months or years before actual harvest or production of the commodity.

Price, realized The price obtained by a seller. Realized prices are often quite different from the estimates made when farmers commenced production.

Prices, seasonal pattern A set of prices within a year that varies somewhat regularly as a result of the regular influence of the seasons on production, marketing, and/or demand.

Pricing system A market mechanism or process (organized behavior) by which market participants discover, negotiate, or fix prices.

Pricing, timing of Because farmers are price takers and commodity prices typically vary considerably within a year, farmers are motivated to get their prices set at the most favorable time. Various contractual arrangements facilitate such timing of pricing. *See* Contractual exchange.

Principle of comparative advantage States that, under free trade, people should specialize in producing (when specialization yields efficiencies) those commodities that they can produce most efficiently and then trade freely. Suppose that an Iowa farmer can produce 9,000 pounds of corn or 200 pounds of beef calves per acre per year, whereas a Wyoming rancher can produce 5,000 pounds of corn or 200 pounds of beef calves per 10 acres. If each farmer does both, they produce a total of

$$\frac{9,000 + 5,000}{2} = 7,000 \text{ pounds of corn}$$

and

$$\frac{200 + 200}{2} = 200 \text{ pounds of beef calves}$$

whereas if each specializes in her comparative advantage, they produce 9,000 pounds of corn plus 200 pounds of beef. Even though Iowa land is great cow pasture compared to Wyoming land, the comparative advantage of Iowa is in crop production.

Private labels The branded products owned by retailers and other distributors. *Cf.* Manufacturers' brands.

Private trucking A firm transports its goods by owning and operating trucks rather than hiring that service.

Processor's margin The differential between selling price and buying price that rewards an intermediary for her services.

Procurement pricing A typical procedure for a commodity handler is to compute purchase price as selling price minus a desired margin—subject to what competing prices will allow.

Product The output of a firm that has added some value to a raw commodity.

Product differentiation A characteristic of a market in which buyers perceive significant differences among the products or services offered by various sellers. Product differentiation always exists in monopolistic competition and usually exists in oligopoly.

Product life cycle The sales path of a product over time as it passes through the stages of introduction, growth, maturity, and decline.

Product marketing The marketing of most processed foods (such as canned fruits, cake mixes, and frozen entrees) provides profitable opportunities for promotion and reduces the emphasis on price competition. *Cf.* Commodity handling.

Product needs Those specific needs to which a consumer can relate definite products and services.

Product positioning A seller's strategy of placing his product into a target market in a desirable position relative to those of competitors. For example, a seller may try to position a soup as more healthful or better tasting.

Production contract Agreement in which, for a fee, a farmer (called the *contractee*) produces poultry, livestock, or even crops that are owned by another party (called a *contractor*). Because the farmer does not own the production, he cannot sell it when it is ready for market.

Production lag The period it takes to increase or reduce production of a commodity. *See* Biological lag.

Promotion The communication of good, positive public perceptions of a person or firm. For a marketer, promotion includes advertising, personal selling, and sales promotion (e.g., free samples).

Public Law (P.L.) 480 The 1954 U. S. legislation that authorized U. S. export subsidies for agricultural commodities.

Put option A futures market instrument that gives its buyer the right (without an obligation) to sell a futures contract at a specified price during a specific time period. Because the put option provides insurance against market price declines, the buyer pays a premium for it.

Quality The sum of the attributes of a commodity that influences its acceptability and value to many buyers.

Quantity control devices Rules in many marketing orders that are used to obtain a more orderly flow to market and may also increase short-term returns to producers.

Realized prices *See* Price, realized.

Reciprocity When competition is distorted because a conglomerate firm is using its real or potential purchases from a second firm as an inducement for that second firm to buy items from it.

Reserve stocks An inventory of certain farm commodities held by or under the direction of government to even out the effects on consumption and prices of varying year-to-year production. Such stocks can rather quickly become surpluses.

Retail assortment The particular mixture of many food products carried by an individual food retailer.

Retailer performance An evaluation from a social viewpoint of the pricing, profits, product mix, promotion, and productivity of the nation's food retailers.

Return on investment (ROI) The percentage obtained by dividing annual earnings by the total investment in a firm or industry.

Risk bearing Being in a position to experience gain or loss as a result of externally controlled changes in the amount or price of one's holdings of commodities or other assets.

Robinson-Patman Act Federal legislation in 1938 that prohibits price discrimination that might injure competition and provides for punishment both for sellers that price discriminate and for buyers that seek to induce such action.

Sales branch A processor-owned facility that inventories and sells processed foods.

Sales promotion Those promotional activities other than advertising and personal salesmanship. Examples include giving samples, cents-off deals on packages, and coupons.

Self-sufficiency The degree to which a country produces enough food to feed its own people.

Sherman Antitrust Act A federal law passed in 1887 that has been the basis for most of U. S. policy efforts since then to prevent changes in market structure that would make markets less competitive and to prevent types of market conduct that restrict or damage active competition.

Shipper The person taking responsibility for the transportation of goods.

Sorting out The dividing of a farm commodity into more homogeneous groups on the basis of quality, size, and so on.

Speculation The taking of ownership positions for the purpose of profiting from market price changes.

Spot spread The margin for a processor between its sales prices and buying prices of a commodity.

Staggers Rail Act Passed in 1980, this federal law made a major reduction in economic regulation of railroads.

Standardization The development and use of constant measures of quantity and quality of various goods. For example, the United States is gradually shifting to a metric system for measuring quantities.

Standards of identity The federal specifications that a product (e.g., ice cream) must meet in order to be labeled and sold as such.

State trading The practice of trading in international markets exclusively through a government agency.

Store format The size, arrangement, and quality of fixtures and lighting of a food store. Formats range from the economy look of a small box or warehouse store to the luxurious ambiance of a superstore.

Strike price The price specified by a put option at which a seller has the right to sell a futures contract. Put options are made available at a set of strike prices above and below the current market price of the corresponding futures contract.

Superstore A large supermarket with a great variety of products, specialty and service departments, and a large amount of general merchandise.

Supply The set of alternative quantities that would be produced or sold at alternative prices.

Supply shifters Factors changing the ability or willingness of sellers to supply a set of outputs at certain prices. Examples are technology and weather.

Supply-oriented processing The location of manufacturing activities such as livestock slaughter near the supply of raw materials to minimize transport costs.

Surface Transportation Board The federal agency that has replaced the Interstate Commerce Commission in the economic regulation of interstate transportation.

Tariff A tax levied on imports to hamper or even stop them from coming into the country.

Technical analysis The study of recent futures market statistics for guidance about impending price changes. Usually it includes a study of trends and price patterns using bar charts or points and figures. It may be used in conjunction with a fundamental analysis to study the demand-and-supply situation.

Time value Reflects the time between an option premium quote and contract expiration.

Trade barriers National regulations that impede or prevent trade.

Trademark A brand name, symbol, or other mark that has legal recognition as a branding device. For example, Domino's Pizza has a domino as its trademark, which is a complete *identification* between the name of the seller and its trademark. *See* Brand name.

Trading strategy A managed set of activities of a grain trader to provide flexibility of action and benefits from price changes while maintaining an acceptable level of risk.

Transaction costs All those costs incurred by sellers and buyers as they search for market opportunities and make and complete business deals. For example, a seller's costs of hauling livestock to an auction and paying the auction fees are considered transaction costs.

Transport mode A transportation method such as railroad, truck, barge, or air.

Unit train An entire train and crew that is contracted to a shipper to be operated as a unit at his or her direction.

Utility, form The value of a good associated with its availability in a form convenient to the buyers.

Utility, place The value of a good or service associated with the convenience of its accessibility to buyers.

Utility, time The value of a good or service associated with its availability at a time desired by buyers.

Variable price merchandising (VPM) The continued manipulation from week to week of prices of numerous items to give a price-competitive image for a retail food store.

Vertical coordination A business entity or a group of business entities work toward achieving a set of standards or practices used throughout parts of or an entire marketing system. This coordination may be obtained through information sharing, contracts, or regulation.

Vertical integration A situation where a firm owns two or more adjacent levels of production and/or marketing so that the product or commodity does not move through the market as it normally would in moving from one level to the next on the way to the consumer. Sometimes, contract production is classified as vertical integration. A few economists even consider marketing procurement contracts in vertical integration.

Vertical merger The combining of two firms into a single firm when one firm was a customer (actual or potential) of the other.

Wholesaler–retailer (WR) This term recognizes the contractual or ownership integration that typically links the food wholesale and retail functions.

Working inventory (WI) The minimum inventory (holdings) of a storable commodity that allows normal operations by marketing participants.

WTO (World Trade Organization) An international organization with the goal of reducing trade barriers. It was formerly called GATT.

Yield grades The classifications of beef carcasses (and live cattle) according to their leanness and thus their percentage yield of trimmed retail cuts.

APPENDIX

ADDITIONAL RESOURCES

The additional resources listed here may assist the reader in finding information related to the topics covered in this book. We list the Internet link and topics that can be found on each website.

UNITED STATES DEPARTMENT OF AGRICULTURE RESOURCES (USDA)
WWW.USDA.GOV

ECONOMIC RESEARCH SERVICE (ERS)
www.ers.usda.gov

- Agribusiness/industry concentration
- Agricultural market/trade projections
- Biotechnology
- Crops
- Diet, consumption, and health
- Farm structure, income, and performance
- Food market structures
- Food prices, spreads, and margins
- Food safety
- International agriculture
- Livestock, dairy, poultry, aquaculture
- Trade
- U.S./state facts

FOREIGN AGRICULTURE SERVICE (FAS)
www.fas.usda.gov

- World production, market, and trade reports
- Weekly export sales
- Outlook for U.S. agricultural trade

NATIONAL AGRICULTURAL STATISTICAL SERVICE (NASS)
www.nass.usda.gov

- Commodity reports
- Wheat outlook
- Feed outlook
- Oilseeds outlook
- Quarterly hogs and pigs
- Cattle on feed
- Agricultural prices
- Grain stocks
- Census of agriculture (every five years, last in 2002)
- Dairy products
- Weather
- Farm labor
- Land values
- Cost of inputs
- Agricultural chemical usage reports

INDEX